D1478314

THE YAMBO OUOLOGUEM READER

THE YAMBO OUOLOGUEM READER

YAMBO OUOLOGUEM

Edited by
CHRISTOPHER WISE

Africa World Press, Inc.

P.O. Box 1892
Trenton, NJ 08607

P.O. Box 48
Asmara, ERITREA

Africa World Press, Inc.

P.O. Box 1892
Trenton, NJ 08607

P.O. Box 48
Asmara, ERITREA

Copyright © 2008 Yambo Ouologuem
First Printing 2008

All rights reserved. No part of this publication may be reproduced, stored in a retrieval system or transmitted in any form or by any means electronic, mechanical, photocopying, recording or otherwise without the prior written permission of the publisher.

Book design: Aliya Books and Saverance Publishing Services
Cover design: Zachary Wise and Ashraful Haque

Library of Congress Cataloging-in-Publication Data

Ouologuem, Yambo, 1940
[Selections. English. 2008]
The Yambo Ouologuem reader / by Yambo Ouologuem ; edited with a preface by Christopher Wise ; translated from the French by Christopher Wise.
    p. cm. Includes bibliographical references and index. ISBN 1-59221-600-5 (hardcover) -- ISBN 1-59221-601-3 (pbk.)
1.   Postcolonialism--Africa. I. Wise, Christopher 1961- II. Title.
PQ3989.2.O8A2 2008 843'.914--dc22 [B]

2008005892

Contents

Preface to *The Yambo Ouologuem Reader*[1]

by *Christopher Wise*

The critical reception of Yambo Ouologuem's *Le devoir de violence* forms one of the most interesting chapters in the history of African literature. Many credit Ouologuem with delivering the final death-blow to Senghorian negritude, with clearing the way for a more honest literature divested of the sickly longing for a false African past. For these readers, *Le devoir de violence* signaled an important new direction in African letters, a fiercely courageous, post-independence literature. For others, Ouologuem's "untimely" portrait of African history revealed far too much, bringing to light horrors that many preferred to forget. While early European and American readers celebrated the "honesty" of *Le devoir de violence*, Wole Soyinka, Mbeloko ya Mpiku, Tunde Fatunde, and other African critics worried that Ouologuem might be an "apologist" for colonial oppressors, both French and African. In the early 1970s, these important questions ebbed in the wake of largely pedantic controversies surrounding *Le devoir de violence*'s status as a literary property. The legal entanglements that ensued led Ouologuem's publisher to withdraw *Le devoir de violence* from the shelves of French bookstores, but the novel continued to live on in translation and as the subject of countless theses, dissertations, articles, and book chapters. In the United States, critics like Kwame

Anthony Appiah, Christopher Miller, Thomas Hale, Henry Louis Gates, Jr., and many others debated its meaning, although none questioned its importance as a major work of literature. In time, Ouologuem came to be recognized as one of Africa's most influential writers, his work regularly compared to that of Wole Soyinka, Chinua Achebe, Ngugi wa Thiong'o, Naguib Mafouz, and many others. To the chagrin of those who once hoped that Ouologuem's great novel would quietly fade away, critical interest in *Le devoir de violence* has never been more intense. Today, it is no longer possible to deny *Le devoir de violence*'s literary importance. History has passed its verdict on the question of this novel's alleged lack of "authenticity," for no merely "plagiarized" text could command so much sustained critical interest. The novel itself offers the best possible proof of Ouologuem's original-ity, an irrefutable testament to both his integrity as a man and genius as a writer.

Yambo Amadou Ouologuem was born in 1940, the son of Ouologuem Boukary Yambo and Aïssata Oumar (*née* Karambé)[2] at the Ouologuem family residence in Bandiag-ara, Mali, capital of the Toucouleur Empire of El Hadjj Tall Oumar and the administrative center of the *pays Dogon*. The history of Tall's *jihad* in 19th century West Africa has been well documented by both African and Western historians.[3] Originally from northern Sénégal, El Hadjj Oumar Tall brought into West Africa a new version of Tidjaniya Islam (distinct from the Tidjaniya of Morocco), which he learned from Sheik Mohammed El-Ghâli, Caliph of the Tidjaniya in Mecca. El Hadjj Oumar's interpretation of Islam, which differed from other Sufi brotherhoods across the Sahel, stressed the importance of Islam as a *total* way of life, an all-encompassing belief system affecting every aspect of one's daily existence. Though Tall himself was a Toucouleur (or "sedentary") Peul, he established his Tidjaniya Empire in the heart of the *pays Dogon* among Yambo Ouologuem's immediate ancestors, all of whom were prominent members of the Dogon aristocracy. Although the Dogon had resisted Islam for centuries prior to the founding of the Toucouleur

Empire, most were unable to resist El Hadjj Oumar's militant call to conversion in the late 19ᵗʰ century.

The extent to which Yambo Ouologuem's own family cooperated with Tall, employing Islam to their own material advantage, would become a question that would later haunt the young author of *Le devoir de violence*.[4] While Western scholars have long debated the origins of the Peul (both Macina and Toucouleur), most Africanists who have written on the Peul agree that they have some "Semitic" or "Levantine" (possibly Yemeni) origin. European and American scholars, especially those influenced by German and French Romanticism, have promoted the theory that these "black Arabs" (or "white" Africans) first migrated into West Africa from Palestine, speculating that the Peul, a word with a possible etymological relation to the words "Philistine" and "Palestine," may be one of Israel's so-called "lost tribes." In opposition to such theories, which contemporary Peul complain relegate them to the status of "Philistine" (a catch all term for the Jew's Palestinian Other), prominent Peul like the late El Hadjj Sékou Tall nonetheless insist that they are descendents of an uncle of the Prophet Muhammad, who journeyed to the Western Sudan and brought Islam to historically black African peoples (Tall "The Origins of the Fulani" 22).

In an effort to assert the Peuls' blood lineage that is traceable to the Prophet Muhammad, El Hadjj Sékou Tall argues that the Peul intermingled with "black Africans" like the Dogon, Songhay, Bozo, Mossé, Mandé, and others as the result of the marriage of this legendary Arab ancestor and indigenous Sahelian peoples. Tall's own version of the Peuls' origin militates against popular views of other Sahelian ethic groups that the Peul (or "the wiley red ones") are fraudulent interlopers, or recent arrivals in West Africa (if a 1,000 year residence can be called "recent"). Tall also insists that the Peul are one of the three remaining indigenous "white" ethnic groups in West Africa, along with the Arabs and Berbers (the Sephardic Jews having absconded). In *Le devoir de violence*, Yambo Ouologuem savagely parodies the Peuls' claim to racial privilege as the "black Jews" of West Africa. Ouologuem is a Tidjaniya Muslim like the Toucouleur Peul, but he is also a black African, specifically a Dogon; that is, Ouologuem is a member of a community that has experienced nearly one hundred and sixty years of racial oppression from Peul chiefdoms, beginning with the 19th century *jihad* of El Hadjj Oumar Tall. Many Peul men belong to Sufi brotherhoods that are linked to Al Kadir, the legendary "hard" teacher of Moses, who is reputed in the Qur'an to be even wiser than the great lawgiver. It is significant that *Kaidiara*, the major Peul epic which was transcribed by the Toucouleur Peul author Amadou Hampâté Bâ, is in fact little more than a mnemonic device for Sufi initiates to memorize Kabbala in oral form. The evidence of Bâ's text also suggests that the version of the Kabbala that is memorized by Peul adepts is linked to one of the earliest known, 2nd century Palestinian transcriptions of the Kabbala.

In Yambo Ouologuem's early years, he was profoundly influenced by the religion of the "black Jews" of Northern Mali, his birth coinciding exactly with the death of Tierno Bokar Salif Tall, the renown "sage of Bandiagara."[5] As one might expect, he was also unable to escape feelings of alienation from his fellow Dogon, in part due to his family's close ties to the Toucouleur Peul ruling caste of Bandiagara. The ancestral privileges of Ouologuem enabled him to gain access to the top educational institutions in both Mali and France, as well as inherit extensive land-holdings throughout the *pays Dogon*. Given the great poverty of his fellow Dogon, as well as the Talls' historical complicity with the French colonial administration (both in the case of El Hadjj Oumar and King Aguibou Tall[6]), the contradictory alliances behind Yambo Ouologuem's early identity profoundly complicated his perspective on Islam and French colonialism. If we may not doubt the great religious integrity of the Oumarian Tidjaniya (both Toucouleur and high-caste Dogon), we may equally be certain that political pressures during the era of French colonialism left few local leaders with unsoiled hands. It is easy to imagine the impatience of the young Ouologuem with the "hypocrisies" of previous generations, the lifestyles of those men caught between the demands of faith and necessity. What must be emphasized, however, is the relatively *small* impact of French colonization in Bandiagara and the outlying regions of the *pays Dogon*; that is, the writings of Yambo Ouologuem cannot be comprehended apart from the Islamic-Sahelian culture of Northern Mali, that wonderfully rich mosaic of Dogon, Bozo, Toucouleur Peul, Songhay, Tuareg, Bella, Macina Peul, and other peoples. Not unlike the Concord of the "American Renaissance," the Bandiagara of notable figures like Tierno Bokar Tall, Amadou Hampaté Bâ, El Hadjj Sékou Tall, and Yambo Ouologuem constitutes one of the most remarkable intellectual communities in literary history. The original voice of Yambo Ouologuem, a voice that first disarmed in its self-confident *indifference* to the West, emerges from within this specific cultural context.

It is therefore curious that so much critical interest in France and the United States has been generated by legalistic and academic questions about *Le devoir de violence*'s status as a literary property. In fact, the latest flurry of critical interest in Ouologuem in North America has centered on his alleged "theft" of European literary sources in an effort to aggressively "deconstruct" Western writing practices. During a RELIS conference in Burkina Faso, where I gave a paper on the critical reception of *Le devoir de violence* in the United States,[7] such arguments provoked indulgent smiles from my African colleagues, many who wagged their fingers at me about the "antics" of American critics. For most of my Burkinabè colleagues, the idea that Ouologuem may have deliberately "stolen" from authors like Graham Greene, André Schwarz-Bart, and Guy de Maupassant seemed to have relatively little bearing in ascertaining his significance as an African writer today. In his brief defense against plagiarism charges, entitled "Polémique: *Le devoir de violence*," Ouologuem stated that his editors had revised his manuscript by removing citations from Greene and Schwarz-Bart.[8] In his "In Defense of Yambo Ouologuem," Kaye Whiteman also testified to having actually seen the manuscript in question, including handwritten lines by Ouologuem such as "Here ends *The Last of the Just*." During a visit with Ouologuem in Sévéré, Mali in 1997, he told me that both the manuscript of *Le devoir de violence* and its English translation went to press without his full prior knowledge or consent. In other words, the novel's final "cut" (or its final published form), in which references to European texts had been deleted, was never authorized by Ouologuem himself.

Responding to erroneous statements made by Eric Sellin, Paul Flamand wrote to the editors of *Research in African Literatures*, especially to defend himself against the allegation that Editions du Seuil had commissioned Ouologuem to write *Le devoir de violence*.[9] Flamand demonstrated that this was not the case; however, Ouologuem himself never made such a claim, only Sellin did. In this letter, Flamand said nothing at all about whether or not unauthorized editorial changes had been made to Ouologuem's manuscript by Editions du Seuil. In fact, Flamand made clear that Editions du Seuil was fully cognizant of the fact that Ouologuem had made use of Schwarz-Bart, which is why they bothered to contact Schwarz-Bart about this matter in the first place. It is likely that Editions du Seuil was aware of Ouologuem's use of Schwarz-Bart because this was made plain in the manuscript that Ouologuem had submitted to them. If this were not the case, at the very least Editions du Seuil would have been guilty of gross negligence in approving publication of Ouologuem's book after detecting evidence of such "blatant plagiarism" and then not bothering to question the likelihood of further instances in the manuscript. Flamand's letter only exonerated Editions du Seuil from charges made by Eric Sellin, which were largely irrelevant (as well as "inadvertently tendentious,"[10] to quote Sellin).

Far more hostile to Ouologuem was the published response of someone named "B.P" in an article ironically entitled "Le Devoir de vérité." As a matter of fact, it is unclear whether or not "B.P." actually edited Ouologuem's manuscript or was in any way associated with Editions du Seuil. However, B.P.'s article in *Le Figaro*, which was strategically wedged between the response of the author (mentioned above) and the response of Graham Greene's literary agent, Ms. Marie Schébéko, clearly illustrated the dishonesty of the French literary establishment in responding to this situation. B.P. listed a few brief points in his/her response to Ouologuem's defense, none of which addressed Ouologuem's claim that his publishers had made unauthorized revisions in his manuscript. For example, B.P. stated as follows:

> Yambo Ouologuem defends himself from plagiarism charges by claiming that the [missing] quotation marks may be found in his own [handwritten] manuscript. The trouble is that they are absent from the book which, need we say, only critics and the public have access to. [*Yambo Ouologuem se défend de cette accusation de plagiat en invoquant des guillemets qui figureraient dans son manuscrit. L'ennui, c'est qu'ils sont absents du livre auquel, faut-il rappeler cette évidence, les critiques et le pulic ont seulement accès.*]

Of course B.P. was correct, but such a statement merely begged the question: Did the editors of *Le devoir de violence* remove references to other works without Ouologuem's consent? If so, why? Furthermore, why did his editors not request necessary revisions from Ouologuem if they were truly concerned about plagiarism? Given the unusual nature of Ouologuem's borrowings, would it have been possible for Ouologuem to revise his novel accordingly? Such complications may have led the novel's editors to conclude that simply deleting references to Greene, Maupassant, etc. offered to them the easiest solution to the creative problems his manuscript posed. In the same article, B.P. deliberately misread Ouologuem to the point of absurdity. In his statement, Ouologuem had implied that Graham Greene should have responded to this crisis by coming to his aid (much like Schwarz-Bart had at an earlier date); instead, Greene sided with the publisher of *Le devoir de violence* who took the liberty of pleading "guilty" on Ouologuem's behalf—without bothering to consult him. "It is significant," Ouologuem stated, "that this publisher should plead guilty in my name, without even asking me, and that, without the slightest protest from Mr. Graham Greene, he [my publisher] went ahead and removed my books from sale throughout the world. [*Et il est significatif que cet éditeur plaide coupable en mon nom sans même m'interroger, et que, sans la moindre réclamation de Mr. Graham Greene, il retire mon livre de la vente dans le monde entier.*]"

B.P. responded as follows:

> To write that Graham Greene did not complain is false. It was at the great English novelist's request that Mrs. Schébéko, the head of Clairouin Agency, which represents Greene's interests in France, contacted Paul Flamand... [*"Écrire que Graham Greene n'a émis aucune réclamation est faux. C'est à la demande du grand romancier anglais que Mme Schébékok, directrice de l'agence Clairouin, qui représente ses intérêts en France, est intervenue auprès de Paul Flammand..."*].

However, Ouologuem never stated that Greene did not complain about the alleged "plagiarism" of his novel, *It's a Battlefield.* What Ouologuem stated was that Greene, as a fellow author, should have taken the initiative to intervene on Ouologuem's behalf, preventing the unnecessary removal of the novel from the bookstores. B.P.'s final remarks were simply insulting:

> When Yambo Ouologuem borrows from himself, his thought is obscure and his prose entangled. It would not occur to Graham Greene to plagiarize him. Nor to anybody else. [*"Quand Yambo Ouologuem n'emprunte qu'à lui-même, sa pensée est confuse et sa prose emberlificotée. Il ne viendrait pas à l'idée de Graham Greene de le plagier. Ni à quiconque."*].

The arrogance, evasiveness, and dishonesty of B.P. were emblematic of French responses to this crisis. As an African student in a foreign capital, only twenty-eight at the time his novel was published, Ouologuem's situation could not inspire envy: the full weight of an embarrassed intellectual community was exerted against him. Many of those involved may have had a vested interest in obscuring their own role in producing a "plagiarized" text, specifically through altering Ouologuem's original manuscript. What almost no one bothered to consider was the possibility that Ouologuem told the truth in this matter from the earliest days of the controversy: that is, the original publishers of *Le devoir de violence* made numerous unauthorized changes in his manuscript, deleting references to European sources while leaving references to the *Tarîkh el-Fettach*, the *Tarîkh es-Soudan*, and other "unknown" African sources fully intact.[11] In other words, Yambo Ouologuem has suffered a grave disservice at the hands of his former publishers, a disservice that has had long and painful repercussions for him. Ouologuem's reputation as a writer was damaged by vicious ad hominem attacks on his character and other red herrings. Despite the fact that Éditions du Seuil never produced a single piece of evidence to substantiate their claims, Ouologuem was widely presumed guilty of producing a "plagiarized" text. In fact, it is significant that, while Ouologuem's brief response to plagiarism charges has been analyzed in some detail by his detractors, the written responses of his publisher have escaped close scrutiny altogether.

There can be no doubt that intensive and harmful scrutiny was brought to bear upon Ouologuem in ways unthinkable in cases when European artists have freely borrowed from African sources. For instance, few art historians speak of "plagiarism" or "theft" when discussing the paintings of Picasso, Braques, or Mogdiliani. Yet Ouologuem has been subject to a series of highly refined attacks on his character for nearly thirty years, more recently by those who congratulate him for his "cleverness" in deliberately "stealing" from European writers.[12] More importantly, prolonged discussion of

Ouologuem's "plagiarism" of European sources has diverted attention away from urgent historical questions many would prefer to ignore: a fact that is probably not incidental to the proliferation of a particular kind of critical discourse on him.

Though Ouologuem has declined to discuss his writings in French, he remains an active member of the Tidjaniya community in Sévéré-Mopti and Bandiagara, collaborating in writing projects with Amadou Hampâté Bâ before Bâ's recent death, and working for educational reform in both Mali and Mauritania. Above all, he seeks to bring an end to the racial oppression of black Muslims throughout the Sahel and elsewhere, especially at the hands of Arab Muslims. Thanks largely to the tireless efforts of Ava Ouologuem, the daughter of Yambo, a new edition of *Le devoir de violence* has recently been set before the French reading public. Ms. Ouologuem has performed Herculean labors on behalf of her father, and on behalf of the Ouologuem family name, which has been unfairly attacked for nearly three decades. The reedition of this great novel in its original language has truly been a cause for celebration. But at the same time that *Le devoir de violence* has become available once again in France, the earliest English translation is no longer available in the United States or anywhere else in the Anglophone world. Moreover, Ouologuem's two other French-language books, *Lettre à la France nègre* and *Les milles et uns Bibles du sexe* have never been translated into the English language. *The Yambo Ouologuem Reader* is offered in order to remedy this situation and in hopes of attracting a new generation of readers to Ouologuem's books. Once again, the reader has Ava Ouologuem to thank for making this new volume of her father's writings available. It is therefore in sincere gratitude and appreciation that I dedicate these new translations to her.[13]

NOTES

1. This essay is a revised verision of my French-language preface to
    Le devoir de violence (Paris: Serpent à Plumes, 2004), as well as my
    prior introduction to *Yambo Ouologuem: Postcolonial Writer, Islamic
    Militant* (Boulder, Colorado: Lynne Rienner Publishers, 2001). It
    is included here at the request of Ava Ouologuem, the sole executor
    of Yambo Ouologuem's literary estate.

2   Throughout Northern Mali and elsewhere in the Sahel, it is cus-
    tomary to give the family name first.

3. See, for instance, David Robinson's *The Holy War of Umar Tal*
    (1985), B. O. Oloruntimehin's *The Segu Tukulor Empire* (1972), and
    Brad Martin's *Muslim Brotherhoods in 19th Century Africa* (1976).

4. See Linda Kuehl's "Yambo Ouologuem on Violence, Truth, and
    Black History" (312).

5. See Amadou Hampâté Bâ's *Vie et enseignement de Tierno Bokar: le
    sage de Bandiagara* or Louis Brenner's *West African Sufi: the Religious
    Heritage and Spiritual Search of Cerno Bokar Salif Tal.*

6. Not unlike Ouologuem's Saif, El Hadjj Oumar alternated in his
    relationship with the French between antagonism and collabora-
    tion, depending upon the need of the moment. As David Robinson
    points out, "It is ironic that the image of an intransigent Umar,
    largely generated by the French, has been retained and belabored by
    modern Senegalese nationalists anxious to portray the Fulbe leader
    as a hero of resistance to European conquest" (40; also see 5). In
    the case of El Hadjj Oumar's son Aguibou Tall, however, the rela-
    tion was obviously more collaborative if not subordinate (Abun-
    Nasar 143; Robinson 27-31). Also, see Yves Saint-Martin's "Un
    fils d'El Hadj Omar: Aguibou, roi du Dinguiray et du Macina
    (1843?1907?)."

7. Yambo Ouologuem dans le postmoderne: les débats littéraires sur
    Le devoir de violence depuis 1985," Vè colloque international delit-
    térature, Réseau d'Études Littératures Sahéliennes, Université de
    Ouagadougou, Burkina Faso, November 21, 1996.

8. Yambo Ouologuem, "Polémique: Le devoir de violence," *Figaro lit-
    téraire,* June 10, 1972.

9. Paul Flamand "Letter to the Editor," *Research in African Literatures*, Vol. 2, No. 2 (1971): 116.

10. See Sellin's reply, *Research in African Literatures*, Vol. 2, No. 2 (1971): 116-117.

11. See Kaye Whiteman's "In Defence of Yambo Ouologuem."

12. See "Something New Out of Africa?" Though such arguments are now bolstered by reference to poststructuralist theory, the seeds of this critique were already present in the earliest, most slanderous accounts of this controversy. The anonymous writer of this piece asks, "[I]s Ouologuem on to something: a style of literary imperialism intended as revenge for the much-chronicled sins of territorial imperialists" (525).

13. A note of thanks to students of my Winter 2008 graduate seminar at Western Washington University, especially Matt Atwood, for their help in proofreading the final draft of this manuscript.

WORKS CITED

Abun-Nasr, Jamil M. The Tidjaniyya. *A Sufi Order in the Modern World*. London: Oxford University Press, 1965.

Appiah, Kwame Anthony. *In My Father's House: Africa in the Philosophy of Culture*. New York/Oxford: Oxford University Press, 1992.

B.P. "Le devoir de vérité," *Figaro littéraire*, June 10, 1972.

Bâ, Amadou Hampâté, Kaïdara: *A Fulani Cosmological Epic From Mali*. Trans. & Ed. Daniel Whitman. Boulder, Colorado: Lynne Rienner Publishers, 1988.

_____. *Vie et enseignement de Tierno Bokar: le sage de Bandiagara*. Paris: Seuil, 1980.

Brenner, Louis. *West African Sufi: the Religious Heritage and Spiritual Search of Cerno Bokar Salif Tal*. London: Hurst, 1984.

Es-Sa'di, Abderrahman ben Abdallah ben 'Imran ben 'Amir. *Tarikh es-Soudan*. Translated by O. Houdas. Paris: École des Languages Orientales Vivants, 1898-1900; 2nd ed., Paris: Adrien-Maisonneuve, 1964.

Fatunde, Tatunde. "Images of Working People in two African Novels: Ouologuem and Iyayi," *Marxism and African Literature*, ed. Georg

M. Gugelberger. Trenton, N. J.: African World Press, 1985: 110-117.

Flammand, Paul, "Letter to the Editor," *Research in African Literature*, Vol. 2, No. 2 (1971): 116.

Flammand, Paul & Sellin, Eric. "Letters to The Editor," London Times Literary Supplement of May 19, 1972: 576.

Greene, Graham. *It's a Battlefield.* London: Heinemann, 1934.

Hale, Thomas. *Scribe, Griot, Novelist.* Gainesville: University of Florida Press, 1990.

Kâti, Mahmoud. *Tarikh el-Fettâch ou chronique du chercheur pour servir à l'histoire des villes, des armées et des principaux personnages du Tekrour.* Translated by O. Houdas and M. Delafosse. Paris: Ernest Leroux, 1913.

Kuehl, Linda. "Yambo Ouologuem on Violence, Truth, and Black History." *Commonweal.* June 11, 1971: 311-314.

Martin, Brad. *Muslim Brotherhoods in 19th Century Africa.* Cambridge: Cambridge University Press, 1976.

Mbelolo, J. Mpiku ya. "From One Mystification to Another: 'Négritude and 'Négraille' in *Le devoir de violence.*" Review of National Literatures 2, no. 2 (Fall 1971): 124-47.

Miller, Christopher L. *Blank Darkness: Africanist Discourse in French.* Chicago: University of Chicago Press, 1985.

Oloruntimehin, B.O. *The Segu Tukulor Empire.* London: Longman Group Limited, 1972.

Ouologuem, Yambo. "Polémique: *Le devoir de violence,*" *Figaro littéraire,* June 10, 1972.

Robinson, David. *The Holy War of Umar Tall.* New York: Oxford University Press, 1985.

Saint-Martin, Yves. "Un fils d'El Hadj Omar: Agibou, roi du Dinguiray et du Macina (1843?-1907?)," *Cahier d'Études Africaines* 8 (1968).

Schwartz-Bart, André. *Le Dernier Des Justes.* Paris: EEEditions du Seuil, 1959.

Sellin, Eric. "Letter to the Editor," *Research in African Literatures,* Vol. 2, No. 2 (1971): 116-117.

"Something New Out of Africa?" *Times Literary Supplement,* May 5, 1972: 525.

Soyinka, Wole. *Myth, Literature, and the African World.* Cambridge: Cambridge University Press, 1976: 104-106.

Tall, El Hadjj Sékou. "The Origins of the Fulani," translated by Christopher Wise. *The Desert Shore: Literatures of the Sahel,* Edited by Christopher Wise. Boulder, Colorado: Lynne Rienner Publishers, 2001: 11-26.

Whiteman, Kaye (K.W.) "In Defence of Yambo Ouologuem." *West Africa,* July 21, 1972.

Wise, Christopher. "In Search of Yambo Ouologuem," *Research in African Literatures.* Vol. 29, No. 2 (Summer 1998): 159-182.

_____. "Yambo Ouologuem dans le postmoderne: les débats littéraires sur *Le devoir de violence* depuis 1985," *Littératures du Sahel,* Edited by Joseph Paré, Sanou Salaka, and Christopher Wise. Bellingham, Washington: CamNexus / Kola Tree Press, 1998: 117-122.

_____. (ed). *Yambo Ouologuem: Postcolonial Writer, Islamic Militant.* Boulder, Colorado: Lynne Rienner Publishers, 2001.

THE DUTY OF VIOLENCE

BY
YAMBO
OUOLOGUEM

Dedication

To a humble companion
in hard times and in times far worse

I

THE LEGEND OF THE SAIFS

O ur eyes drink the sun's rays and, vanquished, unexpectedly brim with tears. *Maschallah! Wa bismillah!* ... The
bloody adventure of the black-rabble—shame upon these
worthless wretches!—could easily be recounted from the first
half of this century; but the true history of the Blacks begins
much earlier with the Saifs, in the year 1202 of our era, in
the African Empire of Nakem, to the South of Fezzan, long
after the conquests of Okba ibn Nafi al-Fitri.

To dwell upon the glories of this empire—renown as
far as Morocco, the Sudan, Egypt, Abyssinia, the Noble and
Holy City of Mecca, and known by the English, the Dutch,
the French, the Spaniards, and, of course, the Portuguese—
would merely rehash stale folk tales.

Of much greater interest, when the elders, the notables,
and the griots gaze off into the abysmal deserts and speak of
this Empire, is the desperate flight of its population—born
along by God's implacable "blessing," *wallahi!*—baptized
by torture, strewn along the Rande, dispersed upon the arid
mountains of the Goro Fato Zinko, staked on the isles of
the Yame River for more than two thousand kilometers
downstream of Zinko, dwelling on the furthest fringes of
the Atlantic coast, scattered finally along the lengths of the
Savannah Limitropes of Equatorial Africa, in clusters of
varying significance, separated from one another into diverse
tribes: the Randinques, the Fulani, Gondaites, Berber-
Nomads, N'Godos, warring among themselves to win impe-

rial power, in intestinal rivalries, vying with one another in acts of horrifying violence.

In order to stifle these uprisings, the Saifs bloodied their spears in acts of infamy and tribal blackmail, proclaiming "For the Light of the World!"...

In that feudal age, great choirs of slaves sang their devotion to the justice of their masters, not only through forced labor, but also as they were butchered alive, smeared with the blood of slaughtered children and disemboweled pregnant women ... This is what happened at Tillaberi-Benita, at Granata, at Grosso, at Gagol-Gosso, and in the many places mentioned by the Arab historians of the *Tarikh al-fettach* and the *Tarikh es-Sudan*.

Afterwards, a tumultuous wail arose from the village, echoing as far as the gloomy den where the hyenas sleep. A pious silence followed, as the griot Koutouli, of beloved memory, brought his lament to its conclusion. Not far from the piles of butchered children, seventeen fetuses could be counted, all torn from the gaping entrails of their mothers, who had died in agony, but not before they were publicly raped by their husbands. Crushed in humiliation, their husbands later took their own lives. Nor could they avoid the duty of performing this suicide, in order to save the life of one of their brothers, an impotent and despondent witness to this spectacle, whose pitiful response—*Al'allah!*—was deemed "more tearful than frightened" or "insufficiently traumatized."

The village chief, his lips parted in deaf and dumb resignation, concluded that human life was in vain. Frightened out of his wits, he nonetheless knew that it was his duty to preserve order by dangling the earlobes of the rebellious from a neighboring village upon a long, sinewy rope. The bodies of these men were burned into cinders, their ashes strewn into the river. It is said that the maleficent djinn of these villains contaminated the water for three years or so, which made it necessary for a few of the elect to dig wells at a safe distance from the river and to remain constantly on watch in the nights against their evil spirits. May God the Most High bestow His grace and most favored blessings upon them!

But this tale has been told many times before now: countless others have offered their own accounts of the terrible deeds of the tyrants who stifled the least hint of resistance from within the Empire. Patiently traversing the expanse of two centuries, the heart of the Nakem endured many similar forms of discipline and ignobility; the crowned rulers, forcing life down the throats of their subjects like the boa gagging on an antelope, rolled from obscure dynasties into those with more sibylline genealogies— each infamy more vicious than the one before ...

... Within this gallery of horrors, the destiny of Saif Isaac al-Heit stands out like no other. Distinguishing himself from all his peers, he brings to the legend of the Saifs a splendor that sustains to this day all those who dream and theorize about African unity.

To attribute the historical renaissance of the Nakem Empire to this singular figure, one would have to give credence to the sinister litany of the imperial dictators from days past, recited from the mouths of the elders. Thus, it happened that Saif Moche Gabbai of Honaine—according to the prophecies of a seer, who had foretold that on a certain day in 1420, the Saif would be overthrown by an infant who hailed from Tillaberi-Bentia, capital of the Nakem Empire—no longer heeded the whims of pregnant women and put to death all newborn boys, whose decapitated heads he sat in a row on the long wall of his antechamber. But, there was at least one mother by the name of Tiebiramina— far more fortunate than the rest !—who was able to hide her newborn son under the cover of night, fleeing with her husband and three faithful servants to Gagol-Gosso, where they later resided.

After reaching manhood and growing to become as strong as he was brave, Isaac al-Heit, who was the son of this couple, enlisted his services with a troop of militants.

Here, we reach a contested point where tradition becomes mired in legend and is finally consumed by it; for the scribal accounts fail to provide extensive commentary, and the versions of the elders diverge from those of the griots, whose tales contradict those of the chroniclers.

According to one version, Isaac al-Heit was already a powerful lord before becoming a militant. It was said by some that he lived with his elderly parents, who dwelled among the nobility in a province along the Rande. According to others, he lost his parents in a massacre, during the days of the punitive raids of Saif Moche Gabbai of Honaine, and was himself pierced by a spear. A poor Gondaite farmer saved his life by tending to him during many long days and nights, until he fully recovered. Still others claim that he joined the troop of militants because he was not insensible to the splendors and glories of military life.

When God the Most High makes the sun—diamond in the mansion of His celestial power—set against the evening sky, the following tale is recounted in the talismanic manuscripts of the ancient sages, in the recitals of the oral traditions, as well as in the famous epic (contested by some because it denies the Saif's Jewish origins and claims instead that he was an ordinary black man) of Mahmud Meknud Traore, a descendant from a long line of griots, who was appointed griot of the contemporary African Republic of Nakem-Zuiko, the sole vestige of the Ancient Empire of Nakem:

The Lord Almighty—holy is His Name—granted us the favor of bringing forth, at the founding of the Black Nakem Empire, our illustrious ancestor, the Black Jew Abraham al Heit, the child of a black father and an Oriental Jewish mother from Kenana (Canaan), who was descended from Jews of Cyrenaica and Tuat, late-coming migrants to Nakem who traveled across the Aïr Mountains, following in the footsteps of Cornelius Balbus.

God the Most High acted thus in order to bestow His blessings and special favors upon the royal lineage of the Saifs—prayer and peace be upon it!—among whom none was more illustrious than the very pious and devout Isaac al Heit, who was reputed to have set free one slave during each day of his rule. The secret of his strength was his pious renunciation of all the trappings of princely life, preferring instead to run off with a troop of passing adventurers.

Thus it was that the valorous and extraordinarily brave Isaac al Heit came to know hunger, thirst, fevers, the shocks of battle, and the agony of the dying. A hundred times he was left for dead. Thanks be to the blessings of the Meek and Just Master of All Worlds, he always managed to escape death, for his demise was deemed unacceptable to God and to all men of goodwill: *wassalam!*

And thus it was that the noble ardor of Isaac al Heit (God refresh his couch!) was rekindled amidst the piles of rotting corpses that were left in the wake of Saif Moche Gabbai of Honaine (the curse of God be upon him!). When Isaac at last drew forth his sword, the sun and the moon alike gleamed upon his blade, and the image of the earth was mirrored in its steel.

In short, God the Almighty bestowed great blessings upon Isaac al Heit, who managed to assemble a mighty army from a throng of fugitive slaves, rebellious peasants, courageous but impoverished townsfolk, warriors, adventurers, orphans, who all assembled under his banner.

The ranks of his army swelled. He became famous. His council was sought from all quarters.

Time and again, he defeated the Berbers, the Moors and the Tuareg; he was formally recognized by the Sheikh Abderrahman es Soyouti; he was helped in his hour of need by the Sheikh Muhammad ibn Abdelkerim al Meghili, the Sheikh Chamharuch of the Race of the Djinn, and the Hassanide Mulay al Abbas, Prince of Mecca: God be merciful upon them all! At Benghazi, he fought the enemies of the Imam Abubakr ibn Umar al Yemani; at Tripoli, he destroyed the blasphemous usurpers who wished to assassinate the Cadi Abdelquahhar ibn al Fizan; and, once, when he found himself not far from Alger amidst the tribesmen of Beni Tsa'aleb, the Sheikh Abderrahman al Tsa'albi himself informed him of the prediction of the Imam Mahmud, Grand Sheriff of Mecca: "So that the thirst of the men of the Nakem Empire may be satisfied, a new Saif has been ordained to be sent unto them. You are the one He has chosen, Isaac al Heit, for you are the water, the salt, and the bread. You are a saint and the appointed caliph of God. Know also that, after you, there will only be one other caliph upon whom God's eternal light will shine, a man who will come from the Takrur region of the Nakem Empire, and who will appear at the end of the eighth century of the Hijra. God will bestow all manner of riches, power, and glory upon you both, which you will spend in ways deemed agreeable to Him."

In the days to follow, Isaac al Heit defeated Saif Moche Gabbai of Honaine—God curse his reign!—of whom it is said that, at the moment of his defeat, the world darkened before his eyes, and his enraged face turned as yellow as pepper. Forced to retreat, he came upon the Yame River, into which he hurriedly descended, following the river as far south as the land of Sao, where he later died from a burst spleen. His death meant that all power would now pass into the hands of the meek and beloved Isaac al Heit, who assumed the royal title of Saif and dubbed himself Saif Isaac al Heit (God refresh his couch!).

Fact or fiction, the legend of Saif Isaac al Heit continues to haunt the dreams of black romantics even in our own days, especially in the rhetoric of the politicians of the modern republics, for his memory continues to enflame the popular imagination. Many historians promote his cult in the oral traditions, praising him for his key role during the celebrated and unparalleled days of the first African States. In those glorious days of old, it is said, the king was both a sage and philosopher, the founder of a prosperous new epoch in human history. The excavation of this glorious era, or so it is said, has become the most urgent task of archaeology, history, numismatics, and the other academic disciplines, including the natural sciences and ethnology.

But the true facts should not be forgotten: traces of the past as it really was—undoubtedly fascinating in its own right— may be found in our own era only in the ancient manuscripts of the Arabs and in the African oral tradition, which tell us the following:

At his death in 1498, the meek and just emperor Saif Isaac al Heit left three sons to inherit his power: the first born, Joshua, a devoted servant of God, took no interest in matters of state; the second born was Saif al Haram; and the youngest was Saif al Hilal; he also left behind eight daughters and four wives: Ramina, Dogobusseb, Aissina, and Awa. Some seven years before his death, however, during the Feast of Tabaski, the Emperor Saif Isaac al Heit slipped while trying to climb into the saddle of his horse and so fell flatly upon his back. Saif al Hilal, the youngest of his three sons, hurried towards his father in order to help the old man back to his feet; but, the elder brother Saif al Haram imagined that the old man's fall was comical: This disrespectful son not only had the irreverence to burst into loud peals of laughter, he even fetched his father's courtiers and stable-boys so that they too might have a laugh at the old man's expense.

That very night, at the hour when the errant jackals howl in the bush, the Emperor publicly disinherited his older son for all time, cursing Saif al Haram before his entire court, the Assembly of Notables, and the Council of Elders. He also predicted a life of woe and decadence for him.

Thus it was that after the death of the just and meek Saif al Hait (God grant to him salvation!), his chosen son Saif al Hilal ascended to the imperial throne, but—to complete his father's disgrace—his rule was fated to last only thirty days. For Saif al Haram, who proclaimed that the royal couple must be made up of both the queen mother and one of the deceased emperor's sons, married all four of his late father's wives in a single night— including his own mother Ramina—thereby taking total power of the kingdom, but not before binding the feet and hands of his younger brother—the legitimate heir to the throne—and throwing him into a dungeon.

The deposed son was shackled, his hands and feet tied behind his back, forced to relieve himself in his clothes, as well as to grovel for the food that appeared at the door of his prison cell. Sometime on the twelfth day of Ramadan, he began to be eaten by maggots, eventually dying on the twentieth day of the same month... A prayer for him.

... Later, the Emperor Saif al Haram—the curse of God upon him!—returned in victory from a war that he had waged against the Fulani, bringing with him twelve thousand Toucouleur slaves. At the hour when the sun is at its most cruel, this evil brother and accursed son waved to the ecstatic mob of on-lookers, as his noble steed pranced before the gates of Tillaberi-Bentia. Upon his right, the notables, the chiefs from various provinces, court dignitaries, and, upon his left, the women, children, and the elderly. Behind him, his victorious army formed a lengthy hedge around the Toucouleur slaves, who were shackled in iron at the ankles. In an instant, it seemed as if all of the Saif's evil deeds had been washed clean.

After entering the courtyard of his palace in full glory, he attempted to descend from his horse in order to greet his wives, who were also his step-mothers, when—as befalls all those who blaspheme against Your Holy Name!—he was knocked to the ground by a sudden jerk from his horse. As the Saif fell with a thud, he tore open the breeches of his blue tunic, displaying his lower extremities—not unlike Adam on the day of his birth—to the stunned crowd of on-lookers.

The fanatic and stupefied witnesses revealed their profound idiocy by interpreting this event to be a divine omen… More than one witness, however, later confirmed that the saddle-strap of his horse had been deliberately filed, in order to cause this public humiliation. The Saif's men seized all possible suspects by the ears, shaved their skulls, tattooing a cross upon the soles of their feet, so that their every step would be displeasing to God; then, they were threatened with eternal damnation, they along with their fathers, their mothers, their ancestors, and all their descendants. The disgraced courtiers, who were named as the principle suspects, were also required to confess their crimes to God, who replied to them in the guise of the Saif's sorcerer. In the end, they were banished and exiled to Digal, where they were promptly trampled underfoot by the Saif's horses; a Tuareg dagger was ritually blessed before it was thrust seven times into each of their eye-sockets, their ears, their testicles, and then rotated into the hollow of their navels. All the blood from their bodies was slowly drained before they were at last pitched into a great bonfire, called to eternal glory by the meek Master of all worlds.

And yet Saif al Haram, seemingly in dread of his father's prophecy, or perhaps desiring relief from the guilty memory of his dead father and murdered brother, eventually decided that he would "abdicate" the crown following a long (and strategic) illness, which was punctuated by several brilliant (and equally strategic) foreign expeditions against the Gutes, the Jakuks, and the Vantungs. The newly appointed "emperor" was a Tuareg slave, who was actually a petty attendant of the Saif al Haram—an imperturbable figure of lava and laterite—who did everything in his power to undermine the nobility; the name of this "emperor" was Abdul Hassana, a man who was sly, dishonest, and yet strangely subdued in his cruelty.

On the advice of Saif al Haram, this "devout" petty official took the pilgrimage to Mecca, from whence he returned one year later, bearing the title of "al Hadj" (a pilgrim from the Holy Land). Dispensing holy water to the sick from the town of the Prophet Muhammad, he imagined that he could placate all his political enemies, cause the lame to walk, restore the sight of the blind, and convert the unbelievers to the "true" faith: *alif lam!*

He was compelled nonetheless to show evidence of his spiritual gifts; for, the water from Mecca the Holy did not win for him a single friend, nor did it restore the sight of the blind, nor did it cause the lame to walk. In fact, it did not even taste very good—sacrilege!—or, so the infidels claimed.

Since his rosary ticked off nothing but evil deeds, Saif al Haram and his disciple Abdul Hassana decided to manufacture their own miracles. It was thus on the 20th of May 1503 that an enormous pyre, by the grace and mercy of God the Most High, suddenly burst into flames. Eighteen notables, all of whom remained loyal to the memory of the just Saif Isaac al Heit and his youngest son, were tossed upon the fires and then roasted alive. As these men were skewered upon the flames, twenty-eight poisonous snakes escaped from under their robes, slithering from the blazing wood before they disappeared, as if guided by the invisible breath of Satan, into small holes that had miraculously appeared in the sand of the imperial court—where they had, of course, been hollowed out the night before...

The delirious crowd let out a long ululation that sounded like the roar of a lion, before all fell upon their knees and burst into a religious hymn: "Wonder of wonders!"

At the hour of the hooting of the wood-owl, the pyre once more exploded into azure tongues of flames, inspiring yet more melodic psalms from the muezzins, who had, all the while, been busying themselves reciting surahs from the Scriptures.

From that day forward, the Saif and his prodigy al Hadj Abdul Hassana commemorated the historic date of this event, which was followed by many other celebrations that were equally gruesome, lighting an immense bonfire on the 20th day of May of each year, thereafter dubbed, *the Vipers of the Supernatural*. A national holiday was born. A hymn in its honor!

And yet, not long after the death of the just Saif Issac al Heit, it was as if Saif al Haram, the son who had been cursed by his own father, as well as his sycophantic minister al Hadj Abdul Hassana, suddenly became afflicted in the collective soul that they did not possess: At great personal expense, they settled the accounts of the most influential and yet least appreciative families of the Empire: It was on behalf of the Saif's worst critics that twelve thousand plates were arranged for each day's meal, accompanied by ample carafes of wine, generous pensions, and titles of nobility that were as weighty as they were worthless. Together, they concocted a veritable fairy tale world for adults: Some three thousand, two hundred, and sixty horses from the royal stables drank milk from watering troughs that were "lined with gold and ivory." *Allah harmin katamadjo!*

In order to satisfy his hunger for public acclaim and for new lands, the Saif—this splendid King of Black Kings—recruited the help of the southern chiefs to increase the traffic in slaves, blessing each bloody adventure with yet more honeyed litanies. The Black man, who has no soul but only working appendages, was thus—contrary to God's will—sold at a discount price in a devil's pact between religion and trade: Mercilessly hunted like a beast of prey, he was beaten to a bloody pulp, shackled in heavy irons and chains and then thrashed within an inch of his life, before he was finally delivered like so many cheap goods to the Portuguese, Spanish, and Arabs (both from the north and from the east), and to the French, Dutch, and English (who poured in from the west), all of whom tended to their carnal property with scrupulous contempt, before casting them upon the four winds.

When the night vomits forth its starry diamonds, the griots of Nakem sing the lament of one hundred million of these wretches who were deprived of all human dignity and then bound like cut-rate cargo, six by six, before they were stowed inside the Christian vessels where not a sliver of light could reach them. And there was not a single merchant of these bargain-priced souls who would even venture a peek into the lower hatchways, out of fear for his own life. One short hour in this pestilent den exacted a heavy price. Orgies of unspeakable atrocity, of foul air, fever, famine, vermin, Beriberi, scurvy, suffocation, and misery beyond measure were celebrated in the dank holes of these evil ships. Thirty percent died in transit. And, since Christian love for one's neighbor is such a beautiful, nearly inhuman, virtue, the god-fearing merchants who commanded these vessels were required to pay a fine for each slave who died en route; those slaves who became as sick as goats in labor were simply tossed into the sea, left to the mercy of the waves and sharks. The same fate was reserved for the newborn babies, who were tossed overboard with all the other dead weight.

… Half naked and completely stupefied, the black-rabble, wide-eyed as the new moon, filed out of the big boats upon their arrival, venturing forth into the new world, where they were scrutinized and haggled over in the public marketplace. Under the eyes of the Almighty (and Just) God, they at last collapsed into a vast, putrefying heap —, a miserable human tide sprawled along the foreign coast, like an enormous black mass of rotting flesh—, a spectacle of unspeakable suffering for the viewing pleasure of all.

And from the front ranks of this heap of broken wretches, from within the mounds of trampled bodies, the cries and death rattles of the black-rabble were occasionally stirred with a lash from the master's whip. The spectators maintained a respectful distance, watching the local priests, who had come to proclaim the word of Christ, but could only bow their heads in disgust as they fidgeted with the beads of their rosaries...

It often happened that a beautiful but modestly attired young lady, whose voice sounded like a chattering guinea fowl, her eye and throat bobbing in nervous agitation—became aroused by the shiny bodies of the slaves, by the trembling virility of their sex organs—and would seek the advice, if not consolation, of her pink-fleshed mother, a self-proclaimed authority on black sexuality, only to hear in reply: "The Holy Father does not approve of *café au lait*..."

There were others who did not stand upon ceremony but instead rolled their incendiary eyes and—like the English pirate Hawkins, who, among others, was knighted by Queen Elizabeth— restocked their armories with *"a demi-Moor in his proper color, bound with a cord." God save the Queen!*[1]

Meanwhile, back in the court of the Nakem Empire, now that the intransigent nobility had been brought into line, the unpopular Saif al Haram instructed his favorite minister to stir up more trouble among the warring, rebellious, and undomesticated tribes, to "sow as much discord as he possibly could."

Using every means at his disposal, the Saif accumulated livestock, farm produce, and every form of wealth imaginable. The raids of the Massai, the Zulus, the Jagas, organized with a more than Machiavellian cunning, awakened in each people, each race, each tribe (thus it was decreed by the Almighty) a simmering impatience whenever their chief, dispatching his army to attack the "enemy of their race" (and finding himself accused of riling up the various inhabitants in order to enslave them for a profit), would shout in response that they had best be quick about it, for their spears were thirsty for the blood of their foes.

Cruel peoples, whose language is little more than a form of croaking, ferocious killers such as those remote forest-dwellers, living in a state of bestiality, copulating with the first woman who crosses their path, who stood tall and were terrible to behold, men with hairy hides and hideously long fingernails, Zulus, Jagas, and Massai, who feasted upon human flesh and were armed with shields, darts, and knifes, who ran about without clothes, savages in their native garb, barbarians in everyday life, men without faith, without law, without sovereign, without roofs over their heads other than the flimsy huts that they built in the forests, which they gladly abandoned at first light, devastated all those whom they met with iron and fire, plundering the various regions along the furthest fringes of the Nakem Empire, compelling all those who lived in such places to fall upon the mercy of the Saif, or to die of hunger, illness, or deprivation.

During this same period, the Nakem provinces suffered such a terrible famine, combined with pestilence, that even an infinitesimal amount of food became worth the price of a slave, that is, less than ten crowns. Driven by the cruel blows of necessity, father would sell his own son, brother his own brother, as each struggled according to his own manner for survival, no matter what the cost. Those sold during the famine were purchased by merchants from Sao-Tome in big ships that were loaded with victuals. The food sellers pretended that they were slave-merchants, and those who found themselves purchased in this way hastened to confirm their own enslaved status, ecstatic to have escaped such dire circumstances. Great numbers of free men were enslaved in this way, men who sold themselves simply in order to survive.

It was thus that in nearly every corner of the Empire and in its vassal regions that a veritable blood bath without precedent was inaugurated. The capture of rebel tribesmen, of men who were free, of defeated militants transformed into prisoners, the sacrifice of the village chief whose flesh was now turned into a feast, all became ritualized ceremonies for wild-eyed black-boys in native garb, whose barbarity was unleashed at the whim of the Emperor and his notables... In the midst of these raids, Saif al Haram encouraged through the use of intermediaries the ritualized blessing of wounded captives via a saber-blow to the head, so that their severed skulls could be hoisted atop of the army's lances and spears, before being deposited upon the doorsteps of the victorious who were thereby consecrated—such is God's will!—as the brave. And, as if the Black possessed the true soul of a man, the chief of the captives and his family were delivered over to the women and children of the village, who promptly spat upon them in a whirl of dances, leaps, screams, chants, and sarcasm, followed by a ceremony during which their souls were purified of their Satanic blackness. On the third day of their captivity, his eyes sparkling with the lust for vengeance, as well as with arrogant hatred, the sorcerer flayed rather than shaved their skulls, which were then coated with karité butter.

Each villager danced before the captives, wielding a curved wooden knife that chaffed in the hand, "stabbing" the chief once for every year of his life and once more for every relation who had ever been taken in a slave raid. And, before ceding his place to the blood lust of the next villager, each squatted before the captive, cursing at him and reviling him, spitting in his face and whacking him three times with the wooden knife, all of which was punctuated by a loud clicking of the tongue. Everyone grew merry at the sight of the ecchymosis of the victims, who gently bled into the night.

The evening of the third day, encumbered by the din of the jingling irons that weighed at his ankles, the chief of these prisoners was—his feet and hands bound as women provocatively danced about him, tantalizing him with glimpses of their naked bodies, thrusting out their breasts with arched backs, stroking the hairy tufts of their sex with the palms of their right hands— castrated by the sorcerer to the ecstasy of those assembled, whose collective pleasure now bordered on hysteria.

In the light of the torches, the unmanned and impotent husband, paralyzed in his pain, thighs gooey with blood, beheld each of his wives transformed into—first, standing upright and then rolled about in the dirt for yet another turn on the ground— randy whores who were compelled to service the conquering village, as they were each undressed and then raped, one after another, to the intoxicating rhythm of the tam-tam, by each and every villager, men and women alike…

Two days later, during the vigil before the sacrifice— washed in a "purifying" tub, and then coated in cow butter up to their shoulders (their children having already been disemboweled while in flight) —, they were all painted in peanut oil and tethered to a post. It was the seventh day of their captivity, but the men and women of the village had thus far failed in their efforts to kill them by sheer provocation, by depriving them of all speech and bodily movement. The wretched captives, feverish at the thought of their imminent deaths, their eyes aflame and their mouths drooling with saliva and insults, sought to kill their enemies by ramming them with their heads; they clawed, bit, yelped, searching for any means possible to avenge themselves.

On the evening of the seventh day, satiated on palm wine and inebriated on millet beer, howling like wounded dogs, the captives exploded within minutes once they were set upon the fires, their fat loudly crackling in the dancing flames, before their meat—as white as that of a milk-fed pig—was peeled off by the expert fingers of the cannibals. The marrow of their skulls, as well as the severed vaginas of the women, were reserved as rare delicacies that were eaten by the "well-to-do" men of the village; the testicles of the chief ended up in a broth that was intended to be an aphrodisiac, which was "digested" by the women in their big communal soup bowl, thoughtfully garnished with red peppers and other strong spices. An orgiastic drinking bout crowned this anthropophagic feast, which, whether it was inspired by hatred, instinct, the thirst for evil, the taste for blood and vengeance, or, perhaps, in order to possess the attributes of the eaten victims, was one of the most sinister traces of this phantom Africa, over which loomed the ominous shadow of Saif al Haram. A tear for it.

On April 20, 1532, during an evening that was as smooth as damp satin, Saif al Haram, in performing his conjugal "duty" with all four of his step-mothers, repeatedly and at the same time, had the impudent weakness to overindulge in the well-known pleasures of connubial bliss, and ended by giving up the ghost... The next day, his crow-eyed minister al Hajj Abdul Hassana, who had set up house with an ephebe and with Hawa, the loveliest of the Saif's stepmothers, was surprised in his bed by a poisonous asp, which he stroked in his hand in the mistaken belief that it was something else. He opened his mouth wide three times before he died, pricked to death! ... His successor was his cousin Holongo, "a horrible biped with the brutal face of a buffalo," humpbacked in front and back, who, in the midst of a fevered moan of supplication, expired in the arms of Aiosha, a wench who strangled him during the most jubilant moment of his ecstasy, following two years of a reign that was carried on by Saif Ali, a righteous-seeming pederast, mischievous as a donkey with a thick hide, who was killed six months later by the sin of gluttony, and then followed in his turn by Saif Djibril, kid brother of Ali, also killed by the sin of indiscretion, only to be replaced by one of the sons of Ramina (mother of Saif al Haram, who had been knocked up by her own son, albeit not without a few difficulties)—a certain Saif Youssoufi—a notoriously ugly albino who had been assaulted on two separate occasions by some suitor or another of his wife, before he was finally overwhelmed on the third time, at last carried off by a fatal wind of which he remained completely oblivious, ceding his crown to Saif Medioni of Mostaganem, who was himself called to glory only ten days later, torn between, it was said, the contrary angels of Mercy and Justice. One after another, the remaining children of the accursed Saif and his stepmothers took their turns upon the throne: Saif Ezekiel, who ruled for four years and was then dethroned; Saif Ismael, thwarted for seven months, then dismissed; and the third, Saif Benguigui of Saida, who dozed through five years of rule: it was as if the Court spoke with an eternally forked tongue.

Years without glory, their shame was drowned in forgetfulness. It seemed that all three of these later Saifs were born of a serpent—their accursed father. Lacking in hope or courage, they welcomed the coming of icy death with empty hands. At Tillaberi-Bentia, things reached such a nadir of debasement and impotence that, from morning till night, the old men did little more than snooze under the village palaver tree, dreaming of the glory days of the just Saif Isaac al Heit. Their perseverance in remaining vertiginous dreamers was finally rewarded by the tender mercies of Heaven: for they were all attacked in the same night by ... three poisonous serpents. Ah, those were the good old days! Ah, traditional values...

Thus, it was in 1545, the noble riff-raff, who had made a vocation of dominating and debasing the Nakem people, discovered themselves in the same situation that they had been in back in 1532: living in instability and constant peril and seeming, more than ever, to be bound to a lifestyle of total corruption, *Maschallah! Wa bismillah!* The name of Allah be upon them and beside them!

... Coffers were empty, hearts were weary, and corruption was immeasurable. While waiting for the Black Messiah to save them, the Commander of Believers who would restore the imperial tradition, the families of notables throughout the Rande province took to baptizing their children with the name of Saif the Just, Saif Isaac al Heit. It was a wasted effort, for the Eternal, in His mercy, brought forth an epidemic of yellow fever that dashed all their hopes within a single month, weeding out these diverse and youthful pretenders to the throne...

Hardened by this paternal festival of divine will, with his turban enshrined like a halo upon his head, the last descendant of the accursed Saif, Saif Rabban Yohanan ibn Zaccai, mounted upon his royal steed, which seemed to have galloped out from under his shorts, drew forth his cutlass and split the luminous air of dawn that now broke over Tillaberi-Bentia.

Drawing near the bed of evil spirits of the imperial court, he brought to account with a single blow all those who were guilty of the sin of sleepiness. Henceforth named Emperor, he was showered for eight years with honors, during which he domesticated the throng of envy-sodden notables; but, at the time of the Feast of Tabaski, while basking in his popularity among the more acrimonious of his subjects, breathing in the air from the perfumed armpits of his ladies of honor, he suddenly dropped to the earth with a thud, where his puckered lips were greeted by the shit-splattered hoofs of his horse. "The evening rose moistened his temples," as it is written in the chronicle, "and his hands clasped the shaft of the arrow that had pierced him, depriving him of the chance to even say *amen*, or to become a mere victim." A tear for him.

And thus, certain that Saif Rabban Yohanan ibn Zaccai was destined only for the earth below, which slept along with him, the Gondaites, who now cracked the knuckles of their crapulous but contented fingers, leveled the copious knolls of clay earth-dwellings, the last outposts of the Saif's partisans, before hurling themselves upon his imperial throne.

Two hundred years had passed during which the courtesans, farmers, militants, men and women of rank, slaves, and blacksmiths had together sung the Saifs' praises, all the while lining their pockets and growing fat on imperial cheese, the mere stench of which, for the cunning few, could obtain them entry to the bloody festivities of the corrupt, where by aping the Court they could procure land, livestock, titles of nobility, money and all that it could buy, starting with women.

In this dissolute and thoroughly dizzying era, when all castes freely intermingled, when embezzlement and vice were openly displayed, the Arab conquest, the history of which dates back several centuries, burst upon them from the north like the violent laugh of a dog with dazzling white teeth: subjugated slaves and various defeated tribes were sold off to Mecca, Egypt, Ethiopia, the Red Sea, the Americas, and Arabia at prices that were as ridiculous as the besotted dignity of the black-rabble.

An able-bodied man who was robust and strong cost a little more than a she-goat and a little less than a he-goat, the tenth of a cow, and the eighth of a camel; in the marketplace, he fetched about a thousand of the shells called coweries, or two tablets of salt. And, as if grateful for his own debasement, the slave found himself sold at an unprecedented scale, a commerical industry that was masked by the cult of spiritual values and by the creation of Arab universities (hitherto rare) at Tillaberi-Bentia, Granta and Grosso, universities which were well-known in the world of international commerce and oriental trade …

… The Empire began to fall apart … The Saif dynasty disintegrated along its paternal branch, among the grand-children of Saif Rabban Yohanan ibn Zaccai, the oldest being Jacob who, the griots say, spent his evenings "lecturing upon intricate theological conundrums to his cat." The discretion of the cat was such that, in order to spare Jacob from his fears of life in the hereafter, it would steel away upon its two hind-paws at the dawn of each new day. After a brief nap, Jacob, who dressed as a simple Levite, would submit to the discipline of scholarship, inculcated by whip and rod, which hammered into him many fine sentiments and numerous spiritual values. But, since he hardly ever spoke, the Court found him to be amiable, if completely worthless. After the death of his father, his younger brothers took control of his portion of the inheritance, not contenting themselves with stealing the throne by intrigue. They did such a thorough job that Jacob, his hairy mouth as tiny as a bird's beak, was compelled to live upon their charity.

One day while he sat in the shade of the tree where the green rock of forgetfulness is buried, his head sunk deep in reverie, he noticed that the imperial palanquin happened to be passing by. It was a warm day, and the men who carried the palanquin upon their shoulders asked if he could lend them a hand. His eyes smiling with gentle reassurance, Jacob obediently arose, saluting the Emperor, his brother, before taking his place as a common porter. But, the further he advanced, the more the palanquin was jostled about, for,

Jacob, in marching with the other porters, hopped rather than walked, to avoid crushing the ants, insects, and toads underfoot—since he revered them as well as the lives of all living creatures.

At last the Emperor cried out, "Don't you know how to march, you imbecile? Let go of the palanquin at once!"

Jacob looked at his brother Saif Tsevi, and, in a voice as smooth as honey, replied, "To whom do you speak in such a rude manner, calling an imbecile? In all of Nakem, beneath its clear blue heavens and along its mother-of-pearl horizon, do you know of a single living man who is not the mirror image of yourself? How therefore can you be angry at yourself?"

An immense light shone forth from Jacob's eyes as he spoke; those who heard his words were awestruck. The Emperor climbed down from his palanquin and prostrated himself before the sage: "May I eat your diseases, venerable lord, my brother, in the abode of the quick and the dead!"

Jacob thus sat down upon the roadside, and for many hours, his eyes wide and his brow bent upon the supernatural, instructed the Emperor Saif Tsevi in "the true wisdom," doing such a thorough job that the heart of his pupil at last vibrated in unctuous harmony with his own ...

But the beautiful union of knowledge and morality is fragile, for it happened that Saif Tsevi not long afterwards seduced his own sister, whom he succeeded in transforming into his mistress, and that his sister, for her part, once she was married and finally grown to adulthood, was allowed to turn ten-year old boys into her own personal concubines...

... After bewailing the passing of his favorite wife, the Berber-Jew Yehochua, Saif Tsevi, who was an obstinate swine, hastened to marry Lyangombe, a black sorceress affiliated with a secret society of sorcerers and magicians, whose consecrated ancestor is depicted as a bisexual being—equipped with a phallus on one side, and three vaginas on the other. In the private lives of the people of this society, who had about as much courage as a wet chicken, the rule of hospitality for the master of the house decreed that he must—in a quasi-tragedy for one and all—consent to allow all manner of guests to enjoy the sexual favors of his wives.

In their public life, they honored terrible Sabbaths, to which their members would steal away in the nights, traversing the bush, making themselves known to their fellow conspirators by imitating the howling cries of the hyena. During these saturnalian festivities, incest was licit and even recommended, combined with rites such as human sacrifice followed by incestuous orgies and coitus with beasts; as if the Black was required to be—*Ya atrash!*— nothing more than a savage.

The presiding sorcerer and sorceress ordered all those assembled to sit in a circle upon the ground, their legs crossed, where they sang gentle hymns about the virtues of their sex organs, disrobing until they were completely in the nude, before they publicly copulated, urging—with tears of happiness at their own conspicuous appetites—each man who was present to copulate with three, four, or five women, repeatedly and with as many as his strength allowed him. Saif Tsevi and his two other brothers, Soussan and Youssef, who were present on this particular night—guided by the insolent genitals of Satan—were discovered the next morning by peddlers, all three in the nude, their throats bloodied with teeth-marks from the very bitches whom they had pleasured the night before, now asleep in their arms, strangled.

Thus it was that the only survivor of the paternal branch of the Saifs turned out to be Jacob, a man who was as humble and wise as he was luminously poor, and who, eight years later, was busy counting stars at the hour of his death. A desolation upon his tomb.

However, in the midst of this dreadful intersection of tradition, extortion, violence, and dilettantism that encapsulated the lives of the pious, the feudal, the landed, the lazy, as well as the sensuous, some of the most powerful Muslim families endured: for instance, those who dwelled in some remote province, circle, or canton, or who exercised power in an unambiguous though relatively limited fashion. It was because local authority had become compartmentalized that colonial conquest was first made possible, as indigenous conflicts were brought to heel in locale after locale, but not within wider zones of cultural influence or in the most important capitals. The white man had spoken of the right of colonization, the necessity of partition, "the sacred duty of international charity." He believed that it was imperative that he bring "civilization" to those less fortunate, to abolish the slave trade that scorched the continent like a flaming torch.

And, much later, addressing the people, the Saif observed: "No one denies the more constructive aspects of colonization: but, it should not be forgotten that, along with its benefits, such as education, it was accompanied by very great evils— such as 'assimilation,' the scorn of indigenous culture, etc. —; one should therefore not neglect to ask if, given the tardy character of these various benefits, they are not actually the result of colonization itself, but of decolonization. Universal suffrage, a strong work ethnic, self-determination, reparation from the profits of colonization between colonizer and colonized are not therefore the fruits of colonization, but of the war against colonization."

Or, consider the following:

At the time that the White Man, arriving like a mournful dirge in Lent, launched the conquest of Africa, the chiefs among the Randigue, the Gondaites, the Fulani, and the N'Godos, agreed, including the minor tribes, that mutual respect was a necessary precondition of gaining independence, including the cessation of all wars and outbreaks of hostilities against one another. But, once the necessary conditions had been met—for practice makes perfect—, the same chiefs, desiring to reestablish their authority during this fortuitous time of calm, donned the mask of modernization, promising their serfs, both their domestic help, as well as their slaves from time immemorial, that, due to their fears of an anticipated aggression from a neighboring tribe, they would temporarily be—*oye!*—"considered subjects with provisional liberty and equality." Then, once peace was restored among the diverse tribes, civil war having not yet broken out—hee, hee—the same notables promised to these same subjects that after … hmm… um… hmm… a brief "apprenticeship" in compulsory labor, they would at last obtain the Rights of Man in recompense… No mention was ever made of the rights of citizenship. Halleluiah!

Compulsory labor was therefore regimented as a vital feature of the economy of each province of the Nakem Empire, now dismantled by a multitude of petty kings, who aped one another in province after province. The religious aristocracy (cooperating with the notables) announced to the illuminated people that, with the end of compulsory labor and the inauguration of "labor undertaken in absolute freedom" all would obtain— bing!—*iru turu inè turu*, "true liberty and complete citizenship" …

Every aristocrat, every notable therefore allotted—what could be more democratic!—a plot of land to his serfs, who were compelled to cultivate every centimeter of property "for the improvement of their souls."

Hence, eighteen years after the arrival of the Whites, thirty years after the birth, in the maternal branch of the Saifs, of Saif ibn Isaac al Heit (that is, the son of Saif Isaac al Heit)—the notables exhorted the Nakem people to remember "the much elevated path of calm living and traditional values, of which God himself offered the most luminous example."

… While waiting for the dawning of this glorious day, for the coming of a new world in which serf would at last become equal to king, the black-rabble—a short-leash for these wicked curs!—accepted it all. Forgive us, Lord. *Amba, koubo ouma agoum.*

Thus it was that Saif ibn Issac al Heit—who resembled, it was said, trait for trait, his ancestor Saif Isaac al Heit, and who became the spiritual son of the later with help from the sheikhs, the emirs, the ulemas, who granted to him sovereignty over the Nakem Empire and proclaimed him to be an apostle according to the theory of *spiritual succession*—reestablished the alliance between the empire's aristocrats and notables, all of whom, having removed their lemon-yellow slippers and deposited them outside the door of the mosque, now practiced Islam with pious humility, assiduously applying themselves to the conversion of the fetishers, who had the misfortune to succumb to the inclinations of their own black souls. The exploitation and domination of the blackrabble could not have been more complete. May the Evil One be forever banished!

And, in fact, by this point, the slave trade was long known by the aristocrats and notables to be a bad business, having laid waste to entire regions, whose people vanished like water in thirsty sand, making it increasingly difficult to find reliable workers. In the end, they decided that it was far preferable to fleece the people by way of taxes, public fines, and various other forms of levies, both direct and indirect, by pressuring them to cultivate the land on behalf of the notables in exchange for a reward in the Afterlife, where their hard work would surely be compensated, and, finally, by cooking up for them a steady diet of religious exercises—the ultimate insurance—, beginning with Islamic prayers five times a day, so that homegrown spiritual idiots could busy themselves in seeking the Eternal Kingdom of Allah. In truth, religion in Nakem was brutally vomited up, forsaken in preference for a cultish, idiomatic, and confused mumbling about human dignity—exchanged for a mystifying pedagogy that was instilled by mindless method and rote memorization, the aims of which were finally political. Marabouts and notables alike used religion to enrich themselves, entering into showy polygamous alliances with the wealthiest families, thereby consolidating their interests, as each hurried off to take the pilgrimage to Mecca, the "Holy Land." Intelligence is a gift from the One who settles all accounts: *wassalam!*

And yet the fact is that the nobility, after having waged war from the time of the first Saifs (glory to God the Almighty!), had schemed in order to increase their own personal power: *Amen.* At the death of the accursed Saif (blessed be the Eternal One!), understanding the need for political stability (such as it was), the nobility schemed to burden the people with every known form of pseudo-spirituality, all the while materially enslaving them in their daily lives.

The Imam Mahmud, Grand Sheriff of Mecca, had he not predicted that, in the thirteenth century of the Hijra, a Caliph who was of Takrur origins would appear? Was it not also true that Saif ibn Isaac al Heit's mother, "in obedience to the decrees of the Eternal," had given birth and baptized her son in the Takrur at the very dates foretold in prophecy and in legends of old? …

Thus it was that this later Saif had the good fortune to have been sufficiently groomed to play the role of Black Messiah, compared to many other sons of the nobility, who squandered their personal fortunes in vain. But, it is not Christ himself who elects a messianic vocation! Forgive us, Lord, for chasing after the cults that are dressed up in Your Name…

… Launched from every possible quarter in the second half of the XIXth century, multiple geographical societies, international associations of philanthropists, pioneers, economists, adventurers, bank agents, educational institutions, the Marines, and the Army set in motion a veritable struggle to the death between the various European powers, who swarmed across the lands of the Nakem, fighting among themselves, conquering, pacifying the natives, securing treaties, burying, as a token of their peaceful intentions, their stockpiles of flint, gunpowder, and bullets. "We will bury war so deeply in the bowels of the earth that our children will never be able to dig it out again," they said. "The tree that takes root on this site will attest to the eternal alliance between Whites and Blacks. Peace will endure between us, so long as its branches do not bear the evil fruit of bullets, cartridges, and gunpowder."

And thus began in earnest the scramble to exploit the black-rabble. The Whites, defending colonization as an international right, championed the theory of zones of influence, which legitimated the claims of the first occupants. But these "first occupants" arrived too late, for, thanks to the efforts of the notables and the aristocracy, the true colonizer had long ago set up shop in the Nakem—the Saif, for whom the European– whatever he may have imagined!—was merely the pawn. In fact, the European "conqueror" offered little more than technical assistance to the Saif, feeble though it was! So be it, oh Lord! May Your Word be eternally sanctified and exalted!

Note

1. Both of these italicized phrases appear in English in the original text.

II

THE ECSTASY AND THE AGONY

A thoroughly displeased Saif ibn Isaac al Heit, with perfumed mouth and honeyed tongue, now orchestrated the mobilization of his fanatical people's energies against the foreign invader, manufacturing new miracles upon a daily basis throughout the Nakem Empire: the earth shook; tombs fell open; countless saints returned from the dead; streams of milk flowed whenever the Saif happened to pass; visions of archangels appeared in the misty twilight; wooden buckets from the village wells now brimmed with blood; during one of his travels, he transformed three pages from the "Holy Book," the Qur'an, into as many doves, which fluttered before his path, as if urging the devotion of the people to the sacred cause of the Saif; and, with the skill of a true diplomat, he feigned his profound disdain for the material things of this world: all of this was business as usual.

But no matter how refined his religious stratagems—May Allah protect him from the evil eye!—he was finally compelled to renounce supernatural miracles in preference for the military arts, which had fallen into complete destitution.

From then on, throughout the Nakem, the Ziuko-Nakem, the Goro Foto Zinko, the Yame, the Geboue, the Katsena, and the lands of the Sao, the Galibi, the Gohou, the Gondaites, the Dargol, and the N'Godos, weapons began to amass: spears, lances, poisoned arrows, javelins, swords, daggers, sabers, muskets, and military arms of all sorts, each blessed three times by Saif ibn Isaac al Heit, were delivered to the keeping of the militants. At the same time, sorcerers, who were mounted upon black mules, charmers of boas and cobras, magicians who were versed in the black arts, criminals specializing in painful forms of death, herbalists cunning in methods of poisoning, of befouling wells and watering troughs, assassins who were connoisseurs of lethal plants, dangerous weapons, and terrifying beasts, and who, with the dawn of each new day, became more and more devoted to the cause of fatherland and religion. Fetishes, warriors, serpents, wasps, cheetahs, arrows, elephants, panthers—all became assault vehicles of the Nakem resistance.

The entrails of more than a hundred scouts from the invader's army literally exploded after a few sips from the poisoned ponds; terrified at what their eyes beheld, black *tirailleurs* deserted the army of the Whites in droves. Slain by arrows, as well as by poison, the ranks of the invaders were soon infiltrated by spies who stole their rifles, gunpowder, bullets, and uniforms, and who kept the Saif informed of their every footstep.

With his sword suspended in his right hand, Saif hewed a path as wide as a village road. The brave militants who were blessed by Saif imagined that they were invincible: yet, they ended up as pale shades under a moonless sky, slaughtered by the thousands; as it was remarked in those days, however, "They did not actually die; they merely returned to their celestial abodes on High." *Djallè! Djallè! Amoul bop! Makoul Fallé!*

And that is why the night lingers, whiter than the dawn of every passing day.

The long row of officers in charge of the loitering *tirailleurs* wearily slog their way upon a winding path overrun with straggling brush. Each seeks to appear calm and ruthless, but Africa is always there, awaiting them in the bush. The rainy season brought a truce between the insurgents and the foreign troops, but, early in 1898, the whites invaded Groure and Nieke, bordering territories of great wealth and vast populations, where gold powder was hidden in the hollowed out tusks of elephants, in the crooks of ivory curios, in small antelope horns encased in red leather.

Throughout all the provinces, the black insurgents conduct raids to kidnap black captives; with the money they earn, they buy horses, gunpowder, armory, augmenting, as if by design, the ever-growing ranks of black slaves, while the Whites, for their part, take control of the land.

All is raped, sacked, violated—and the captives, numbering around eight thousand, are rounded up into a herd, which the colonel parcels out. At first, he carefully records everything in his ledger, but he ends by throwing up his hands, crying, "Just get them out of my sight!"

And thus every White Man obtains more than ten black women of his choosing. The return trip to headquarters is made in forty-kilometer stretches, all the captives in tow. Children, the sick, and invalids alike are killed with slashing bayonets and rifle-butts to the head. Their bodies are strewn like garbage along the roadside. A woman is found squatting. She is pregnant. They jostle her, propelling her onward, kicking her from behind with their knees. Still marching, she gives birth while standing up. The umbilical cord is barely cut and tossed aside, when the baby is kicked to the side of the road: the march goes on as before. The haggard mother hobbles for a bit, delirious, reeling, and wailing in her misery, before she finally collapses a hundred meters down the road, where she is soon trampled.

Time goes by. Fresh tornadoes assault the land with massive gales of water, flooding the trails and roads with rivers of mud. The Yame River swells, widening its tributaries along the lower plains.

Those Blacks responsible for carrying the rations go for five days without food, receiving forty lashes if they so much as help themselves to a handful of the ten to twenty-five kilos of food that they carry upon their naked, shaved heads. The *tirailleurs*, enlisted men, non-commissioned officers, and commissioned officers are in charge of so many slaves that it is impossible for them to count them, much less feed and lodge them. After arriving at Gagol-Gosso, which has by now capitulated to the Whites, they ask for food and shelter for the captives, to which the chief responds with a shrug, "You must sell them." And, so they did. Those who did not fetch a price were drowned in order to preserve cartridges. And the march continued, peopled by a nightmare of towns and villages that resisted them, attacking them in the nights behind their columns, dropping hundreds of bee-nests upon them, flooding the air with poisoned or flaming arrows, encircling them in rings of fire.

But such efforts amounted to little more than mild annoyances that did not prevent the Whites from regaining their composure and later dispatching black *tirailleurs*—the true shock troops—to "break the spirit" of the village, once it had been sacked by the invading soldiers.

In the course of these raids, villages were burnt to the ground, fields and harvest ransacked, slaves sold in droves, countless half-breeds conceived in violence and then abandoned as soon as they were born, not to mention another unforeseen consequence of the invasion:

Relatives of the black *tirailleurs*, those who were devoted to the cause of the Whites, were sometimes accidentally given away or sold. To remedy these blunders, innumerable "travel passes" were issued on behalf of those adversely affected. "Permit Moussa, who is on his way to Granta, accompanied by a man and a small girl who are *non libres*, to travel freely in order to redeem one of his captured relatives at Gagol-Gosso..." "Permit Ali, who is en route to Zemba, to travel freely in order to look for a captive named Niama Kimane, who was accidentally given to Amala, a non-combatant in Borgnis Desborde's regiment, who took part in the assault upon the town of Buanga-Fele..."

... But, at very long intervals, a caravan journeyed across the infinite expanse and knolls upon the abysmal plains, black caravans, processions of men, women, and children, driven forward with the lash of a bullwhip, covered in ulcers, gasping for air in their iron collars, hands bloodied from their chains.

In spirals above them, crows, buzzards, bald vultures with long, hairless necks flew overhead, monitoring the progress of the caravan, confident that, when the time came, they would get their chance to feast upon these walking cadavers, who, weakened from their festering wounds, their bellies swollen with famine, would finally succumb; and from those wretches who were abandoned on the road because their feet, worn to the bone with open sores, refused to carry them any further... Throughout Upper-Rande, as well as across the Yame, to the north and to the south of the Grand River, from Krotti-Bentia to Dangabiara, there is neither road nor footpath without such outposts of death and criminal activity, the only sites where commerce flourishes in these desolate lands, now under the protection of the White Man... According to every credible source who had visited these lands, or who had lived there, a caravan of slaves that was captured in war, whether its was guided by a native or not, lost about a third of its cargo in human flesh before it finally arrived at its destination where the slaves were distributed.

As for the "friendly" villages, they were required only to supply the provisions that had been formally requisitioned, as well as beasts of burden, men who had been drafted into service because they were robust enough to serve as carriers, and who were often abandoned without resources a few hundred kilometers down the road. Let us forever glorify He who both rewards the just and punishes the wicked! All praise to the Master of joy, intelligence, and happiness. *Amen.*

The next year, there was a long and terrible siege before the fortress of Saif ibn Isaac al Heit, during which he was compelled to abandon his palace at Tillaberi-Bentia on a somber night in August 1900, retreating to Kikassougou in a hasty flight that soon became a riot of disorder. In the process, he abandoned more than eight hundred horses, four hundred camels, a thousand donkeys, driving the starving mob before him like a herd of crazed cattle, leaving only ruins and desolation in their wake. The spectacle of legions in flight fomented yet more revolt, as doom hung over all. Murder now became the rule, rather than the exception, especially for those marked men, who did not bear the imprint of the Saif upon their foreheads, but who were instead tattooed along their temples. Racial war now unleashed, the Saif extended his bloody and savage raids all the way towards Yame.

Subjected to massacre after massacre, entire villages, their huts in flames, threw themselves upon the mercy of the *Flencessi*, whom they blessed, while the Saif, in exasperation, countered by invading the Tetenoubou and by attacking Doukkamar, surrounded by his faithful retinue.

Before the assembled griots, Saif swore that he would return from battle with the heads of the white chiefs, launching his campaign the very next morning. At Toma, the Gondaites were given formal notice when two emissaries of the Saif told them, "Submit to the Saif, or, by Allah, your land will be ransacked, your father and mother will be burned alive, and your sons will be executed."

Without a moment's hesitation, Ali, the Gondaite chief of Toma, a soldier with a distinguished military record who had been wounded in conflicts against the Mossi more than twenty times—the latter whose ancestors had, once upon a time, defeated the Saifs and the Dia in battle—replied, "*Wallahi!* Upon my head and eye! Tell the Saif that if he is a better man than me, he may go ahead and take my country from me; but I will defend it until the last drop of my children's blood has been shed: *wassalam!* I have already sworn an oath of allegiance to the *Flencessi*, agreeing not to submit to this impious Saif."

Thus the old Empire, faithful to its custom of tribal warfare, tore itself to shreds over hundreds of kilometers of massacres, razed missions, slashed throats, fire-storms launched by the Emperor, who ordered that the heads of all white captives be mounted upon the shafts of his men's lances and spears.

At the gates of Toma, the Saif decreed to his soldiers, "Let us set three white sheep and seven white chickens before the ramparts. If these fetish animals enter the town without being killed, then we will know that the attack will succeed…"

This recourse to paganism had a surprisingly powerful effect, rallying thousands of animists in the region to the Saif's cause, and inspiring them to poison the drinking water of many nearby French troops, thereby paralyzing them. For his part, Ali, when he saw the chickens and sheep, grasped at once that the Saif's troops would be redoubled in size. Hence, immediately setting fire to a gigantic stack of wood in the midst of three thousand of his men, he shot off six hundred muskets into the flaming whirl of smoke, first three and then seven times: exorcism.

The three white sheep and the seven white chickens, when engulfed in the smoke that the wind blew in their path, beat a quick retreat from the gates, just as the ears of the Saif's men were greeted with the sound of the muskets.

A sorcerer, emboldened at this exorcism, fired his rifle at Saif, who, having turned towards the smoke of Toma at exactly the right moment, unwittingly avoided the volley that was aimed in his direction, and that blew out the brains of his master-atarms. In retaliation, one of the Saif's officials hurled javelins at the sorcerer, whom he gravely wounded, also killing his horse by piercing it through the head.

Seventeen thousand faithful militants retreated at once, hurrying off to save themselves, followed by hundreds, in fact, nearly all of the Saif's remaining army. This debacle went on for more than an hour. And Saif cried out, "An army of men is all I have asked for! An army of men! ... All the subjects of my Empire have arisen against me, fleeing like frightened monkeys in armor. With a real army, I'd turn back these white macaques!"

... But History is mysteriously silent about certain facts, about selected acts of villainy, tragic derelictions of duty, cowardly appeasements, and sudden about-faces. Thus it was that Saif, surveying this disaster from the bush outside of Toma, and realizing that all was lost, unsheathed his saber in order to cut his own throat. It was not to be, for his son hurled himself upon his father, just in time for his father's golden blade to sheer off his own head, which fell like a stalk of wheat upon the earth. More than anything else, this incident dispirited the Saif, who capitulated to the French that very morning.

The Empire was pacified, now parceled out in numerous geographical zones, partitioned by the Whites. The black-rabble, rescued from slavery, joyously welcomed the white man, whom they hoped would make them soon forget the organized cruelty of the Saif.

... Meanwhile, forced to retreat to his palace at Tillaberi-Bentia, the Emperor, with his only young son seated upon his right, as the marabouts prayed, and the griots of the court sang his praises, endured a period of imposed silence until December 20, 1900, the day he was compelled to sign a peace treaty with the French.

Surrounded by his Court, which was as brilliant as ever, and decked out in all the trappings of imperial splendor, the Saif sat upon his throne, his feet at rest upon a satin carpet with embroidered flowers of gold. He wore a short tunic, a magnificent boubou with intricately woven stitching at the neck, from which dangled two fetishes. A jet black turban sat upon his head, wrapped around a red tarboosh; on his legs, he wore somber pantaloons, and, lower still, Moorish boots with soles that were made from the hide of a hippopotamus.

After a moment, Saif raised his arms to adjust a golden diadem that was encased with fine pearls, so that it sat squarely upon his forehead.

His entire entourage of faithful vassals seemed only slightly more dejected than was normal, their depression betrayed by their eyes, which seemed to drown in pools of blackness. All were somberly, but richly dressed. Forgetting the *salam*, Saif did not arise at the approach of the French representatives, contenting himself with motioning for them to be seated. Behind the Emperor, two masters of arms, all decked out in red, which was the traditional garb of the barbaric nobility, stood with spears erect, their arms extended in featly. In their left hands, they clutched razor-sharp hatchets and silver maces that were encased in the hide of a lion, the insignia of royalty.

From their leather shoulder straps, two muskets gleamed inside the holsters. Their faces were hidden in magnificent tufts of hair, the terrifying mane of the king of all animals.

Upon right and left, the twenty-seven favorite wives of the Saif, all young and comely, wore silks and heavy broaches.

In the rear, there were sixty servants, as well as forty domestics, slaves and the sons of slaves who were loyal to Saif. Further back, children sat like Turks upon their rugs. In a vast semi-circle, the royal guard of six hundred militants stood at attention, each wearing small bells that jangled upon their arms and ankles, as a spiral coil hung from the holes of their right ears.

Saif beheld this dazzling world that was arrayed before him. It felt as if his soul was being torn to pieces. He signed the treaty in a flash of somber impotence. Glory be to the Only Living God!

Six months later, the *Flencessi* extended an invitation to Madobou, his young son. Saif accepted the offer on his son's behalf with these words:

"A thousand salutations… May these expressions of gratitude be sweeter to you than honey and sugar. May they bring comfort to your valiant people, the sight of which causes our eyes to rejoice, and whose presence is as agreeable to our hearts as the fruit of the tree of perpetual happiness."

This was vintage Saif.

In a gesture of good faith, and to demonstrate the friendly esteem for the French that he did not possess, Saif entrusted his son to the emissaries, so that he might accompany them upon their return to France.

The Lord, holy is His name, had decreed that the arrival of the conquering delegation in France, and above all in Paris, would be an event for the ages. The most important personalities in France received the young Maboudou. The Champs-Elysee, the Arc de Triomphe, and the animated life of the great boulevards left the inexperienced young man speechless. On July 14, 1901, he attended Longchamp's military review. Mabadou was utterly enthralled.

The fanfare, the decorous ceremony of the officers who stood at attention beside the solemn major-general, decked out in sparkling gold lace and metals, overwhelmed him. "It was like a blinding swirl of lights," he said later, "in a world that had been turned upside down." The charging cavalry of black and white horses filled him with such enthusiasm that he even asked if could have a cuirass of his own. The son of Saif now stumbled from event to event with touching naivety.

The curiosity mixed with admiration that Paris observed in the son of the Saif was reminiscent, it is written in the chronicle, of the visit of Aniaba, son of the King of Assinia, to the court of Louis XIV. Bousset affectionately adopted him upon his arrival, and the king, who had served as a god-father at his baptism, awarded him the certificate of king's officer. Then, one morning, news arrived of the death of the King of Assinia. In parting, Aniaba received a blessing from the Cardinal of Noailles at Notre Dame, and, on the day of his departure, Louis XIV remarked to him: "Prince Aniaba, there is no more difference between you and me than there is between black and white."

Commenting upon these words, the Governor-General Delavignette notes, "It seems that the words of Louis XIV to the Prince Aniaba retain a hint of truth even in our days, for they speak to what is taking place in Africa right now. When Louix XIV remarked to Aniaba: 'There is no more differ-ence between you and me than between black and white, he was commenting upon the fact that they were both kings, and that they shared a certain solidarity by virtue of the fact that they were royals, and that, although they were different in color, they were united in their royal blood. And now, by way of comparison, we may affirm that it is a common royal nature that binds us to the Africans at this current historical juncture."

Frenzied applause erupted, and the Parisians gaily loaded up the son of Saif with a cornucopia of gifts, hoping to gain his cooperation upon his return to the bosom of his presti-gious father.

When he came back to Nakem, the son found that his father had not been idle, having in one year populated his palace with twenty three newborns, who were birthed by twenty of Saif's twenty seven wives.

An unexpected consequence of Madoubou's visit: the cruel dictator of a dynasty that was infamous for its tyranny, was, upon the return of Saif's son, now viewed by the Nakem people as a defeated genius of sorts, a man who should be numbered among "those great men whose spiritual righteousness quenches the thirstiest of hearts, even at the moment of their greatest agony." *La illaha illallah, la illaha, illaha! Mahamadara souroulaio...*

Twilight of the gods? Yes and no. It seemed more like a fading dream, or, perhaps, a turning point, the convulsion of an entire civilization. Before its ultimate demise? Before its rebirth? Or, was all of this mere sound and fury? A tear for the black-rabble, Oh Lord! May you always take pity upon them! ...

III

NIGHT OF THE GIANTS

1

The only vestige of these aborted dreams –the true poison lies in the tail! ...—was the serf, whose days of hard labor harkened to the era of forced captivity.

Awaken at five in the morning to prepare the bath of the master, who is off to his prayers at the mosque; hurry to open the doors, while the other captives quietly bustle about to make the master's breakfast: couscous, lamb sauce, milk, sugar, pastries. All is calm—a light gently streams into the court yard. Meanwhile, it's already time to fetch the day's water from the shores of the Yame.

Three women sweep the courtyard, while five others pound millet, preparing gruel for all those who till the land of the master. The laundry comes next, in piles from two days back, which is rung in water and then scoured with soap that is distributed to each of the laundry women. Next, baths must be drawn for the twenty-seven wives of the lord and master: the servants in waiting are dispatched to hear, obey, run about, execute their orders, assist them in the tubs. The mistresses of the house face difficult choices that require consultation: which robe, camisole, pagne, scarf, or tunic—lugged across the courtyard for the second time that morning—works best? Cotton or wool must be spun, wound into balls or upon the distaff; the thread goes to the weaver, and then there is just time to hurry back to inform the ladies, who are too distracted to pay much attention anyway; there is now another errand to run, only to be interrupted to perform yet another task, this one less urgent than the first. Banana-leaves are also required, or perhaps those from a kola-tree, in order to wrap the feet and hands of the great ladies, primed now to be dyed in henna or to be painted red on the fingernails... Then better make yourself scarce!

At last, the aristocrats take their breakfast in silence, and without water, according to the custom of the land.

Meanwhile, the male captives stand to one side and wait before clearing off the tables, washing the dishes, hurrying down their own food. Finished at last.

Time to clean the stables, carry out the piles of manure, bring hay to the horses, which—as etiquette dictates—must be fresh and grassy.

The female captives wash the dishes of the male captives and then breakfast in their turn. At last the day begins. It is seven o'clock.

Palanquins, mats, couches, beds, mosquito nets, drapes, and covers are in order. All of this merits some reward for the serf: one hour of rest.

Each captive makes his entry to pay his compliments to the lord and his wives, wishing them a good day. Respect.

The well-to-do men of the quarter are profuse in their civilities. The lords make their morning rounds, calling upon the notables and discussing recent events.

In small isolated groups, the serfs converse among themselves and then return to their diverse courtyards.

The news of the day is exchanged, and twenty serfs go off to the fields with the farm slaves.

At the head of ten servants, Tambira walks to the market to sell a hundred liters of the lord's milk. For his part, Kassoumi, the cook who was purchased from the marabout al Hajj Hassan, follows the three other serfs to help load up the house donkey with twenty-seven sacks of kola nuts, all to be dispensed the same morning in the marketplace: such is the will of Saif. Once this task is performed, they depart for the fields to slaughter one of the Saif's cows for the day's food: they cut up the meat into manageable portions, stacking it on the donkey's shoulders, the intestines already emptied and washed in the Yame River. The hide is sold at the shoemaker's along the waterside, or at the blacksmith's to make bellows for his forge, the money delivered upon their return, precisely at ten o'clock, into the waiting hands of the master; the slave next oversees the grilling of the filets and the roasting of the shanks, which are divided between the domestics and those portions intended for the table of the master. The serfs, captives, and slaves are allotted whatever remains of the animal, the tripe, gristle, and bones.

One Thursday towards one o'clock when he was at last free, Kassoumi decided to go out for an afternoon stroll. It was a hot and humid day. The sun lay in wait, poised to assault all those who dared to show themselves beneath its forceful rays.

Kassoumi veered to the right after leaving the courtyard of the slaves, crossing Tillaberi-Bentia with big strides upon his spindly legs, hoping to chase away the familiar feeling of boredom. His spirit grew calm in the solitude. After passing beyond the last of the houses, he followed the dusty footpath that led to the Yame River.

He felt himself to be utterly alone, small, worn out, at sea in his ill-fitting tunic with enormous sleeves that swallowed up his hands, the flaps now entangled in knee-britches, compelling him to walk at a too quick pace—merely so he wouldn't get tangled up and then fall over on his face. He hurried along the path, barefooted. He was a sad figure of a worker without means, both weary and naïve. His big black eyes, which were punctuated with a birthmark on the right eyelid, exuded the gentle calm of a dumb animal.

He did not seem to notice the sun but walked like a man with a clear destination, occupied by his private thoughts, for he had once discovered a shady spot under a banana tree, a place that reminded him of his lost homeland. It was only here that he felt truly at peace.

At path's end, where the footprints trail off into the sand, he removed the hat that rubbed against his forehead and then wiped the sweat from his brow.

He paused to catch his breath on a mound that over-looked the water. The river was mercurial and soothing under the brilliant sky.

For a moment or two, his body stood motionless, as if enflamed by the phosphorescence of the afternoon. But he was soon haunted by vague memories of his country—images from his childhood—that flooded upon him: a patch of field, a hedge, the door of a hut, a mother, a distant raid, and the house of the Saifs.

When he came to the banana trees, Kassoumi reached for a piece of fruit, carefully removing the peels, as he thought of all the people he had long ago left behind.

From time to time, his monotonous voice murmured a name, an indisputable fact from his childhood, for which only a few syllables were required to evoke a memory. And, little by little, his native land, so far away, would steal upon him, transporting him across vast distances, back to a land of green horizons and gentle breezes, where he was inundated with familiar shapes, sounds, odors, and tastes.

He took his seat under the banana tree, satisfied and yet depressed, full of tender sorrow, like a caged beast who knows its true worth. For a long time, he sat against the banana tree with his fingers interlaced, as if in mute suppli-cation before his master. With insects buzzing in his ears, he once again became engrossed in his thoughts, his black legs lazily stretched over the weeds beneath the banana tree. The brilliance of his white boubou and the gleam from his saber silenced the chirping sparrows fluttering in the branches above him.

He cast his eyes towards Tillaberi-Bentia. On the edge of the knolls, he made out the shape of Tambira, now wending her way towards the river. Under the flaming sun, she carried a calabash that spilled over with the day's laundry. The servant woman waved a palm leaf across her half-opened lips, as if kissing it, and Kassoumi suddenly felt an inexplicable bolt of joy when he saw a flash of amber that had escaped from her calabash.

She was a big, vigorous woman, black and supple, with beautiful, almond-shaped eyes. When she saw him sitting under the tree, she laughed with all the benevolence of an intelligent woman, instinctively sensing his timidity. "What are you doing over there?" she asked him. "Watching the bananas grow?"

Kassoumi perked up, laughing: "Well, maybe…"

"*Yeeee reti!*" she replied. "It is certainly is getting hot out here!"

Still laughing, he said, "Yes, quite hot indeed!"

She continued on her way, but then, ten meters later, changing her mind, she returned upon her steps: "Do you have any clothes that need washing? I'm washing mine."

"No, thank you," said Kassoumi, but he was touched by her gesture. She remained standing before him, hands upon her hips, the calabash balanced upon her head, happy at the pleasure that her proposition had clearly provoked.

She returned to the path, calling back: "Goodbye, then. Some other time!"

He followed her with his eyes, for as long as he could possibly see her, watching as her beautiful silhouette receded upon the horizon, as if vanishing in the pale ocher of the sand along the river.

When she spotted him the following week in the same place, she said, "Hello to you, Kassoumi."

"Hello to you, Tambira. Straight be your path."

"God hear you and reward you. Do you always come to this spot?"

Delighted, Kassoumi managed to stammer: "Why, yes.. I come here quite often … to relax."

That was all. But the next Thursday, she laughed when she saw him yet again, his eyes flashing like two stars, and his smile as bright as the sun's rays. Stirring her finger into something that was hidden in her calabash, she modestly asked, "Would you like to try something that may remind you of home?"

With all the instincts of those who belong to the same race, being herself far from her own native land, she had divined and hit upon the right spot.

Both of them fell silent. She poured a little honey, not without difficulty, into a small wooden bowl that she had wrapped in clean, white wool; Kassoumi took a sip from the bowl, careful not to exceed his own portion. Then he handed it back to Tambira.

She gently lapped up the honey, savoring it on her tongue, as she stood before him. He watched her drink from the bowl, nearly as agitated as he was charmed.

Then she returned the bowl to the calabash.

She sat beside him to make small talk, and, the two of them, now sitting side by side, abandoned themselves to the intoxication that comes from simply being alive, their arms clasped around their knees, gossiping about the small details of village life. The calabash that was filled with laundry lay on the ground, reminding them of the shortness of their time together.

But the woman soon ate the banana that he offered her and willingly drank from the goat's milk that he poured out from his goatskin.

… Often, in the days that followed, they brought one another sweets and other goodies, for it was harvest time when pastries of all sorts flowed in the house of the Saifs. The safe haven of this providential spot took the chill off the two slaves, who now cheeped away like happy sparrows.

One Thurday, Kassoumi asked permission to be absent for a few hours—something he had never done before. He had a queer air about him, as if occupied with a difficult problem, his thoughts elsewhere. Saif did not understand the reason for the change in him, but he vaguely suspected that something was afoot.

The slave went to his familiar spot, where the weeds were now worn flat from frequent use; he was soon lost in thought. Then, taking a long detour, he ambled towards the Yame River, where he waited behind a tree. At last he saw her.

The light of the moon seemed to emanate from her gentle body, and her face shone like the rays of the sun. She wore a necklace that fell between her swollen breasts, with a scarf upon her head, as a hundred beads formed a long row between her long legs and supple arms, gathered together in a double knot at her waist.

She walked with slow, undulating movements, as if carried along by a boat. As she approached his hiding spot, she seemed to rise and fall upon the horizon. Eyes riveted on this apparition, he trembled with an immoderate desire for this woman. Maddened by a deaf and furious rage, he felt a cold sweat along his back. He was seized with impotent anger. He calmed himself as best he could, and, with an air of detachment that he did not really feel, he deliberately attempted to relax his muscles, trying to logically reason with himself, to forget this unwelcome folly.

As if carried by the sun, she came nearer to the tree where he was hidden. For a brief instant, her flashing eyes seemed to look directly at him, but it was clear that she believed she was alone. His lips quivering and face alit, he allowed himself to now take a long look at her.

No one else was in sight. No movement anywhere. He heard neither the cry of a bird, nor the song of the cicada, not even the sound of lapping water from the river. All seemed numb beneath the sun's blinding rays. In the pungent air, Kassoumi imagined that he heard the gentle crackling of a fire.

She disappeared behind a shrub; then, without warning, there was a soft movement from behind a half submerged rock. Standing on his toes, he could see her at last, nude with opulent thighs, taking her daily bath, believing that, beneath the sun's sweltering heat, she was completely alone. The water—Praise be to God!— only came up as far as her knees...

She turned her head towards the Yame, her body awash in the sun's blinding tears: the birth of Eve from crystal waves, transparent in the light's brilliant reflection. And he saw that she was marvelously beautiful, this large, naked woman—a living sculpture—caressed by the dying day, her breasts as full as they were insolent.

Suddenly, she turned and let out a cry. Half swimming, half walking, she sought cover from behind a rock.

But, sooner or later, he knew that she would have to get out of the water, so Kassoumi seated himself against the tree and waited. Timidly, she lifted her head from the water. Her hair was braided in furrows like the nubs of a porcupine—or, a medusa. Her large mouth opened, taunt and alive, revealing a row of sparkling teeth, whereas her inquisitive eyes accentuated the sweet velvet of her flesh—the color of old mahogany, hard and desirable, glimmering like satin in the air of the Yame that never fails to stir up the blood.

"Hey, get out of here!" she cried out to him. Her voice, vibrant and profound like everything else about her, lapsed into a troubling guttural accent. Her voice pierced him like the ray of the sun from on high, like the scent of newly grown flower. But Kassoumi did not budge. "You shouldn't be here," she cried. "Do you think this is right?" The syllables in her mouth sounded like the yaps of a dog. Kassoumi did not move in the slightest. Her head disappeared.

In the time it takes to walk a hundred steps, her antenna-like nubs of hair peaked out again from behind the rock, then the rest of her hair gradually became visible. At last her forehead and eyes could be seen, appearing and reappearing, like a child playing hide-and-seek.

By now, she was infuriated. "You're going to make me sick from the sun," she shouted. "I won't leave as long as you're here."

Thus, Kassoumi finally arose, feeling sorry for himself. Regretfully, he departed, turning back every so often for another look. When she thought that he was far enough away, she swam out from the water, her curvaceous, undulating body streaming with life. She completely turned her back to him, disappearing beneath a wave, and then behind a shrub, under a cloth that hung from its branches.

The next morning, which was a Thursday, Kassoumi came back to the same spot. She was again taking her bath, the shameless hussy, but this time she was fully dressed. As sprightly as a hart, she pranced about with a malicious gaiety, clucking with little hiccups of cheerfulness. She laughed with joy at the sun, dancing before the moon, and he—now thoroughly annoyed— abandoned her and returned to his spot under the banana tree. With his hat on his knees, as though he needed to cool off his brow, he broke the silence by saying in a haughty voice: "All right, she's a beautiful woman. So what? The world is filled with beautiful women." But he stayed there all night, couched on his mat, where he awoke the next morning. He felt neither depressed, nor unhappy, but there was something that had taken root within him that he could not quite define. It was as if something had grabbed hold of his soul, an indescribable longing, a vivid sensation that was somehow beyond his reach, that could not be chased away, killed, or made to sit still. He was obsessed, irritated, ready to explode with the very thought of Tambira. He was nearly beside himself, hurtled towards her by a tremendous explosion of his own heart and body. He wanted to hug her, to strangle her, to swallow her whole. Full of rage and impatience, he trembled under the crushing weight of his impotence—all of this because she did not belong to him.

One Friday afternoon, she stopped to rest under the banana-tree. It was hot. After the harvest, the weeds had grown back again, protectively covering the surrounding earth. She returned from the Yame, her clothes now washed, wearing only a short camisole, which was damp against her loins as she lifted her arms to hold the calabash aloft. She was a veritable feast for the eyes! And Kassoumi once again began his dance upon a spiritual tight rope: he felt as if his soul was suspended over hers, a careful balancing act over the empty space of her immaculate body, onto which he might tumble at any moment. Suffocated by a sudden chill, Kassoumi found her so desirable that he began to feel dizzy. Then, asking her to sit down, he resolved to speak to her, stammering, "Now, see here, Tambira, this cannot go on."

She looked at him in gentle distress, "But Kassoumi, what is it that cannot go on?"

"Me, thinking about you every waking minute," he replied.

Then, with a smile that was really more of a grimace, she said in a natural voice, "But it's not me who's to blame for that."

"Oh, yes, it is," he retorted. "It is you... You have stolen my sleep, my peace-of-mind, my appetite... Everything..."

Half-surprised, and fixing her somber and anguished eyes upon Kassoumi, she murmured in a low voice, "What... What must be done to cure you?"

He remained transfixed, arms dangling, even frantic: "My sun... oh my light!"

Directly above the banana tree, flying near the top of the thick screen of high leaves overhead, a bird unexpectedly began to sing its head off. It launched into a series of high-pitched trills, piercing notes that filled the air before they were dissolved across the horizon, dissipated over the riverbanks and further up into the thick foliage.

They were very close to one another, their faces full of memories, but their mouths remained taunt: they slowly sucked in the silence between their palpitating lips. All was still. Kassoumi put his arm around Tambira's waist, gently holding her next to him. She took his hand without anger, and without embarrassment, pushing it away whenever he went the least bit too far with his caresses, as if all of this was exactly as it should be. Lost in ecstasy, she listened to the rapturous bird. Invaded by the infinite desire for happiness, by a sudden tenderness that radiated from her—what revelations of unsuspected poetry!—she shook from such a weakening of the nerves and heart that she could only press ever harder upon the hand of the man, who, for the moment anyway, merely held her against him. She no longer spurned his caresses: the very thought of refusing him seemed unimaginable.

They stayed like this for some time. The woman calmed herself, penetrated by the most gentle of sensations. The head of Kassoumi rested upon her shoulder; and then, suddenly, he kissed her fully on the lips. Furious, she revolted and to avoid his lips, rolled over upon her back. He tumbled her back over. But she quickly thrust back her clothes upon her thighs, desperate to flee. He scrambled up on top of her, covering her entire body with his own, clawing at her, stroking her luxurious skin, hindered by the fleshy protrusions of her ample breasts, the heaving of this proud woman's chest. For a longtime, he pursued the mouth that shunned him, and then, joined at last, he fastened his lips upon hers. Bewildered, she at last kissed back, surrendering to him now. As he furrowed ever more deeply into her moistening loins, she felt herself growing swollen, overwhelmed in delicious defeat, crushed under his weight, as if she was falling...

A wet breeze glistened, rustling up the murmuring leaves; they were naked amidst the tall weeds, conjugal sighs escaping from their satiated lips. Transfigured and nearly delirious, they lay motionless, consciousness of nothing other than the fact that they had possessed one another, the profundity of the act of penetration that they had experienced. They lay coiled in each other's arms and legs, supersaturated by the intermingling of their bodies, reveling in one another's flesh. Reason now forsaken, they gave themselves up for lost: wanderers in a strange land. They were numb from head to toe, stunned in expectation of the wonders to come. The woman carried the man like a ship on the ocean, with a slow rollicking motion, rising and falling above the violent depths. They murmured, sobbing throughout the course of this unexpected voyage, and their incessant movements propelled them forward at a speed that they surely could not sustain. The man let out a growl, thrusting his weapon more deeply and with greater force between the thighs of the woman. The venom gushed out; and suddenly they felt as if they would explode or die! It was a second of intense happiness, a perfect union of spirit and flesh—maddening.

They awoke, vibrant, crazy, and mute. Ears buzzing, they felt exhausted and completely depleted. They were both satisfied and obsessed with the knowledge that they now belonged to one another.

After parting that day, they met each other in the ditches, the sunken fields, the tall weeds under the banana-tree, or even, at the day's end, along the shores of the river, when he returned with the pack animals that were laden with tanned hides or cow meat, or when she brought back the washing or fetched water for the house of the Saifs.

Their fellow slaves, of course, had much to say about the couple... It was whispered that they were made for one another. Informed, Saif promised that they could be married the very next month, transforming the serfs' respectful hatred of him into adoration: the curious mob enjoyed vicarious intermittences of the heart.

The surveyors Waguli, Kratonga, and Sankolo, as well as the agents Wampulo and Yafole took full advantage of the occasion, following Saif's prompting, to increase the daily chores of the domestics. But, they performed their new tasks with light hearts, little suspecting that the marriage of Tambira and Kassoumi was merely a subterfuge of the master, enabling him to assume paternalistic airs at very little cost to himself. *Alif minpitjè!* —all glory and power to God on High...

Two weeks before this marriage was to take place, the military commander of Krebbi-Katsena, who controlled the French colony of Nakem from Mount Katsena, invited Saif to a ceremony that was held in the court of honor of the buildings of the colonial administration, newly constructed. The guests consisted of notables and indigenous dignitaries, French soldiers and various representatives, including the governor and his family, whom the officers welcomed with great pomp and ceremony, as well as forty-three other recently arrived French citizens—seven of whom consisted of missionaries and the Abby Henry —, other officers, ten wives, who accompanied the settlers, flanked by thirty more men: adventurers, businessmen, idealists, or administrative employees.

That afternoon, when the bishop Thomas de Saignac disembarked, Chevalier, Saif, and the people of Nakem welcomed him with unbelievable joy. From the Yame River to the capital of the former empire, hence a distance of about five kilometers, the people had been instructed to clear away all the stumps and brush along the trails, covering the footpaths with mats to soften the bishop's every step.

But more remarkable still was the fact that the lands bordering the road, as well as the fields, treetops, and hills were now covered with men and women who were anxious to get a glimpse of the bishop, whom they believed to be a true saint, sent to them by God—so beautiful was this man's colorful robes. He was offered gifts of lambs, goats, chickens, partridges, wild game, fish, and other victuals in such abundance that he did not know what to make of it all, and so he ended by simply giving it to the poor. In this way, the great zeal and obedience of the Christians became widely known.

Throngs of men and women, girls, boys, and the elderly came unto him, throwing themselves in his path to ask for the holy water of baptism, manifesting unique signs of the true faith, and refusing to allow him to pass until they had received it. Thus the bishop was compelled to make frequent stops to comply with their wishes, and to carry water, salt, and other necessary personal supplies wherever he went.

The bishop was borne along in procession to the church; after he gave thanks to God, he was brought to the lodgings that were destined for him. Immediately, he began to regulate the organization of the Church and clergy, including the ordained priests and the laity.

He elevated the Church of the Holy Cross to the rank of cathedral, which at this time boasted eighteen canons along with their various chaplains, a head chaplain, as well as a choir, an organ, bell tower, and all other necessary accoutrements of the cult.

Public speeches buzzed with edifying words like "militant humanitarianism" and the "civilizing mission" of the French, as an impassive Saif heard it proclaimed, that "henceforth, education would become obligatory, that routes, rail-road tracks, and canals would soon be built, for the greater good of all those who lived in the colony, and for the promotion of liberty, equality, and fraternity." It was necessary to applaud on such occasions, and Saif certainly applauded.

When he returned to his house, he called a secret gathering of important local families. Agents of the French informed the authorities about this meeting, but Saif assured those in charge that its aim was merely "to extend the white people's hopeful message of peace, happiness, and civilization to the most influential black families." He was left to do as he pleased.

This gathering of notables took place on the first Ash Wednesday in the year of 1902, following an unusually spectacular convocation that had been ordered by Saif ibn Isaac al Heit.

As was the custom, the notables took their seats before the regional chiefs, sitting cross-legged upon the floor, behind the Saif's advisors and facing the throne of the Emperor, who was fastidiously dressed for the occasion, surrounded by his most important dignitaries: his son Madoubou, "a man so strong that he was capable of splitting a slave in two, or of cutting off the head of a bull with a single blow from his sword"; the famously wise Black-Jew Moise ibn Bez Toubaoui, "a doctor deeply versed in the law, the Qur'an, the surahs , and the Zohar"; the Berber-Fulani scribe al Hajj Dial; the Sudanese Doumbouya, a wealthy black man with the face of a horse, "an expert on the current state of the clandestine slave-trade."

In this memorable assembly, evil incantations were inter-mingled with each of the nobles' responses to the Saif's imprecations, punctuated, here and there, with Pharisaical truisms drawn from the cult of traditional morality.

When the views of the notables and aristocrats were solicited by Saif ibn Isaac al Heit regarding the appropriate response to these recent political developments, they hesi-tated to reply.

A cold dread filled the hearts of all:

For suddenly, they saw that al Hajj Ali Gakore, a well-known idealist of advanced years, had now arisen from his seat, ambling before the Saif like a drowsy vulture. Trembling under his great boubou, he kneeled in submission, pouring three pinches of dust upon his handsome silk turban. "If it is indeed true," he argued with the voice of a dialectician, "that the children of Ham, of whom the Scriptures speak, labor under a curse, and if it is true that we are indeed the descen-dents of Black and Jewish peoples, born in the lineage of the Queen of Sheba, why then should we revolt against the white man?" Then, as if suffocating from his own audacity, the timber in his voice trembling with each word, he added: "Noble lords, did not the Imam Mahmud, Grand Sheriff of Mecca, predict that after Isaac al Heit, following the apparition of another caliph, blood and tears would at last disappear from the world? True or false? Did he not foretell that servants and masters alike would devote themselves to the service of God? Did he not say that a new power would be justly enthroned, and that a grandeur without end would henceforth flow like…the sea? Did he not say that this new empire would be strong beyond measure, and that the people of the kingdom would be united in the amassing of wealth, power, and glory, so that all worldly goods could now be spent on things agreeable to God? True or false?" he asked, as if illuminated.

Finally, his eyes rheumy, timidly looking up at the imposing figure of Salif ibn Isaac al Heit, he added with a sigh, "What would one think, noble caliph, if you were to neglect to tell the people about these things?"

The consequences of this audacious act are recorded by Mahmud Meknud Traore, paternal descendant of the ancestral line of griots and current griot of the contemporary African Republic of Nakem-Ziuko:

"Afterwards, Saif decreed that only the sons of slaves would be compelled to attend the French schools, to partake of the missionaries' masses, to be baptized by the white fathers, to adopt French dress, and to shave their skulls, while their families would be sworn to secrecy and suffer dire penalties should they prevaricate from their oaths. He decreed that all the *Holy Bibles* of the missionaries be burned, by way of a strong wind from the Yame to be guided by expert hands towards the huts of these Jesuits in cassocks. Moreover, he decreed that the notables of the neighboring colonies of the former Nakem Empire be called to sedition, and that Tama, a black poisonous snake that had been raised in the house of the Saif, along with three other poisonous snakes, younger but no less cruel, be let loose in the room where the chief governor and his family, the hosts of the married administrator, slept in the nights. Finally, for the edification of all, he decreed that al Hajj Ali Gakore, "a man of dubious faith and a hypocrite with expertise in the art of defamation," be submitted to the twice-just punishment of fire and poison, dying in the winter of 1902, his body exploding like an infernal machine from resinous poison, his enflamed intestines gushing upon the smoldering coals." A tear for him.

Who could say how many were exterminated by Saif? After the auto-da-fé of al Hajj Ali Gakore and the "accidental" death of the governor, his wife, the administrator, including his wife and daughter, Saif made an appearance before the colonial administrator, along with his cohort of dignitaries, to deplore these terrible deaths, to express his regrets for their negligence, to lament as well the arsons during which six hundred and fifty-three *Bibles* had been incinerated.

The call of Saif that was secretly delivered to the neighboring colonies did not fall on deaf ears: some imitated his actions, burning down the lodgings of the colonial administration, incinerating hundreds of copies of *Bibles* and *The Life of Jesus*, to the great sorrow of the missionaries. And, at carefully chosen moments, *the Vipers of the Supernatural* assassinated the most undesirable settlers and administrators. Other local chiefs, as well as collaborators, and those who were merely prudent, fearful, or servile, quietly bowed their heads in submission to the Whites... But the morning following these events, imperial order was quickly restored: the deaths of the administrative personnel led to telegraphed requests for replacements, as well as more copies of *Bibles*. Africa, the white man shrugged, was still the dark continent. It was therefore hardly surprising that a few imprudent white men, suddenly catapulted from the cradle of European civilization into this dangerous black land should ignore the advice of their superiors and allow the weeds to grow too tall around their dwellings, thereby inviting in "a few poisonous snakes from the burning forests." The Whites were therefore oblivious to these perfect crimes, which did not fail to repeat themselves. *Maschallah! Wa bismillah!* The name of Allah be upon us and around us! Forgive us, Lord.

The next day, Saif—*Ya atrash!*—had intented to marry Tambira and Kassumi. But, reserving for himself the right of the lord, and this being the first marriage among his servants, he upheld the traditional moral value "that the bride should be a virgin." Since this did not seem to be so in the present case, the marriage of Kassoumi and Tambira was delayed by a month. After having offered to the couple the gift of a cow, three sheep, four cooking pots, money, and other diverse household gifts, Saif dispatched two elderly women to verify that the bride was indeed not a virgin.

The matron asked Tambira to sit with her legs crossed upon a big mortar that had only recently been rolled into her hut. And, while the first matron held Tambira immobile, the second cut into her clitoris—*bâ'al ma yallah!*—with a soiled knife, excising it and then sewing both lips together, pressing them their fingers, holding them tightly in place, and then clasping them together by way of thorns. Considerately arranging in this "stitchwork" to leave a small orifice for Tambira's natural needs, she next introduced a small grooved stick that was coated in black butter, and, finally, the operation now having ended, she applied a bandage of millet cane, shaped like a triangle, upon the woman's lower extremities, from the knees to the haunches. Tambira was forbidden all movement until completely healed. The old woman made her lie down upon a woven wicker mat, forbidding her all visitors of the opposite sex, and personally bringing her all her meals, as well as attending to her every need.

Meanwhile, Saif deepened his alliances with the notables, the servants, even the *tirailleurs* and translators of the *Flencessi*, if the truth be told, by proclaiming that traditional moral values clearly dictated that all women should be considered the instruments of men. So that no woman should ever fall into error on this question, the practice of infibulation (or the sewing up of the vagina)—rare before this time—was now enforced by law: to prevent a woman from betraying her husband by way of ruse, her clitoris was removed at a stroke; this stratagem, combined with the terror of the punishment that was meted out to all female adulterers, weighed so heavily upon the black woman that she tended to immediately sober up in the face of all temptation. Finally, the vast number of men who made concubines of the weaker sex were delighted to have discovered, upon the occasion of marriage, an entirely new carnal pleasure, the sadistic union of ecstasy and pain, the joy that comes from deflowering a thorn-laced receptacle. Their ravaged mistresses too, thighs bespattered with blood, reeled in sensual agony, more than half dead from this intoxicating combination of pleasure and fear.

An adulterous wife in such circumstances incurred merciless sanctions: at the very least, she was stripped naked and completely exposed in view of the royal court. She was also shackled in irons at the ankles and submitted—as decreed by custom—to a vaginal douche of peppered water in which swam—*wallahi!*— red ants. In certain instances (if an adulterous woman was found to be in a state of pregnancy or had already aborted her fetus), the Saif instituted yet another innovation during which "the woman's thighs were opened above a burning fire that singed the hair off her vagina." In contrast, a woman who had been deceived by her husband could merely proclaim to the world that she had indeed been deceived. She might then seek out her rival, and, after finding her—hee! hee!—slap her and insult her.

Thus it was that on the first Thursday of the following month, after feverish preparations, the wedding took place as anticipated.

As custom decreed, the slave Kassoumi, sought through the use of magic to insure the love of Tambira with the aid of a salamander, a cockroach, and an old piece of cloth that his fiancé had once used to wipe herself after they had copulated. When these implements had been dried, he ground them with a pestle and then mixed them into a treatment that he was to serve his wife after Saif had exercised his seigniorial right. As the old folks urged, he next burned fingernail clippings, three eyelashes, seven hairs from his head, seven more hairs from his genitals and armpits, which he crushed together into a powder that was seasoned with red peppers, all to be sprinkled on the food of his bride throughout the night of their wedding celebration. Finally, to insure that he would be vigorous during the first seven days of marriage, he crushed three lion penises, along with the sperm of a he-goat, and three cocks' testicles into a bowl of mashed yams that was later cooked in a red sauce with strong spices.

On the first Thursday night of March, in the year 1902 (the religious union having been ratified by the proper authorities that morning), the antechambers burned with incense, defusing the odor of camphor, aloes, Indian musk, and gray amber, as the guests dyed their hands with fresh henna and their faces with saffron; the drums, flutes, fifes, cymbals, koras, and balafones resounded in the air as they did during the days of the great festivals; Tambira, now refreshed and bathed in sweet perfumes, received the visit of the matron, who came to verify that her needlework was still in place. One hour later, Saif—the magnificent lord whose every step was a source of great happiness— burst through the connubial stitch-work, which, happily for Tambira, had by now rotted.

To the Saif's great anger, Tambira experienced very little pain at the moment of penetration, but he was nonetheless mollified by a stratagem of the woman, who, after grimacing at the appropriate moment, let flow a sack of sheep's blood from beneath her, wetting the thighs of the sadistic Saif, who imagined that he had penetrated her innermost depths. As soon as the right of the lord was consummated, the matron displayed the bloody sheets for the eager public, and three salvos soon rang out into the night. The new couple was saluted with chants, cries, screams, and dances: *oye oye oye, gouzi-gouzi!*

Kassoumi thus went into the hut to greet his new wife, whom he symbolically slapped and then went back outside again in the view of all those assembled. He did this three times before he sat down to eat. Later the same night, he consumated their sexual union, which was necessary to repeat at frequent intervals, it was said, "during the six other days of the first week, so that the perforated wound would not close up again."

The same month, one thousand six hundred, and twenty-three marriages were performed from province to province, and from district to district, as the notables geared up for the assault.

The foolish people applauded these marriages, while the notables were busy planning their futures. From these new and now legally sanctioned couples were born scads of children, whom the notables sent to the French schools and missionaries in place of their own. Because it was necessary that the French laws apply to someone, the notables made sure that they would apply only to the black-rabble, whom they bred in large numbers on behalf of the settlers, to build their roads, railways, and public works. And the Whites never suspected that the notables were not allied with them! All the while, the notables murmured in the ears of the people, *Azim bouré ké-karato warali*, "The white man has condemned you to a life of forced labor, to building his roads, thoroughfares, and railroad tracks, all for the sake of colonial commerce." The credulous people entered into devils' pacts with these wicked notables and aristocrats, who continued to prosper at their expense: meanwhile, the indigenous masses silently cursed their forced submission to the Whites, fallen demi-gods who were formerly adored as their saviors.

And yet numerous local scholars whispered in low voices that "the truth" of the Saif was a complete fraud, that Saif was little more than an imposter, and that his fabled "noble" blood was no more Jewish than the black-rabbles' blood was green. "He pretends to be Jewish, this miscreant, merely so he can take pleasure in claiming to be superior to other Blacks. But the truth is that he's no different from the white colonizers. Both of them want to "civilize" the Nakem, as if blacks are wholly lacking in the ability to tend to their own needs and govern themselves."

Besides, whoever heard of a Black Jew? Others retorted that what the Saif had said about his Jewish ancestry was certainly true, that he was indeed a Black-Jew, citing the genealogy that linked him with the Gaonins of Kariouan, the Rabbih Enca Oua of Tlemcen, Yossef Lackkar, the Gabilou, Amram ibn Merouas, Jacob Sasportes... Finally, when all else failed, they evoked the Queen of Sheba... *Allahou Akbar!*: Pray to God for His Infinite Mercy...

Fifteen days after these events, a cablegram from Paris arrived at Mount Katsena (three kilometers from the local village of Tillaberi-Bentia): Jean Chevalier, the local vice-administrator, was promoted to the rank of administrator and interim governor.

Fearing for his own life, Chevalier summoned Bouremi, the sorcerer of Krebbi-Katsena, an ambitious man who had betrayed the Gondaites and then rallied to the Saif's cause, only to betray Saif on behalf of the French, whom he soon betrayed to help out the Gondaites, before he at last got everything hopelessly mixed up and decided—an unapologetic sorcerer who was an expert in the occult arts—to kill on behalf of the highest bidder. Chevalier interrogated Bouremi about the Saif, learning all about his spies and killers.

The translator, a man with six fingers on his left hand, was a slave who belonged to the Toucouleur. His name was Karim Ba. Many times in the past, he had participated in the extortions and back-stabbings of the black *tirailleurs* to fatten his own wallet, but he was nonetheless a translator without parallel, the only one who completely understood French, Arabic, and seven vernacular languages of the Nakem.

CHEVALIER: How many men do they have?

BOUREMI: Twenty-eight.

CHEVALIER: Twenty-eight? Did you say 'twenty-eight'?

BOUREMI: Yes, I said twenty-eight.

CHEVALIER: You bastard! You son of a bitch! You're a bold-faced liar! We already know that they have at least three hundred. Saif's men told us so.

BOUREMI: I'm telling you the truth. Besides, it's easy enough to prove it. After the Saif attacked and capsized their pirogues, very few of them survived. All you have to do is count the lit-up windows of the village in the nights.

CHEVALIER: Shut up, you son of a bitch. You are terrified by the accursed Saif! (*He slaps him*). So you call me a liar, me, the administrator Chevalier? I tell you that there are a least three hundred men. Do you really think that a mere twenty-eight men would dare to rebel against the Saif? He would make mincemeat of you, mincemeat!

BOUREMI: ...

CHEVALIER: Are you a Muslim?

BOUREMI: No, by the grace of God the Most High and of Muhammad, his prophet.

CHEVALIER: It's just as well. Then you will serve me. You will teach me how to assassinate with the use of snakes. In return, I will give you gold, women, houses, land, anything that you like.

BOUREMI: The snakes do not assassinate. It's simply a matter of chance whom they choose to attack.

TRANSLATOR: *interjecting*: If I translate your words, your head will roll...

BOUREMI, *to the translator*: It's all the same to me. I cannot tell this man the truth. Saif has all the important snake trainers. If we try to train the snakes ourselves, they will turn on us and their secret will be revealed to all the tribes—and to the Whites.

CHEVALIER, *agitated*: What is he saying?

TRANSLATOR, *to Bouremi*: May the God of the bush prolong your days... *To Chevalier*: My lord, he says that he would like to have some time to think things over.

CHEVALIER: That's fine. Get him out of here. You take care of him. But he'd better play along, or there'll be hell to pay!

And Bouremi was taken away. The translator Karim Ba brought him to his house where Bouremi could see his many wives, domestics, and horses. Ba pointed out to the sorcerer that it was in his own best interests to serve Chevalier, that, by doing so, he too would acquire all these fine things and more. He need only join the other deserters, the elite of the white man's counterespionage. Bouremi struggled to find the right words, fully aware of the danger of his position. To become an open ally of the French against the Saif meant condemning his family to occult death.

When questioned the next day, Bouremi once again deferred his response, pretending that he needed another night to reflect. While waiting, he asked to be taken towards a large patch of ivy, where he might find the herbs to prepare a secret beverage. His wish granted, he then asked his guardian to allow him to satisfy his natural needs. Bouremi urinated behind the bushes in a thick copse, near the shore of a thicket where he could hear the toads croaking. The alarm was sounded. The guards searched next to his hiding place and then looked for him further down the shore. Suddenly, the sorcerer felt a wet muzzle press against him: it was one, no, … two hyenas… He fled from his hiding spot with the dogs at his heels and was soon caught. Shackled at the hands and ankles, he was brought once again before the furious Chevalier, who, from the look of his face, seemed ready to sentence Bouremi to death, but, in fact, only conscripted him.

A valuable collaborator was thus acquired. May he chew upon the offal of a jackass in hell!

The assassination of Saif was arranged for the next month. His death would have to appear accidental, since an outright murder might result in uncertain consequences.

But the discretion of the project had already been compromised by the failed flight of the sorcerer, the news traveling with light speed to the agents of Saif, who at once informed their master. That very day, Saif dispatched a courier on horseback to the village chief of Krebbi-Katsena, who was instructed to send a splendid Fulani woman named Awa to the home of the French administrator, a widower.

Twice during the week, Chevalier made himself "at home" to receive visits from prospective mistresses, procured with the help of his translator or the village chief of Krebbi-Katsena.

Although Chevalier was ignorant of the fact, Awa was the fiancé of Sankolo, an agent of Saif; moreover, she spoke French.

From the moment he saw her, the administrator was completely conquered by her freshness, by the velvety sheen of her skin, which was similar to the hue of the Berber-Nomads; her gentle eyes gleamed like two small fireflies; her hair was silky— and her nose was delicate, like the refined noses of the Tuareg women. She was dressed in the style of the Egyptians, wearing a satin dress, elegant pendants, a necklace of big pearls, and gold bracelets set with rubies.

Her turfs of hair were like watery silk: her eyes burned like ardent coals. In sheer physical presence, she was without rival.

He asked her to be seated, gently placing his hand on her knee. The pressure lamp that had been brought in by a soldier shot a bright stream of light across the somber interior of the antechamber; and Chevalier, perceiving a smile of anticipation from his companion, coyly withdrew his hand. Tonight was not a night to rush things. He wanted there to be no misunderstandings. With soft steps, he led her to the veranda, which was connected to the salon and other rooms of the house.

"I live here by myself," he said with a sad air, and then he added, somewhat formally, "My wife died some time ago." He lit a match, turning up the flame in the petrol lamp. The white walls surrounding them now dramatically came into view. "Have an orange while I light the other lamps."

He kneeled down near similar petrol lamps, the gentle flames crackling to life at the slightest touch of his match.

"It's very nice here," murmured Awa with effrontery. "I can't believe all the books you have!"

"I wrote them myself," lied the administrator.

"It would be wonderful to write."

"Well, you try to say something worth saying… Hmm… Can I show you the rest of the house now? It's tastefully arranged, isn't it? Naturally, it lacks the touch of a woman," Chevalier added, lowering his voice.

Then, moving about from room to room, the administrator lit the various lamps: everywhere he went with his match there sprung forth, like mysterious sentinels hidden in the shadows, long white panels, tinted glass paintings, cream walls, ceilings of pale jade…

He did not once turn around to look at her, contenting himself with sensing her quiet approbation. She suited his tastes perfectly. In his svelte Louix XVI salon, he showed her various odds-and-ends that he had acquired throughout the years, a rich Persian rug, diverse objects brought back from Indochina and North Africa, which helped to soften the severity of the salon; silverware and a Louis XVI buffet in the dining room, presided over by an alabaster vase, an opal Buddah, and an Arabic tea service.

The man conducted his tour with measured steps, speaking of nothing but his various treasures, as if he wished to make her their humble guardian.

"My bed chamber," he said, half hiding before a rose-colored door, peering around with a lamp in his hand.

Awa gasped in pleasure when she saw the rose-tinted room. The semi-circular bed was draped in fine silks that were embroidered with rose petals.

"Goodness!" she said before an ornate plate-glass mirror. The image that she saw looking back at her—her own—was far more flattering than any of the man's sweet words. "Oh my!" she said, letting out a sigh, when she saw a single portrait that hung from the wall. "How pretty! Who is it?"

"My wife," responded Chevalier, without looking at it.

The portrait was directly in front of the bed. It was the first face that Chevalier saw upon waking up in the morning. Each day, this face greeted him, irradiating its beauty, spitefulness, and virtue.

"You must have been in love with her!" hazarded Awa, fascinated by this face.

For a moment, Chevalier was tempted to tell her the truth: that he hung up this portrait before his bed, not because he adored her, but because he didn't know where else to hang it, and because it reminded him of the one creature who had clearly seen through him.

"Come, I'll take you into the kitchen," he hastened to say.

The kitchen was like a culinary fantasy, with its white windows, buffet, and ensemble, its charcoal enameled oven, its immaculate walls, and blue pastel ceiling.

Through an opening in the curtains, Awa happened to see in the neighboring house a splendid black woman, standing completely nude before a mirror, brushing out her hair: behind her was an enormous bed where two of her clients reclined in anticipation. An orderly set the table for breakfast the next morning, while Captain Vandame, in another part of the house, wrote something in his notebook. Not far from him stood a corporal at attention.

"They're all doing something different," she murmured. Meanwhile, her eyes returned to Chevalier's enormous bed lying before her, with its silk sheets and embroidered rose petals. She remembered the words of Saif.

Chevalier sensed something touching his elbow, tenderly pressing against him. He turned around, vaguely confused. He was ever equipped with a gentle and aristocratic smile, containing a little of everything: affected courtesy or simple embarrassment. He regarded Awa anew, conscious that his elbow was now touching her breast, and of the fact that the woman *truly understood* that he was touching her in so flagrant a manner. She made a slight movement, sensing the pointed nubs of her breasts harden against the elbow of the man.

The two of them had nothing further to say about the gilded tapestries on the wall, the zebra skins, and the elegant paintings. The air was heavy with fear and incense; at their feet was the soft hide of a panther.

In a gentle, languid voice, convinced that the woman would consent to his advances, the administrator offered her champagne: "To sleep with a black woman!" he murmured, gesturing towards the bed with hungry eyes. "To bed down with a black woman is the delight of kings and the gods of Olympus! It is the supreme pleasure, the most illicit of extravagances. Come, my little black treasure, I'm going to teach you a thing or two."

Caressing the hollowed cusp of the woman's belly, he kissed the long black wings at the nape of her neck and then momentarily left the room—before he returned wearing a silk smoking jacket with two beautiful and robust setters at his heels.

The beasts darted into the room with wide, eager eyes. Their master whistled, and Medor jumped on top of Awa, his snout moist and simmering.

"Medor!" he said in a clipping voice. "Go on, boy! She's all yours!"

Before the woman understood what was happening, she felt the muzzle and fangs of the dog ripping her clothes to shreds, tearing off her dress and underclothes, denuding her with its heavy, lumbering claws, and yet it did not once graze her skin. Medor was obviously accustomed to this type of work.

Paralyzed by the conflicting emotions of terror and appetite, Awa found that she had been divested of her clothes within seconds. When she was completely nude, Chevalier crouched down towards her, guiding her to a sofa that was upholstered in soft furs and draped with a shawl of red silk.

He laid her down upon the sofa, gently gliding his tongue over her coppery red lips, her bluish, iron-colored hair, her black eyes that shone with silver flecks, her tepid breasts, soft as handsome doves of living wool—and, suddenly, a profound moan escaped from the lips of the woman, which was quickly stifled by the hand of Chevalier.

Her fingers tucked under her armpits, she languidly arched her back—and then she let out a harrowing scream: for she suddenly felt the pungent and raspy snout of Dick, while Chevalier, no longer grimacing, merely caressed her belly and thighs, before the sticky and bludgeon-like tongue of Medor furrowed deeply into her moistened vulva.

She became frantic as the lapping and nibbling of the dogs continued, but she ended by taking the perfumed tongue of Chevalier into her mouth, struggling and groaning beneath him. At last ordering his dogs to retire, the man plowed into the woman as if she was fallow earth, as if she was an ocean that was cleft by the prow of a vessel. And, when he saw that she had recovered from the emotional blow of this transgression, he said, "How do you feel now, my little black treasure? Have you enjoyed yourself a little?"

"My god! I have never felt anything like that before," she groaned. He slapped her sharply on the face, and she cried out in fear, before once again coiling up in pleasure, heaving under his cruel caresses, reeling him in like a haughty queen or an experienced whore. Her mouth seemed eternally hungry for his swollen pink mollusk, whereas his own tongue probed ever more deeply into her open orifice, as if seeking to extract the most sumptuous pearl of the orient, which flowed, almost regretfully, from her stem...

The profound peace that ushers from sensual excess drowned all their fears, all the worries of the day; and the woman was forced to admit that she had never felt better in her life than she did at this moment, lying in this man's arms.

A cup overflowing—Awa—a smorgasbord of desire! Eve with feverish loins, she cajoled the man, hugging him, biting him, scratching him, slashing him with her fingernails, sucking on his nose, ears, throat, armpits, navel, and member with so much passion that the administrator, having discovered the ardent land of this queen among women, decided that he would keep her for good; his soul reeling in ecstasy, they abandoned themselves to their frantic, breathless, and unbridled passion.

One week later, Awa succeeded in loosening his tongue and communicated to Saif his worst suspicions.

"As for Saif... you need not worry about him ... He won't be around much longer to make trouble for anyone. And, I'll tell you something else," the imprudent Chevalier added, verbatim. "the people will thank us for it."

Informed of Chevalier's intentions, Saif waited.

Three weeks later, an invitation in the handwriting of Chevalier communicated to Saif that, "as a natural consequence of the untimely demise of the governor and of the administrator, that he, Chevalier, had been promoted to the rank of governor and that Captain Vandame was accordingly to become commandant and administrator. In fact, this promotion impacted virtually everyone who served in the region."

Saif was therefore invited to dine with him, following the decorating ceremony in which all would be formally promoted; Saif agreed to attend along with his personal bodyguard: Hamed, the One-Eyed.

It was an evening in May. The fiery sun had set along the far hills of Mount Katsena, the land buried in a shroud of dust. A red hue glowed along the ochre trail, upon which loomed the interminable shadow of Saif. He wore his turban-wrapped tarboosh, walking along a row of felled trees, a somber stain upon the horizon.

A small cloud of impalpable dust gathered near the feet of the man, rising up and hovering near his vast robes, while, in the far distance, the obscure prayer of a missionary could be heard: "Come to Jesus," the voice said. "Come to the Lord."

Saif walked with long, slow steps, exuding an air of power and dignity. Smiling slightly, he put his hand on the cutlass that hung at his side, beneath his boubou—and, refreshed by a slight breeze from the savannah, he sponged the sweat off his head of short, gray, and close-cropped hair. His squarish face seemed more the face of a militant than a religious leader. When he was a few steps from the threshold of Chevalier's house, he dramatically removed his headdress, revealing a head that was simultaneously aristocratic, filthy, and handsome. His face betrayed all the unmistakable signs of fatigue that come from a life of precocious debauchery: the full lips, baldhead, hooked nose, and goat's beard radiated his love of earthly pleasures.

He rapped on the round copper doorknocker several times. At first, the sound was feeble, but it soon grew louder and more terrible, ringing out with a vibrant, groan, as Saif struck it with ever-greater force.

The orderly appeared. He stood stiffly at the door, looking at Saif with timid anger, sensing with the instinct of a hunting dog the butchery that this visit surely portended.

The door opened wider—and Saif, accompanied by Hamed, his bodyguard, made his entrance.

Saif made a strong impression. Chevalier shot up from his chair, both confused and charmed: "But, my dear friend, it was supposed to be an informal gathering! You see, I'm only wearing a vest."

Saif responded: "I know. That's what you said. But it is my custom to never go out at night without being properly dressed."

He saluted, placing the turban-covered tarboosh under his arm, a rare object—of massive gold—glimmering at the buttonhole.

Chevalier introduced him to the guests: "Madame Vandame, Commandant Vandame, the new administrator; Madame Mosse, Captain Mosse, and their son Jean; Madame Huyghe, lieutenant Huyghe, their daughter Isabelle, whom we call Isa, for short."

All those gathered took their seats. Chevalier began again: "Let's go into the salon for an aperitif."

Saif replied, "How very kind of you!"

Then he was relieved of his tarboosh, which he would have preferred to keep at hand, now seeking out the eyes of his bodyguard.

Everyone took their seats; they looked at him at a distance, across the table, at a loss for words. Chevalier asked him, "So how are our far neighbors getting along these days? I hope they are not overtaxing you with their frightful squabbles."

Saif, with a neutral tone, responded, suavely: "Not at all. But in any case, with the help of friends gathered here today, we should be able to bring things to a conclusion. It's an extremely complicated affair, of course, but who is better suited to resolve it than us? That goes twice over for the governor and his administrator."

The orderly entered, pushing the door open with his knees and holding with both hands the tray with glasses and liqueurs. Chevalier served all those present.

As if by an oversight, Saif took the glass of Madame Huyghe, who brought the glass of Saif to her lips, before Chevalier quickly said to her, "You have taken the wrong glass, my dear friend.."

Feigning astonishment, Saif stared at the governor, who hastened to explain: "Madame Huyghe, I believe, has taken your glass... which was full ... You see, alcohol does not agree with her."

The woman was about to deny it, when she received—*nak gudwa!*—a sharp kick on her shin from under the table, which made her cry out in pain; meanwhile, her husband made excuses for her. Now amiable, Saif smiled as if he was perfectly satisfied by the explanation. With a face that was nearly condescending, he once again picked up the glass that had been originally destined for him and gave his own to the woman—all the while, he kept one eye on his bodyguard.

In an instant, Saif calculated that the other guests knew nothing of Chevalier's plot: otherwise, when the moment had come, would the woman have wished to drink from the wrong glass? And would they have all brought their own children here *for this*? No... The entire affair was therefore hatched in the brain of Chevalier alone.

At that moment, the governor cried out: "Shall we go to the table? Place yourself there, your Majesty, at my right, near Madame Vandame and Madame Mosse, facing Mademoiselle Isabel. I doubt very much you are afraid of the ladies."

Hence the dinner began without Saif having taken a sip. Chevalier did his utmost on the occasion, aware of his responsibilities as host, rushing to the aid of the most banal of conversations, which had come to a full standstill at all the ordinary places. With a look of near radiance on his face, he spoke in a loud, jovial voice, telling jokes, pouring champagne, and serving the ladies. "A little of this famous Moët, your Majesty," babbled Chevalier. "I do not say that it is an extraordinary vintage, but it is excellent all the same. It still has the must of the cave upon it, as is natural. In fact," he lied, "I have friends in France who regularly send it to me."

Saif, all smiles, agreed to everything, clinking his champagne flute against the raised glasses of the other guests. Holding his own glass at eye-level, after carefully focusing his eyes for a moment, he could at last see *it*! The potion that the sorcerer Bouremi had prepared of extremely fine, nearly imperceptible powder called *dabali*, mixed with the poison of a deadly viper. The dose was sufficient to kill him, not immediately, but before the next morning, as if by heart attack. The perfect crime.

Setting down his glass, while recounting an obscure hunting story, Saif discretely scraped the dried out potion that was hidden in the fingernail of his left thumb—the venom of an asp that had been treated —dispersing its contents inside his champagne flute.

The meal went on, an interminable, magnificent, and veritable banquet. Opulent plates followed one after another: champagne and white wine swirled fraternally in their glasses, intermingling in the stomachs of the guests. Scraping clean every bit of sauce with a table knife, Saif did not shrink from eating all the spicy dishes that he was served, gobbling them up with an imperturbable smile. The noise of the plates, the voices, and the music playing in the background, created a continuous and profound hum, which was dissipated into the clear night sky—where the notes of the bugle sounded the call to the curfew. Madame Vandame sat erect in her chair, fascinated by Saif; her breasts jiggled extravagantly inside her corsage, and the commandant, growing ever more excited, talked nothing but politics, as the Saif, in the meantime, ate the dishes that were served to him but did not drink at all. He asked for seconds, once again scraping the surface of his plate, as if he had only just realized that he should do a better job of masking his fraudulent ignorance, by taking even more helpings of the good things that had already entered into his mouth and filled up his belly. He had begun to discretely touch his foot against the foot of Madame Vandame's, caressing it with his toe; then, made slightly uneasy due to the unexpected heat that he felt emanating from the woman, he looked at her with a fixed stare—tender, attentive, studious—for, at that very instant, he inserted his toe deep inside her, raping her with slow, powerful, and serene strokes.

The hour of the toasts had at last arrived. A great many were proposed, all worthy of applause. The night lengthened.

Fine, milky vapors floated at a far distance, mild garments of the calm and mysterious night.

A pussycat that belonged to Chevalier rubbed against the legs of the guests. With a deliberately clumsy sweep of the hand, Saif knocked over the poisoned glass that he still seemed to nurse, quickly catching the glass, which did not shatter; then he regretfully contemplated the drops of fatal liquid which had spilled upon the floor, and which the cat now greedily lapped up.

Meanwhile, the conversation, having briefly lapsed, picked up exactly where it had left off and was soon proceeding in the most agreeable fashion. But a quarter of hour later, writhing about in convulsions, the cat began to slobber, claw, hiss, and meow— four paws high in the air. Dead.

Saif roared in anger. A true diplomat, he played his part perfectly, blaming everything on the Chevalier's orderly, whom he accused of wanting to poison him, to kill him, and—moreover—to spoil a perfectly amiable gathering among friends...

Devastated by this masterpiece of horror, the bodyguard of Saif hurried towards his master, near the pressure lamp that illuminated the room, whereas the stunned orderly, who was deeply insulted by the angry yelps of Chevalier in front of the guests, remained silent, hastening to clear off the Saif's fork, plates, and knife from the table.

Suddenly convinced that the opportune moment had arrived, and that it was indeed necessary to carry out his farcical assassination, Saif tumbled over upon his bodyguard, as if he had been shoved into him by the orderly, while his bodyguard crashed into the lamp, extinguishing it with a loud explosion. In the dark, Saif howled, as if he was seriously wounded, while he jabbed something into the moist eye of Chevalier, who began to scream.

The table was knocked to the ground; the guests were plunged into terrifying chaos. Groans followed, and then piteous wails. For several seconds, the sound of shattering glass could be heard, as wine glasses and champagne flutes were knocked upon the floor, followed by the sound of crashing plates in the darkness; in the midst of the women's screams and the shouts of the men, injured bodies could be heard crawling across the floor, and then nothing.

The lamp was broken, and all were plunged into a darkness so black, unexpected, and profound that they felt utterly stupefied. The commandant ordered them to be calm and to stay still. He left by himself. A quarter of an hour later, he returned with a lamp that he had brought back from his house, a hundred and fifty meters away.

Vandame could hear no breathing or any other signs of life. The room was as silent and peaceful as a sealed tomb. When he opened the door, however, he recoiled in terror.

Saif was crouched down against the table, no longer stirring, and the body of Chevalier was stretched out upon the floor, under his chair. Then, the others, with beating hearts and trembling voices, called out, "Your Majesty... Governor..."

There was no response or movement.

"My God, my God," murmured Isabelle, "What have they done? What has happened?"

They did not dare move, but a foolish desire to cry out for help, to flee for their lives and scream at the top of their lungs seized hold of them: they were so terrified that they felt as if their legs would buckle from underneath them, and that they would collapse on the spot. The commander repeated himself, "Your Majesty... Governor..."

But, suddenly, in spite of his fear, an instinctive desire to assist Saif and Chevalier took hold of Vandame, who as a military man had ridden into combat on many occasions and performed heroic acts of terrifying audacity. He approached the bodies. First, he came to Saif, who was propped up against the table and seemed to be asleep; then he saw a smashed lamp and the bodyguard lying sprawled beside him. There was a gash in the back of his neck. Then he noticed a large rip across the back of Saif's sumptuous gown. Palpitating with fear, his hands trembling, Vandame murmured, "My God, my God, what has happened?"

As he advanced with short, slow steps, he slipped upon an oily substance that caused him to fall to the floor. From his new vantage point, he saw a pool of red liquid spilling across the floor, seeping ever closer towards the door. He realized that it was blood.

Not wanting to see any more, Isabelle fled out the front door, throwing down her napkin and running in a frenzy into the bushes, back in the general direction of the village. Her eyes fixed on distant fires, she collided with trees, screaming as she ran into the darkness. Her shrill voice rang into the night like the sound of a wounded beast, "Saif... Saif... Saif..." Her mother was not far behind, calling after her.

When Isabelle reached the first sentinels, she was surrounded by armed men, who were deeply shaken by her hysterical screams; for several moments, she flayed her arms about without responding, for she had by now lost her mind.

From the sobbing explanations of Madame Huyghe, they at last came to understand that a great evil had befallen the governor's house. A troop of soldiers ran off at once to assist him.

Soon, fires blazed in the night across the open earth, through the dark trees near the military and administrative buildings, and directly towards the house of Chevalier. They traveled in silence over the dust-silted weeds, their torches forming a long streak of yellow light. In the darkness, the errant branches of trees looked like wriggling serpents. Suddenly the sinister house loomed before them, turning a reddish hue once it was lit up by the torches of the soldiers. Holding guns in their hands, a sergeant, two corporals, and seven soldiers sprinted towards the front door.

For a moment, the door remained opened, as the soldiers hesitated in fear. At last, the men entered, saluting the commandant. Madame Huyghe had not lied.

Congealed blood covered the floor like a ghastly carpet. It flowed next to Saif, and then against his bodyguard—who seemed to be swimming in it, both with one portion of his leg and an entire forearm. Meanwhile, Chevalier slept the sleep of the dead, a gaping hole on the right side of his face. The pupil of his eye looked like a bloody pear: it was clotted, purple, and round, lying on the floor at the end of a table-knife.

Saif slept too, only he slept the hypocritical sleep of the murderer. When the soldiers turned him over, he groggily awoke, as did his bodyguard, who seemed stupefied by his fall against the lamp. Saif rubbed his eyes, as if completely befuddled. He floundered about like a feeble-minded invalid. When he saw the body of Chevalier, he began babbling so incoherently that even his bodyguard could not understand him.

Thus it was that the orderly, who was prowling about in the vestibule, came to be accused of the assassination of Chevalier and, as a result, he fled at once into the night. A summons ordering his arrest was issued, but in vain. For a minute later, one of the night guards struck him down like a rabid dog. He had paid for his crime.

And all the world believed, for the idea came from no one other than Saif himself, that it was the hapless orderly who had killed Chevalier, not suspecting that Saif himself was the true murderer, and that his bodyguard had deliberately ripped open the sumptuous robes of his master, so that it would appear that someone had sought to kill Saif by stabbing him on the back. (God have mercy upon us.)

Vandame, who was appointed the new governor, wrote to Saif, "Your Majesty, I congratulate you with all my heart for the admirable assistance that you have extended to us in this land, and that you formerly extended to the governor Chevalier, recently deceased in such tragic circumstances. You may rest assured that you have no greater admirer of the important work that you have performed so loyally on our behalf, at the risk of your own life, and in the service of the common good.

"I hope that the colonial minister, to whom I have transmitted my report, will provide you with the recompense that is surely your due. I offer you here my formal congratulations, which are only a prelude to the rewards that await you, and of which France will be both pleased and obliged to bestow upon you.

"I therefore confer my highest accolades upon your Majesty, in the humble hopes that you will deign to accept them."

Signed: Vandame.

Two months later, on July 14, 1902, Saif was promoted to Chevalier in the French Legion of Honor, and his sons were invited, upon reaching the appropriate age, to pursue their studies in Paris at the expense of the French government. Glory be to God, Almighty!

Nine months later, Tambira gave birth to quintuplets, who were baptized with Christian names: Raymond-Spartacus Kassoumi, Jean-Sans-Terre Kassoumi, Anne-Kadidia Kassoumi, Rene-Descartes Kassoumi, and, finally, Rene-Caille Kassoumi— sonorous names that were chosen by their parents and the translator Karim Ba, under the direction of Saif.

Meanwhile, throughout the other provinces, during roughly the same period, the nobility welcomed many other happy christenings, all future pawns in a new era of African politics. The Master of all worlds is powerful! It is to Him that we shall return. Pray then that he will forgive us! *Amen.*

2

And tradition tells us:

"After the betrothal in the desert, Saif struggled day after day for seven centuries of History to form a core of loyal followers at the breast of his people. And the people called Saif "Exalted Lord" and the governor "His Highness." There was rain, and then there was drought: the first year. *Wakoul rabbi zidni ilman!*"

And tradition tells us:

"All of you, baptized in the light of Saif ibn Isaac al Heit, are henceforth cloaked in the protective armor of Saif Isaac al Heit: There is no longer Jew nor Black. There is only the splendor of his benevolent Domain."

It was therefore the duty of the dynasty to transmit its message across the ages and to all neighboring regions, so that all men and women of good will might become the children of Saif. Go ye therefore unto him, all ye good people! *Alif minpitjè!* There was rain, and then there was drought: the second year.

And tradition tells us:

"Thus Saif ibn Isaac al Heit, descendant of the luminous and gentle Saif Issac al Heit and progenitor of the thirst of Nakem, was a light unto the world. When he came to live among us, he carried before him the torch of his celestial grandfather, the appointed guide who had humbly toiled so that all men might be saved and brought under the rule of a single chief. *Allah hamdoulilai rabbi alamin!*

"And Saif sent the children of the people to the government schools and missionary schools, whereas he sent the women to the French clinics, and Saif saw that he was indeed their lord and master."

Saif said: "May the missionaries who have been sent to us relieve the miseries of the humble. May all my worldly goods be a treasure trove for the poor. May French law sow seeds of order and calm that will bear fruit throughout the land." And, all this came to pass, just as he had decreed. The country now manufactured natives on behalf of the French: the black functionaries who were recruited to serve the colony hereafter nourished and enlarged their families according to their respective merits. For the first time, a dialogue began to take root among the people, bearing fruit in direct proportion to the quality of the seeds that were sown—and Saif saw that the old Nakem Empire was shaken to its very core. There was rain, and then there was drought: the third year.

Hanging bouquets from doorknockers, Vandame for his part played the role of the diplomat and instituted—*tjok!*—a Lay School for the sons of chiefs, which the children of the swarthy nobles were now obliged to attend. Like a hyena in a briar patch, Saif simmered with indignation, which he hastened to swallow in the invader's presence, as if the serene secularity of these French apostates calmed his anxieties. A reactionary to the bone, Saif could hardly tolerate the idea of sending noble children to the French government school, so he made certain that only the orphans of the nobility, the illegitimate children of noble families, as well as the offspring of families known to openly criticize his rule would attend. Fine, so let the white macaques with their military helmets and "civilizing mission" waste their time teaching these little monkeys who run themselves ragged merely for a chance to lick the white man's boots and to pray to his Jesus, lapping up the infantile sermons of Abby Henry, the fine words of the Sons of Oratory of Divine Love at Rome, the Theatine monks, Auguste de Merici and the Ursulines, Therese d'Avila and the Carmelites, and all those other blissful Christians throughout history, who herded up the joyful rabble in the service of the Church.

"Hosanna to God on High!" proclaimed the new converts, now whitened by the sacrament of Christian baptism. "Paul, the great apostle of Jesus, was also once a zealous persecutor of the Christians. But on the road to Damascus, he was transformed into the most fervent of apostles!" With untiring patience, the missionary brought the message of salvation to the great and the small, to the rich and the poor, to all men and women without distinction...

And one day, Abby Henry beheld an extraordinary phenomenon: men from far away and obscure regions in the interior now kneeled before him, supplicating him to bring the light of Christ to the mob of natives who thirsted for it... Then, smiling and submissive, the illuminated serfs droned, "I seek not marvelous schemes or great miracles that are beyond my kin, but my soul is humbled in submission before the light of my true master."

And so it was that the souls of carpenters, masons, blacksmiths, weavers, bricklayers, farmers, guards, agents, boatsmen, errand-girls, eunuchs, and the lowliest of serfs, as well as local devils who were famous for slander, were stirred by the story of gentle Jesus as he struggled under the burden of the cross. Meanwhile, the notables watched the new converts to the faith with hatred and scorn in their eyes. The new Christians were cowardly enough to denounce the Saif by no more than vague hints, but brave enough to disclose the names of his acolytes. Swearing upon their beloved *Holy*

Bible, they revealed to Abby Henry that a black Sudanese named Doumbouya not only continued to practice slavery himself–a fact of life that was not uncommon throughout the Nakem–but that he also drugged the black-rabble from the more remote regions and sent them to a neighboring land, where the slave trade was still licit, so that they could be sold to Arab slave-traders and other "pilgrims" on their way to Mecca. Those who could not be sold were fed drugs and aphrodisiacs, so that they might be more inclined to work without wages, compensated instead by a hundred nights of prodigious copulation with local prostitutes, who were themselves saturated with *dabali*, a ticket to colored dreams and unbridled eroticism. *Djallé! Djallé! Amoul bop! Makoul fallé!*

The evidence against Doumbouya accumulated: that very year, it was rumored that he had sold in a single stroke six thousand men to Egypt and to Mecca a few weeks before the dry season. It was obvious he could not have done so on his own. Who helped him? The good Christians held their tongues: all were stricken dumb by a malevolent silence. Alerted by his spies, Saif calculated that Doumbouya was Jesuit enough in his treachery to cast the first stone in his direction: hence, Saif decided that it was high time to call Doumbouya to eternal rest in the celestial hereafter. Determined to aid this humble soul on its journey homeward, Saif summoned his killers Wampoulo and Kratonga, who were sent to pay a visit to the blacksmith Jean Barou.

Here is what happened:

Saif's agents approach Barou, asking him to kill the black Sudanese Doumbouya. "Make it seem that his own pocket-knife *accidentally* slid into the neck of his client," they say.

Barou recoils at the very suggestion. They try money. He refuses. They persist. He is obstinate. Haughty, indignant. What is his price? "You won't do it?... Well, too bad." He remains impassive. They remind him that Saif does not take no for an answer. Barou shuts up. Completely... It's not going to happen, he says at last. He will not commit a murder. His answer is final. They had selected him in the first place because he lacked the impassioned zeal of the recent convert.

But he will never again seek to distinguish himself, he now says. He swears it. In the name of his own dignity.

"Ha! That's a good one," Wampoulo says in exasperation. "That's no reason not to kill a man. There's nothing wrong with killing, and you know it. Why shouldn't you kill? Give me one good reason. In the name of who or what? Do it for Saif. What does a single life amount to anyway? You kill because it's your duty to kill. You kill to destroy the memory of what has gone on before you. You kill because—when the time comes—you realize that your enemy is nothing more than a defenseless slab of meat. He's dirty. He smells bad. He annoys and disgusts you. He gets in the way of your plans. You decide that this stinking idiot bears no relation to you whatsoever. That's when a cold hatred suddenly comes over you. Then you kill, all right."

"I kill!..."

"You kill!" interrupts Kratonga.

"No. That's not how I see things. You think violence is a solution to everything, but it's not." Then, fixing his gaze on the two men, Barou points at his moist eyes. "Look," he says. "I'm laughing so hard I'm crying. I could pulverize this slave trader, just as you ask me, before he even knew what hit him. I might even save the country by killing him, for then you could pretend to the Whites that Black people really are civilized. But you know and I know that the slave trade has been finished for a long time. It's an ancient myth. So to kill for such a lousy reason? To kill *for this*? And then go on and try to live my life, as if nothing happened… and then, to go out and kill again? It's a funny way to show your love of country…"

"But we will erect a monument to you, Barou. You will be immortal. You will dwell forever in paradise."

"Paradise! Ha! No, thanks… The world of the dead is not for me. Too much silence and nothing left to hope for. It doesn't exist."

"But it hints at a better world for all and so therefore entices all men who wish to be numbered among those seeking to bring it into being. What if you are the precious immortal spark upon whom all the world awaits?"

Iho yamoun! Eyé yami!

While his acolyte feverishly recites this ghastly litany, Katonga begins to untie his satchel from which he slowly retrieves–Heaven preserve us!–the horned head of a viper.

At a sign from his tamer, the snake slithers across the floor towards Barou, and then, partially lifting its cabled body in the air, it wags its tongue at him. Kratonga squats down and, like a weightlifter who is poised to lift a dumbbell, he seizes hold of the black creature, jerking it in a single motion over his head.

Paralyzed with fear, Barou finds himself strangled in an instant by the snake that is now coiled around his neck. He gasps for air from under its grip, while Saif's agents coolly watch from a distance. They speak in calm tones to the serpent, which tightens its long black coil around Barou's neck. It hisses its forked tongue in his face. Still glued to the neck of Barou, the reptile now spews its odorous breath upon his body, narrowing its eyes to miniscule slits, while the trainer Kratona at first speaks to him, then scolds him more urgently, until the criminal beast at last releases its grip, sliding off the neck of the man. When it reaches the calf of Barou's leg, it buries its fangs deep in his flesh and then slithers back to its warm satchel.

Kratonga reties the leather bag; Wampoulo makes it clear to Barou that it is up to him to make his choice: to kill Doumbouya and live, or to refuse to kill Doumbouya and die– already he knows far too much.

The snake-tamer then recounts the following anecdote:

"We have our entire life to be unhappy," he says ironically. "There's a well-known fable that may be relevant here. Destiny once promised to keep an appointment with God in the Land of Love. On the way there, he came across some men who were fighting one another in an empty field. He tried to reconcile them, but in vain. At last, he said to the men in exasperation, 'There is no justice without love, nor is there injustice without necessity.' And, so it was in the name of necessity that Destiny rose up and slaughtered the men. Yet, he bequeathed the torch of reason to all those who survived, hurrying off for his meeting with God, to which he was now late. However, God was nowhere to be found. Behind him, the men still held the torch in their hands, but it was now extinguished. God had already made his choice. So had Destiny. So too had the men with the torch. Now, do you understand, Barou?..."

"What do you want from me?" the blacksmith says in a feeble voice.

"The hide of Doumbouya."

The blacksmith signals his acquiescence. Wampoulo and Kratonga smirk when they see how terrified Barou becomes as they approach him with a knife in hand. They are poised to murder him... But, the trainer says instead, "Sorry, but I must bleed you a bit. You'll only feel a slight sting."

He nicks the blacksmith on the calf at the precise spot where the snake had bit him, and then he scarifies the fontanel of his shaved skull. He also cuts him twice in the nostrils, smearing Barou's nose with a medicinal powder, which sets the blacksmith to sneezing at once. A violet discharge flows from the wound, as the snake's venom slowly seeps from his body. The blacksmith submits to everything, before he at last collapses in a state of terrified ecstasy, listening only to the sound of his own raspy breathing and incessant hiccups.

"I'm losing blood," he murmurs, as his spirit flounders in a world of black pain.

"So the blacksmith is running low on blood. I guess he'll make a splendid assassin after all."

"I'll do it as soon as I can."

"You're sure?"

"Yes, masters."

"Sit up."

"Yes, masters."

"We want to speak to you."

"Yes, masters."

"It's very important."

"Yes, masters."

And so he did exactly as they asked.

Doumbouya came to Barou to have his head and neck shaved, but the trembling knife of the blacksmith "accidentally" fell into Doumbouya's juggler, severing the lifeline of the man who was known to be the killer of more than six hundred slaves during the golden age of the slave trade when all manner of brutality was licit. Let us burn incense in honor of this merchant of black flesh.

To complete this masterpiece of horror, Saif sent Barou a token of his appreciation, a cartridge holster with adjustable leather straps.

Raymond-Spartacus Kassoumi, the five-year old son of Kassoumi and Tambira, innocently brought Saif's gift to the workshop of the blacksmith. Later, Wampoulo was sent to bring Raymond back to the Saif's palace and to pay Barou the blood money that was his due. In the workshop of the blacksmith, Wampoulo happened to let a cartridge fall into the cinders near the bellows of the forge—and then he took the child by the hand and headed back to the palace of the Saif.

When they were about two hundred meters from the blacksmith's workshop, a terrific blast lacerated Barou's chest, killing him at once. A tear for him.

That very day, Abby Henry called upon Saif, who happened to be "sick" and therefore unable to receive visitors. The Abby returned the next day and the day after that, but he was not received until fifteen full days after these events, when everyone had already concluded that the cartridge must have accidentally slipped from the loose holster, killing the blacksmith—"a careless man but esteemed by all, starting with the Saif." The Abby's principal witness was now dead, but there was no proof whatsoever that any crime had been committed. Wampoulo had pocketed the blood money on his way out the door, leaving no trace behind him.

The ever-sly Saif, as if warning the Abby not to mettle in the affairs of others, discretely reminded him of the theological foundations of his mission: "The mystery of Israel," he observed, "resides in its refusal to accept the Gospel. Still, it is not for us to pass judgment. For the Church, with its ecclesiastical hierarchy and dogmas, might be viewed by some as hypocritical: the first shall be last."

Saif then gave a brief discourse on the subject of his Jewish ancestry, before he remarked with an evil smile that, "Israel was here, after all, to call the Church to vigilance…"

When he was certain that the Abby had grasped his point, he quickly dissimulated: "Vigilance in the matter of individual conversion," he said, warming to his subject. "For it is erroneous to speak in broad terms of any whole scale rejection or acceptance of Jesus Christ by all the people, for salvation is essentially an individual affair. Thus, to speak of Israel's 'defiance' of the Church, or of its rejection or acceptance of the Church, is to speak in terms that are far too general, if not erroneous.

"Vigilance is also required against the danger that the church may become an end in itself.

"And, finally, vigilance is necessary with respect to the very idea of a 'remnant,' lest we fall into the error of imagining that man's fidelity plays any part whatsoever in ushering in the Kingdom of God. This is certainly not the case, for the grace of God does not require the help of man to be enacted. But, this notion of a 'remnant' that is introduced in the Old Testament is also present in the New Testament, as well as in the doctrines of the Church. It constitutes a bond between the Old Testament and the New, marking their essential unity. It also remains the unifying element between the pre-Christian and the post-Christian Church.

"Your mission to convert the idolatrous Muslims and Black Jews of the Nakem," the Saif concluded, "confronts the Church with the timely question of why it bothered to come here in the first place, if not of its very existence." *Alif lam!*

3

The intermingling of missionary activity and indigenous politics would carry a steep price, especially in the year 1909.

A case in point:

"Let it be known by all those who see this proclamation, mandated and authorized by the eminently just, powerful, and pious Saif ibn Isaac al Heit, King by his Holy Grace, that in the year one thousand, nine hundred and nine, on the tenth day of the month of April during the present year, in the village of Tillaberi-Bentia and within the palace of His Royal Lordship, that it was decreed by the aforesaid Lord in my presence, functioning in my capacity as town solicitor, that this document be delivered to the colonial auditor and schoolmaster, Monsieur, the Governor Vandame, along with a copy of the formal inquest and testimony of witnesses, providing details of the criminal plot against him of Bishop Thomas de Saignac. In hopes that his brother, the white governor of the territory of Nakem, know the true facts, his Royal Lordship has decreed that the present document be made available to him.

"I, Karim Ba, public solicitor and translator for the Governor, His Highness, and recently appointed to the post of town clerk by His Royal Lordship Saif ibn Issac al Heit, will transcribe in its entirety, and without altering a single word, the following:

"This action and inquest of His Royal Lordship is addressed to the auditor and governor, Monsieur Vandame, on the subject of the actions directed against His Royal Lordship by Bishop Thomas de Saignac.

"What is herein recorded transpired in the year one thousand, nine hundred and eight, on the tenth day of the month of June of the preceding year, in the village of Tillaberi-Bentia, within the palace of His Royal Lordship. It was herein decreed by His Royal Lordship, in the presence of all the indigenous nobility, and in my own presence, the aforesaid solicitor, that certain witnesses be interrogated regarding the manner in which Bishop Thomas de Saignac violated the pact that was concluded between the Governor, Our Highness, and His Royal Lordship, in order to forcibly remove the latter and to gain control of his rich lands to benefit his own diocese, the bishopric and his parishes, in hopes that the aforesaid bishop might therein convert all the common people to the Christian religion.

"His Royal Lordship Saif ibn Isaac al Heit has ordered me, Karim Ba, the town solicitor, to draw up this public document and to interrogate all those witnesses whom His Royal Lordship has asked to present themselves–all of whom willingly complied.

"I therefore wrote the following items:

"*Item.* Kassoumi, the servant of His Lordship, a married man and the father of family, after having placed his right hand upon the Holy Scriptures and sworn an oath in the presence of the scholar Moise ibn Bez Toubaoui, testified that he had observed on several occasions the sorcerer Bouremi and Bishop Thomas de Saignac in friendly conversation. The witness further affirms that there have been frequent interactions between the two men who have often privately conversed. He states that he does not know anything further about these conversations. However, the witness declared under sworn testimony that he had observed al Hajj Hassan, a prominent marabout, enter the church and speak with Bishop Thomas de Saignac. During the course of this conversation, the witness certifies that the two men entered into the sacristy and closed the door behind them. As in the previous instance, the witness has no knowledge concerning the particulars of their conversation. In order to verify these facts, the witness has signed the present deposition and registered it with me, Karim Ba, translator and solicitor.

"*Item.* The witness Moise ibn Bez Toubaoui, having sworn an oath on the Scriptures, acknowledges that the aforesaid Bishop Thomas de Saignac called out to him that day as he passed by the front door of the Church. The bishop indicated to him, the aforesaid witness, that he wished to speak to him in private. He then asked Moise ibn Bez Toubaoui, a scholar of well-known reputation, to take an oath of silence, for he wished to disclose an important secret to him. The witness states that he vehemently refused to swear any such oath and replied to Bishop Thomas de Saignac that he could speak freely without fear of having his secret disclosed.

"However, the aforesaid Bishop de Saignac repeatedly beseeched him to take an oath, and the witness at last promised that he would not disclose the bishop's secret. The bishop then whispered that he had decided, in accordance with government authorities, to abduct His Royal Lordship

Saif ibn Isaac al Heit, under the pretext of sending him to Europe to accompany his son, who was planning to study in France. Bishop de Saignac told the witness Moise ibn Bez Toubaoui that he need not have any fears of accompanying His Royal Lordship on this trip–or at least of pretending to accompany him and that by doing so he would bolster the confidence of His Royal Lordship. He also informed him that many loyal subjects of His Royal Lordship would accompany them on this trip, and that they all would return unharmed. The witness refused to comply with the request of Bishop Thomas de Saignac.

"And when the aforesaid bishop saw that the witness was unwilling to cooperate, he offered him gold, which the witness refused. The bishop then summoned al Hajj Hassan and the sorcerer Bouremi to further his efforts to persuade the witness to act according to his wishes. However, the witness refused to listen to either of these men and left the church at once. The next morning, Bishop de Saignac summoned the aforesaid witness and the marabout al Hajj Hassan and informed them that the President of the French Republic had formally ordered Saif ibn Isaac al Heit to depart for the Atlantic coast, where he would embark upon his trip to Europe and France. However, as no such formal summons was ever issued, this disclosure could only have been a fabrication of the aforesaid bishop, who wished to abduct His Royal Lordship and to confiscate his lands for the benefit of the Church.

"*Item*. During the previous four years, in honor of the first Christian baptism performed by the missionaries to the Nakem, on the day of Easter, the third of April, one thousand, nine hundred and five, and in the presence of more than eight hundred men, domestics, and former vassals of His Royal Lordship Saif ibn Issac al Heit, His Royal Lordship donated to the Church eighteen leagues along the length of his fallow lands and four leagues along the length of his orchards as a token of his good will, and as dictated by local custom. Ignoring His Royal Lordship's gesture of cooperation, Bishop de Saignac instead listened to the advice of the white merchants, who urged him to gather the idols of the recent converts so that they might be burned in a solemn rite. However, only the newest and least dramatic of the masks and idols were consigned to the flames. For a number of soldiers outside of Nakem, former servants of His Lordship who were recruited in 1906 by Monsieur Mangin, a colonel of the infantry and cavalry, who oversaw their march as far as Morocco, were surprised to find that these same masks and idols had not been burned at all, as Bishop de Saignac had told the converts, but were instead exchanged for gold and sold to antique dealers, collectors, museums, and boutiques. The profits from these exchanges were turned over to the Church in Nakem, which claimed to have been overwhelmed by the influx of new converts, due to their dire circumstances and extreme poverty, for which the resources of the Church were insufficient to remedy.

"*Item*. Many agents of His Royal Lordship report that Bishop de Saignac had frequently accused His Royal Lordship of seeking to stem the tide of converts to the Christian faith, and of attempting to enmesh the Church in inextricable material difficulties, thereby discrediting it in the eyes of the people. However, there is no evidence whatsoever to substantiate this pernicious defamation of His Royal Lordship. In fact, the evidence suggests precisely the contrary, for His Lordship has been extremely solicitous on behalf of the mission of Church: in one instance, when a number of his own servants deliberately sought to provoke and injure the new converts, he pursued them as far as the front doors of the church, and he was even prepared to execute them for their misdeeds, had not his respect for Your Majesty prevailed, for His Royal Lordship had no wish to embroil Your Majesty in difficulties of this nature, but also due to the fact that some of those involved in this regrettable incident belong to the most important families in the land."

"*Item*. However, after the failure of the plot of Bishop de Saignac, His Lordship, who was traveling in the Gagol-Gosso, returned after fifteen days to find that fifteen of his children, all of whom were approximately eight years old, had been poisoned and then died of dysentery. The sorcerer Bouremi was named as a suspect and while evidence was being gathered against him, the sixteenth child of His Lordship named Hassim, also eight years old, fell asleep one night on the terraces of the palace and, upon awaking, found himself covered with numerous festering pustules, for a poisonous liquid had been sprinkled on his body while he had slept. Exhausted by the efforts to insure the salvation of his soul, he became feverish and, after two days of terrible agony, the blood began to congeal in his veins. Efforts to prevent his demise were now useless: The hands of Death utterly crushed his heart, after he had experienced extreme suffering. A stream of blood flowed from his nose and mouth, and this little one, whom Death so cruelly attacked, could no longer resist the inevitable: The beloved son of the Saif at last surrendered his soul to the Creator, seeking recompense for the glorious pains that he had endured on His behalf. Those who attended the vigil over the body were devastated by this terrible loss. The home of all his loved ones was overwhelmed with sorrow, as were the homes of all those who knew him.

"But this was not all, for, three days later, Prince Madoubou, the eldest son of His Royal Lordship, who had been invited some eight years ago to visit France, suddenly became terribly ill: his heart beat very quickly, and his body burned with fire; his blood began to ceaselessly percolate; he changed color; he became black, then blue, and then pale. At last, he was overwhelmed with the same type of fatal pustules that had only recently killed his younger brother. Appearing the same morning before the king and the royal court in the palace, he said simply, 'It seems that there are those who do not love me quite so well as Death, or as my father. Only eight years ago, you officially recognized me as a prince, and my father also honored me with this title. As time passed, you saw that you had no reason to regret bestowing this title upon me. You and my father promised that I would inherit the kingdom, although I did not myself seek any such honor.

You elevated me to this office, and then you changed your mind and sought to kill me. But God has sustained me and what is rightfully mine.'

"This brief speech so moved the Court and so upset those present that the name of the author of these evils could no longer be concealed. The sorcerer Bouremi was formally charged with the crime, although there was still no tangible proof of his guilt. Bishop de Saignac was also named, as numerous accusations by several families had already been made against him, including the charge of impregnating three black women.

"Your Majesty, as you can see, a great many sordid events of this nature have transpired here, the variations of which are innumerable. However, we no longer have the patience to tolerate them. Our complaints are reasonable. We acknowledge that the Priests of the Society of Jesus who were sent here are certainly virtuous men, who had at one time set a good example for the people. If they are not as respected today as they were when they first arrived, it is because they wished to confiscate the lands of His Lordship, plotting against him and then becoming embroiled in local politics; it is also because they acted without scruple when they carried off the oldest and most expressive local masks, as well as the most artistic doors of their converts' huts.

"Besides these various offenses, Bishop de Saignac defamed the notables of His Lordship from his pulpit, treating them as if they were exploiters of the people, slave-traffickers, and men without learning; and, when he came down from his pulpit, he even stated verbatim, "So far, you have heard me speak about these men, but I have yet to speak on the subject of Saif ibn Isaac al Heit. You may rest assured that I will have plenty to say about this dirty Jew." This was said as he stood on the last step of the pulpit, still wearing his priestly vestments. All those present were enraged to hear His Royal Lordship referred to in this way. May Your Highness accept the testimony of the aforesaid Kassoumi, who has born witness to these events under oath: he is an honest man, who respects the truth.

"This then is the principal reason for the displeasure of His Lordship as well as that of the notables and many of the local peoples who are certainly aware that Bishop de Saignac showed so much disrespect for His Royal Lordship; for God does not tolerate those who defame either the Jews or the infidels, as the example of Elijah clearly shows: Because Elijah allowed his own children to dishonor the tribes of Israel, God did nothing whatsoever to forestall his sudden death, as well as the death of his sons in battle and his daughters-in-law in childbirth. We trust that Your Highness does not suffer defamations of this nature either. Moreoever, we also heard it said from the pulpit, by the aforesaid bishop, that it was a pity we had never actually sought to kill him, and that, after coming to the Nakem, his only regret was that we had not done it so far.

"Similarly, the aforesaid Bishop de Saignac, while traveling in the Goro Foto Zinko, spoke with the local commandant and recommended against the priests coming to this region. In fact, many of the local people were heart-broken when the priests did not show up. Hence, we ask Your Highness to requisition the letters that he wrote about Goro Foto Zinko in order to determine his true intentions and reasons for abandoning the good people of Goro Foto Zinko. Should Your Highness do so, he will see that our complaints are not unjustified.

"*Item.* A friend of Kassoumi, who had recently converted to Christianity, the aforesaid Jean-Pierre Dogo said to Bishop de Saignac: 'Monseigneur, it is necessary that you donate money to his Lordship at this time. Sixteen of his children have died, and the eldest is now gravely ill. It is only fitting that a man who has as many responsibilities as His Lordship, upon whom so many families depend, and who has been so generous to the Church, be given gifts of money to support him at this difficult time. This is the custom of the land.'

"But Bishop de Saignac responded: 'Dogo, I don't have a single centime of Saif's money.' Dogo went straight to the point: 'Monseigneur, if you don't have any of his Lordship's money, you surely have money of your own that you can give to him from the profits of the land that he once gave to you. Ever since you arrived, he has bestowed innumerable riches and honors upon you.' However, the bishop refused. 'It is useless, Dogo,' he said. 'I have neither his Lordship's money, nor money of my own to give him, none that I am aware of, anyway. After all, I'm a priest, not a banker.'

"And so it was that the man who had been given everything by His Royal Lordship now claimed that he had absolutely no money. Despite the personal assistance of Your Highness, your wife, and your many white subordinates, the support that His Royal Lordship required at this time to provide gifts for the poor proved to be woefully inadequate; and, in spite of these deplorable circumstances, Bishop Thomas de Saignac still refused to offer any assistance. Thus, it happened that the poor from every region of the Nakem, numbering not less than forty thousand and six-hundred, came to pay their condolences to the royal family, but nothing could be given back to them. They were deceived by custom, for we normally distribute many gifts and alms upon the occasion of a death in the royal family.

"It is our wish now that Your Highness extend to us the favor of sending someone to conduct further investigations in order to verify the truth of these matters. His Royal Lordship extends to you his best wishes for further cooperation with France and greater friendship between His Royal Lordship and Your Highness. May God the Most High bestow His benign clemency upon you and shield you from all harm.

"Recorded in this village of Tillaberi-Bentia, on this tenth day of the month of April, in the year one thousand nine hundred and nine.

"King Saif ibn Isacc al Heit."

Later that same week, at the same time as the arrival of the medicine that Saif had asked Vandame to send to Tillaberi-Bentia, which saved the life of Madoubo, news rapidly spread of the departure of Bishop de Saignac, as well as the future allocation of a monthly salary to Saif, a personal gesture made by Monsieur and Madame Vandame, and finally of the onset of madness in the sorcerer Bouremi.

There was much skepticism about Bouremi's professed innocence. Rumors of his plotting against the life of Saif—who, it was said, had only sought to protect himself and his family—were heard from all quarters. Each day seemed to bring fresh confirmation of the suspicions against him. More than ever before, Saif saw his popularity soar to new heights, while Bouremi found consolation in a life of unrestrained debauchery.

Not that he raped anyone, or became a complete drunkard, but he was so indiscrete in his behavior, committing so many immoral acts, that his reputation was forever tarnished. Many of these acts, it was rumored, involved violence, sadism, and savagery: private wells were poisoned; some of his neighbors became gravely ill from drinking elixirs that contained human blood and the pus of lepers; potions were circulated that brought panic and hysteria to whole neighborhoods; mysterious and gruesome deaths suddenly occurred; diverse illnesses, some resembling the black death, followed wherever he went; and, finally, a lady who was married to a notable, and with whom he had once had a stormy affair, suddenly became epileptic and then killed herself for no apparent reason.

Like a swashbuckler in revolt, Bouremi swaggered through the streets, accusing Saif of all manner of crimes, seeking quarrels with all those who crossed his path. He seemed to cherish the fits of madness that overcame him, doing everything in his power to prolong them, deliberately preventing any variation in them, and insulting all he knew for the sheer pleasure of insulting them.

Those who thought that they knew him saw him as an idealist, a man who was illuminated for an instant by the blow of some immense idea that had completely dazzled him, often for long periods at a time. He could not conquer whatever it was that had long fermented within him and finally overcome him, they said, for his entire existence—like a man half-crushed under the weight of a boulder—had now become a slow and terrible agony. Was he truly in revolt? Was he a cynic? Or, was all of this mere vulgarity? Had he become the living incarnation of anger, at the mercy of his own neurotic legend? Or, was he simply a failed sorcerer? No. Not exclusively, for many believed that he was little more than a criminal who was enjoying his retirement.

A week earlier, his first wife was on the verge of going to Saif to apologize for Bouremi and ask for Saif's forgiveness, but she fell sick on her way out the door—and suddenly died. Bouremi left his second wife to attend to the burial of his first wife and then wandered about the village proclaiming that Saif was a filthy slave-trader, and that a hoard of Saif's agents had tried to poison him. In order to avenge Saif, they had done everything they could to drive him mad, to kill him, little by little, to drink his life's blood! Saif had sided with the Whites because he wanted to be the Big Man of the Nakem. And so Bouremi was seen everywhere taunting Saif with these accusations, shouting them, singing them in rhyme, harassing everyone who crossed his path and glaring at them with vacuous eyes—as if he defied the entire world and its senseless laws. "So, the world and all its 'stupidities' is to blame for what's become of him!" a supporter of Saif said in disgust after one of Bouremi's harangues. "If you want to talk sense into this animal, you'll have to tie him up first. He's a second-rate madman whose love of causing trouble has now come back to haunt him!" But Bouremi laughed off such criticisms. In themselves, the words that he loudly proclaimed were not all that important, for he had ears for his own 'truth' alone—which was that Saif was an 'incendiary scum,' a slave-trader, a fake leader, a fake Black, and a fake Jew, the assassin of Chevalier, and the murderer of countless others! ..."

"As soon as my folly overcomes me," Bouremi cried, "I am no longer a normal man. I am an imaginary being. The incarnation of the devil, if he existed... which, of course, he doesn't... Besides, even if the devil did exist, he wouldn't amount to all that much... A man becomes a devil when he loses his soul. You watch for the tragic event to occur, but after it does, you're not quite sure how it happened. In fact, you're not even sure *if* it happened. That's how it happened with Saif. That's how he became a devil.

"The coming of the tragic sentiment cannot be foreseen. You feel its slow advance, but it happens too quickly, before you realize what's going on.

"I know that I'm crazy. I can't deny it. I was born in the ravine of a graveyard, and when I came into the world, a hundred thousand stars burst forth from my nostrils, illuminating the night with my brilliant tears. Ah, Saif! ... Do I look so very cold to you? Do you hear my teeth rattling around inside my mouth? No, it's not that! I lost all my teeth in the long struggle that became my life, until I was finally overwhelmed and crushed. Now, I laugh like an idiot with bleeding gums and twenty centuries of cavities. For years, I have longed to speak my true mind, but the wars, upheavals, betrayals, and tensions between the nations of the world kept me in silence. But today at last, I have spoken out, and now the silence itself may be surprised to learn that, after so many centuries of cruelty and inhumanity, I find that some hope still remains... And let's be honest about this: Where else will you ever find a man quite like me? A man who will dare to speak openly about what the rest of the world would prefer to keep silent? Where else will you find a man to speak the complete truth about Man? About those wretched creatures who live in utter misery? Where else will you find a man who will speak on behalf of the impoverished dregs of humanity... Even if it's true that I speak now only for the sake of breaking the silence, or because I have found that, in the long run, silence is intolerable... None of you can see Saif in my words, but when you have at last learned to really and truly see, the echo from the ocean's waves raging inside you will cause the most precious of jewels to gush forth from your unwashed eyes, flowing down in rivets along your crest fallen cheeks—and then you will cry, my dear brothers. You will cry as you have never before cried. But enough of this nonsense.

"Open your eyes!

"Open them, I say!

"My eyes are open!

"I carry a heavy burden ... I do not know if you have understood a single word that I have said, but my madness is certainly a wonderful thing, the best of all possible alibis. It is terrible but also delicious. You figure out how everything works, your accusations are heard by all—and then you suddenly begin to howl like an idiot! And, of course, I have the right to howl like an idiot. No one can keep me from my madness. Just try. I have neither father nor mother, neither god nor devil. In the war against Saif, I therefore choose madness. Some think that I'm merely trying to distinguish myself from others, trying to make myself original, but what if my madness *was* my true originality? What business is it of yours?

The sorcerer howled his philosophical invective at the top of his lungs on the misery of the human condition, haranguing every passerby on the road, supplicating all those who would lend an ear, as he spewed out that he was thoroughly fed up with being slandered. "Certainly, it is true that I have killed more than a hundred and twenty innocent people," he admitted, "but never on purpose." Then, as he uttered these words, something indeed seized hold of him, torturing his spirit, and revolting him to the very core of his being: He scratched, swore, groaned, and raved that these deaths had all been accidents. "They were accidents! Accidents, I tell you! Acci... Oh, why won't you people leave me alone? All I'm asking for is to be left alone! In peace! I want to be left in peace. They were only accidents," he shouted, his face sallow, haggard, and terrified. As for Saif? And Saif's children? ... Had he really killed them? He had not completely lost his wits, it seems, when it came to this thorny subject... But, finally, he grew extremely agitated, pacing about, here and there, retracing his steps, suddenly quickening his gait. Horrified, he shouted that he wanted to put an end to this whole nasty business, but, as if possessed by a devil, *by the devil*, he resumed his invective once again, and, with trembling and haggard lips, he called Saif "a common criminal." As for the Governor, he already knew that Saif was a criminal, but he lacked the proof to catch him. They had questioned all the witnesses! They had verified that he had never sought to kill Saif! He was therefore an innocent man! ... He proclaimed his innocence! ... It was Saif who had knocked over that glass at Chevalier's house, not him... And the retarded cat had lapped it up... Saif's children are dead because Chevalier's cat drank the poison, or maybe it was due to a second of carelessness on his part... In any event, there was no proof against him! He was innocent! There might be moaning and groaning coming from the Saif's palace now, but that didn't prove that he had done anything! So they should leave him alone! After all, accidents sometimes happen…"

"Accidents?

"Yes, things like this happen from time to time! Wait! Listen to me! You need to hear this! You must let me explain it to you…"

But Bouremi explained nothing at all, for everyone took one look at the man and fled from his presence. Be that as it may, a current of opinion slowly began to take shape among the French authorities, as well as the public at large, who were increasingly troubled by the divulgences of Bouremi, and who suspected that not everything that he had said was without foundation. What if it turned out that he was telling the truth? But the sorcerer managed by his own actions to undermine the meager credit that had begun to be accorded to his accusations, and he eventually came to be excoriated by all.

For when Bouremi returned to his house, slobbering with anger and exhaustion, he found that his second wife Bintou was waiting for him at home. He must have seemed frightful to her, for Bintou implored him to pull himself together–for the sake of his child.

"What are you talking about?" he barked.

"Your child!"

"Whose child? Me? Mine?"

"Yes, yours."

"Mine?"

"It's our child, thanks be to Heaven… Our child," she repeated, laying his feverish and cautious palm flat upon her belly. He lives, my love. Our child lives, Bouremi, I felt him moving, our… our baby, Bouremi… our baby… Please respect him.. What will the neighbors say about how you're carrying on…"

"Huh… what? A baby! You are pregnant with this serpent? Ha, ha, so that's why you've been so bloated for the last few weeks. That's why you're been wearing all these big dresses! And here I was thinking that it was some new fashion of yours or that you'd just gotten fat! So you've been hiding it from me, have you? This brat, this living abortion?"

"Bouremi! No, no! No! Don't do this! Not this, Bouremi! Bouremi! Bouremi! No! Ah! Aaaa...."

One, two, three ... seven swift kicks to the belly. The brute kicked her seven times in the belly! Dead center. But not as many times as she deserved, he said. He would have kicked her a hundred times. Free of charge. But, already, she lay without moving and would have been dead, if the neighbors had not intervened and restrained her husband. Everyone without exception was enraged over the actions of the sorcerer. His neighbors quickly turned into a mob, hurling insults at Bouremi, seizing hold of him, tossing him up in the air, and letting him fall to the earth like a sack of soft dough. They did this three times, before the man suddenly stiffened with life, digging in his heels, snarling out a string of insults and threats that he would kill anyone who came near him—and then he bolted towards the river with the mob not far at his heels. Crazy for good this time, he threw himself into the Yame. A cry of horror rang out from the avenging mob, for three crocodiles emerged from the water, sawed him in half with a slap of their tails, and then feasted on his bloody remains.

The next day, Bouremi's wife died while delivering her premature baby, who weighed only a kilogram and was baptized David Bouremi. Ever the magnanimous politician, Saif adopted the child. A hymn in his honor. *Al hamdoulilai rabbi alamin!*

4

A year and three months later, on July 13, 1910, three strangers arrived in Nakem, a German family: Fritz Shrobenius, his wife Hildegaard, and their daughter Sonia, who had only stopped for a brief visit of five days with Vandame at Krebbi-Katsena and then drove off in a camion to Tillaberi-Bentia, loaded down with trunks and cases, baggy pants, shirt-sleeves, colonial helmets, and shoulder rifles.

When his agents and the government emissaries informed Saif that these explorer-tourists were ethnologists who wished to pay him gold for three tons of old wood, and who were collecting as many African artifacts as they could get their hands on, he gave them a magnificent welcome.

He sent the scholar Moise ibn Bez Toubaoui and numerous townsmen to ride out and greet them on the road to the palace, halfway to Tillaberi-Bentia. When they arrived in the village, Saif presented himself to the strangers accompanied by three delegations of nobles on horseback, who were followed by an even larger train of griots and other domestics.

Saif and the nobility came to the meeting in sumptuous garb, the various detachments attired in gold jewelry, leather and brass, to the sound of drums and other sonorous instruments. Horses pranced about in file, and in such a fashion that they evoked the processions of former times, the glorious celebrations on behalf of the victorious warriors. Three of four groups of those on foot sang verses in honor of the guests, and the choir of the masses chanted their verses in response; then, they sang together in loud, clamorous voices piercing the air with litanies of praise that had been selected in advance by the His Royal Lordship Saif ibn Isaac al Heit, on behalf of the German strangers, "for the valorous exploits that they had performed that had brought honor to the Nakem."

All Saif's men then returned in the exact reverse order that they had come.

When they at last arrived at the palace, Fritz, Hildegaard, and then Sonia climbed out of the camion, approaching the throne of Saif, who waited for them in the Grand Court of the Acacias. The interior of the palace was so dark that they only made their way through the corridors with great difficulty.

Enthroned beside his son Prince Madoubou, Saif sat upon a high platform where he could be seen by all. His throne was made of gold and ivory, as well as various pieces of intricately carved wood that were crafted in the local style; all of this harmonized quite nicely with his splendid boubou of ochre velvet that was veined with silver stitching that shimmered from under his damask blouse. On his head, he wore a finely chiseled golden crown, much like that of his son, while he nonchalantly held in his hands an oriental fan, crafted from mother of pearl. He wore Moorish slippers on his feet to complete this outrageous outfit.

When Fritz Shrobenius came before Saif, he bowed in respect, as did his wife and his daughter; the royal personages then greeted them in return, offering them the traditional water gorge as a token of welcome. When these courtesies were terminated, the visitors were at last asked to be seated.

With Karim Ba serving as his translator, the ethnologist revealed the goal of his visit in the presence of all. With the help of a domestic servant, he brought from his camion diverse pieces of cloth, which the ethnologist held up with reverence and respect, as well as pieces of silver, money that was currently in circulation, clothing items, and precious stones. With a magnificent gesture, Saif decreed that it was time for this inventory of items to be terminated, asking the scholar Moise ibn Bez Toubaoui to distribute these displayed goods to those who were present. The crowd kneeled in gratitude before these objects, a prayer flowing from their lips that died down and was then rekindled at the sight of some new treasure.

More popular than ever before, Saif later held a private conversation with the esteemed visitor in the presence of his wives, far from the sight of the black-rabble, so he might examine the remaining gifts in private.

In addition to numerous gratuities for the wives of the notables, Shrobenius offered several bars of gold that weighed two kilograms to His Royal Lordship. The bargain was sealed.

The next day, the ethnologist began transcribing the sayings of the various informants who had been authorized by Saif, while Shrobenius's wife walked with slow steps throughout the corridors of the palace, pestering Karim Ba with endless questions. At her heels, Mabdodou spoke interminably to her daughter of ancient symbols, following the lead of his father who regaled the visitors with copious yarns from days past. "The night of Nakem civilization and that of African History," the prince solemnly intoned, "blew in on a fatal wind, by the will of God the Most High."

Saif nodded his approval with a grave air. From that time forward, ideas began to percolate in the brain of Shrobenius, as they paced back and forth across the courtyard of the Acadias with knitted brows, selling and buying African spirituality by the meter. Hildegaard carefully recorded every cliché that these savants uttered, walking a few paces behind her husband, a fat, serious, and ruddy German, with reddish-blond hair, blue eyes, and the beginnings of a beer belly, *wèrèguè wèrèguè!!*

Saif waxed lyrical on old myths while the translator interpreted his precious words, and Madoubou gave his version in French, refining these jewels of wisdom with ever greater subtleties to the delight of Shrobenius, a human crawfish who was possessed by the desire to resuscitate an African universe that no longer corresponded to anything that actually existed, all in the name of cultural autonomy. Decked out with all the gaudy elegance of a colonizer on holiday, and bursting with jolly laughter, he sought to find a metaphysical meaning in everything he happened upon, including the shape of the palaver tree where the notables gathered. Gesticulating at every turn, he displayed his "amity" for Africa and his proud knowledge with all the assurance of a sophomore in college. He believed that African social life was pure art, a living and sometimes terrible manifestation of religious symbolism. The Nakem today was a great ancient civilization that had, alas, become a victim of the vicissitudes of the white man. But whenever he encountered the spiritual aridity of certain forms of local social life, he fell into a sort of stupefied sleepiness, incapable even of becoming sad. As if suddenly inspired, he consoled himself by driving to the Yame in the camion with his daughter Sonia to film the hippopotamuses and crocodiles. He waited for them at the river's edge during the hottest hours of siesta, taking turns with his daughter, an opulent blond of twenty years, beautiful, with sparkling teeth, who kept on the lookout among the high weeds and tall foliage. Exquisitely fresh with a long white neck, green, almond-shaped eyes, blue eyelashes, and rosy lips, Shrobenius's daughter evoked the delicate color of the shimmering scales of the fish that swam in the profound depths of the Yame.

Madoubo often came along to keep her company, leaning his back against the camion, listening to the slow music of her phonograph, or whispering tall tales about the isle of the Zobos on the Yame and how it contained many pieces of ancient art that had been preserved, and that surfaced from time to time in the village, speaking of these artworks as if he had carved them himself.

Sonia was so interested in the topic that she gave Madoubo confidence to speak at greater and greater length, as she threw herself into the task of taking notes to be interpreted at a later time, smiling at him, repeating "*ya*" or "*nein*" among other German colloquialisms. Madoubou was so enthralled that he could have stood against the camion, listening to her German accent and looking at her until the end of time.

One day they decided to go for a walk along a path that was at some distance from the palace, unaware that they were being followed by Sankolo. Suddenly, Sonia murmured, "I think you're very nice."

Her big brilliant eyes were like two soft lamps. A warm smile lit up her lips, and the son of Saif was overwhelmed with desire.

They descended with slow steps along the shadowy ramparts of the Yame, listening to the sound of a swift wave that was headed towards the shore. It squalled in the distance, as it gained in momentum, growing like a dark stain on the horizon. They remained in the same spot, chatting for a long time, holding hands, and looking out at the dead tree trunks that had been carried along by the flow of the Yame, as the yellow water grew ever darker, as if it was boiling amidst the debris, not far from where the hippopotamuses played.

Sonia nestled against the shoulder of Madoubo. The delicious silence between them was as sweet as a kiss.

Was it the exoticism of the encounter that drew them together? Their youth? Their desire for pleasure? Without knowing or truly understanding why, the young people suddenly kissed one another fully on the mouth, their hard teeth emitting the savory taste of soft seaweed. They kissed for a long moment, so languorous was their fever…

They said nothing and remained facing one another, their heads lowered, their expressions indecisive, as if lost in a difficult meditation, sensing a change in the wind, breathing in the invisible, a mysterious foreboding of their hidden intentions. They were paralyzed by a sort of quivering ardor, the heaving of their chests. A sudden tension overcame them that they could feel along the very tips of their fingers, straining all their faculties of physical sensation, until at last they were overcome by the unspeakable need to commit acts of utter foolishness.

Finally, no longer able to contain themselves, and seeking a place that was safe and hidden from view, the two young people began walking.

Sonia led the way, running along the slopes of the Yame.

"It is far still?" asked Madoubou.

"There in the camion, down below."

"We can't go there!"

"Wait and see! It's very big. Yesterday at the river's edge, I filmed the hippopotamuses from inside it."

She vigorously kicked open the door, climbing into the back seat and knocking over some objects. Her soft voice called to him from the interior of the automobile: "Come on then."

Madoubou craned his neck but did not notice Sankolo lying flat on the ground among the reeds. He climbed into the camion, firmly placing his hands on the corsage of the young woman, whose lips greedily met his.

"Wait a second. My skirt."

After he relaxed his grip, she bent forward, seized the lower part of her skirt and pulled it up over her head. Sonia's slip reminded him of *rhim*, only hers had a lacy border. She sat immobile, intently peering into his face. She was both excited and frightened.

Her bra and panties were sewn from the finest of cloth, as if glossy silk encircled her body in smooth rings.

"Would you like me to remove my underwear? Would that excite you?"

He acquiesced. The phonograph played soft music in the distance. The woman folded her hands over the place where her thighs met, and he could feel his body trying to steady itself by the rhythm of the waves. Her opulent breasts danced before him, as if following the hypnotic motion of the water. It was a spectacle that would have healed the sick and caused the lame to walk.

"This music is extraordinary," she said, on the verge of ecstasy.

"It's… Spanish," Madoubo replied.

"Is it functional?" the woman asked with interest.

"Its function is for making love… to the rhythm of the guitars."

"An excellent idea," Sonia agreed with sincere passion.

Creeping behind them at less than twenty meters, Sankolo watched the woman make a slow and suggestive turn, her arms above her head, as she clapped her hands to the cadence of the guitars.

"Come on then," he heard her say in an impatient voice. "What sort of man are you, anyway?"

In a single motion, Madoubou moved within hand's reach, and his hands now moved freely over her body.

Sankolo felt the humid caress of the Yame wafting across his face; he felt the wild beating of his own heart, jerking inside his chest like a compass gone mad. Moans of pleasure resounded from inside the camion. They kissed. All at once, Sankolo longed to run and throw himself on top of the woman. But a dull ache riveted him in place. He saw Madoubou swell and thrash about on top of her, his lips greedily seeking hers, nervously probing her mouth with his hungry tongue, running the tips of his fingers over Sonia's supple breasts. She was strangely immobile. Stretched out. Her head upright. Her brows slowly furrowed and were then submerged in the same torpidity. She caressed the man. Sankoklo longed to lift his hand to touch her, but his arm and his fingers refused to obey. Suddenly, he shifted to one side, so that he could follow what was going on in the rear-view mirror. He pulled upon the rope of his *touba* and was immediately undressed. He lay his boubou on the ground. His eyes were knocked out of orbit from sheer desire and anguish before the splendors of Sonia's flesh: he then fixed his gaze on her breasts, her lips, her entire body, hypnotized by the rhythmic motions of the couple. A warm and sensual laugh unexpectedly issued from her throat, causing him to breathe heavily and then become entangled in his cotton boubou, which he accidentally ripped. Suddenly, he sneered at himself and then, spitting in the palm of his right hand, he gripped his hard penis and pointed it towards the couple:

"That's something I've never had before! I'll flog myself until my stomach hurts, by God! Say, old friend," he said to his penis, "have you ever seen two white turtledoves in a pigeon house? You see that little treasure that's hidden in the bushes between those white legs? Come on now, taste those sweet lips in that blond thicket of perfumed delights! Again!," he panted, straining for a better look. "Oh, yes, do it again. Come on, kiss her, lick her, harder, right there... Hold her in place. Yes, give her a taste of real flesh... Make me vomit up her pleasure. You like that, don't you? Yes, you do..."

And thus he purred under his own caresses, reveling in his own senses, rubbing his legs together, his flesh vibrating like the string of a harp adroitly played, lovingly caressed. He clutched his fingers on his penis, that cunning little rogue with its own will, welcoming the abundant flow of a red-tinged warmth that made him growl in a superb explosion of pleasure. Then he licked his raspy tongue upon his hand, smearing the saliva over his body, without ceasing to gaze at the swollen and bloody lips of the vulva that he saw in the rear-view mirror. Softly, he began to sob...

He sensed a presence behind him. He turned around and saw Awa, his finance, who had seen everything.

Sankolo lowered his eyes before her. He knew at once that this woman detested him. Summoning up all the ill-will he could muster, he did his best to drive the labored breathing of the couple in the camion from his mind, as well as the taste of saliva that flowed at the corners of his mouth.

Instead, he fixed his gaze upon his fiancé, as if he wished to be saturated with her malignant jealousy.

The courtesan turned away from him, running towards the swelling tide of the Yame, as a flock of swans flew overhead in a V-shape. He saw at once that she was disoriented, desperate–and that she needed him. He knew as he had never known anything before in his life that he was going to make her pay for what she had seen.

She looked at him in horror. He was the first man who had writhed with agony inside her. Awa gasped for air from her throat. With a gesture that was at once hideous and banal, Sankolo pressed his thumb on the tip of his penis and shook it aggressively at her. Naked, he pulled himself up from the ground.

A clean feeling rushed through his body, as the fresh air from the river filled his nostrils. The blood that he could taste inside his throat imbued his lungs with moisture.

Sankolo did not know that he had sneered at her in spite of his asphyxia; but, because his heart beat from under his eyelids, and because he knew that she was going to die, his conscience returned to him for a fraction of a second, as if his brain was a broken mirror that had reflected back a brief glimpse of light. His resolution gushed out from his body in a torrent of intolerable pain. As if he might lie down with his pain like a mother with her child, he emitted a piteous sob. Then, with a quick step, he rid himself of the sensation and followed his child into a desolate solitude.

He struck Awa with a light blow on the cheek. His fiancé raised her hand in defense. Then he hammered his fist fully into her mouth, while keeping one eye on the couple that frolicked in the camion. This gave him an air of terrible detachment, as if in order to completely destroy her, all he needed was a small portion of his will.

He continued to strike her with a series of blows to the face, absent-mindedly thrashing her. He was less interested in administering correction to her than in making her blood flow and inflicting the maximum amount of suffering. The hands of Awa were useless against his blows, and she made no effort to hit him back, for she loved him and was tortured by the horror and the depravity of their physical struggle. A fist smashed into her nose, which she now felt collapsing into her face. She did not say a word, thinking in despair, "He will stop this. He loves me. He doesn't really want to kill me."

Sankolo waited until she was able to lift herself from the dirt, and with a sardonic smile, he began stroking his penis in her direction. The woman hit him in the gut with her shoulder. He staggered backwards, hitting a black stump in the midst of the mud and slime of the riverbank. She groaned in pain for a moment, as Sankolo fought to recover the insane fury that had previously sustained him. Not that he any longer recognized her voice: the voice that cried out to him in pain was no longer the voice of his fiancé but that of a complete stranger.

"No! ... No..." whimpered Awa.

He thrust his hands upon the back of her neck and smeared her mouth into the mud. Awa was still cognizant of what was happening. She tried to cry out, but Sankolo heard only a diminishing whimper, which gave him no satisfaction. She began to cry. Her pain soared like a bird along the veins of her body that imprisoned it. Awa opened her mouth, as if wishing to let the bird escape. She opened wide and then wider, but its talons suddenly grabbed hold of her bowels, settling there, slashing her from the inside, wounding her, never wearying.

"If only I could faint," she thought, "if only I could cry out." Her hand grasped at the small thread of black water that flowed towards the Yame, thick and purple blood intermingling with the mud.

The bird ceased twisting and turning inside her head; it now seemed to be at peace, nestled comfortably in a small corner of the prison that was her body. The slow words spoken by Sankolo disgusted her in the midst of her pain. She felt each of them dripping from the lips of the man, as her body twitched convulsively in terror of expectation of the voice that would shoot through her like a spear, piercing her at the base of her skull. As Sankolo came closer, the bird awoke once again; the walls of Awa's brain vibrated, and the slightest contact of the breath of her lover burned her like fire on an open wound.

Sankolo seized Awa by the throat. He buried his knife in her left breast and rotated it two times. Then he carved a jagged ridge along her lower belly. When he removed the knife, her pink viscera spilled out. He did not even know if the woman screamed. He licked the knife before returning the weapon to its sheath. He buried the body under a wall of mud.

A shadow flitted across the savannah: Kassoumi, who was returning from his banana tree, had seen it all. *Alif minptjè!*

5

Denounced by Kassoumi, repudiated by the notables, imprisoned by Vandame, Sankolo was also banished by Saif, who, a cunning ideologue (and taking advantage of the public outcry over the murder of Awa), further inflated the cost of local black art by concocting a mythological stew of religion, symbolism, and pure aesthetics, further spiced up with the sauces of tradition and "human values," which he served on a platter to Vandame, who, in his turn, passed on the word to his friends, those innocent white vendors–God bless them–who hawked it to the curious, the tourists, the colonizers, the ethnologists, and the sociologists flocking in great numbers to the Nakem. At best sterile and anachronistic redundancies, this black art was nonetheless baptized as "aesthetic" and sold–oye!–in the imaginary universe of "authentic cultural experience"! "Very often," Saif observed, making it up as he went along, "the tools that are used to carve the masks are blessed seventy-seven time by a priest who must flagellate himself as he utters his blessing, repeating this procedure until the third day of the seventh year, marking the date that the tree was cut down. As he recites these blessings, traditional wisdom about the world's creation is ritually chanted"

"The plant," said Shrobenius, following his thread, "must germinate before it bears fruit. It dies and is reborn when its seed germinates. The moon also rises, until it is completely full. Then it grows pale, wanes in the heavens, and finally disappears, so that the process may repeat itself in the days to come. The destiny of man is not so very different from the destiny of black art; like the grain of wheat and the evening star, the symbolic interplay of this art is consumed by the earth and then born again, now sanctified—endowed with the undeniable force that its achievement constitutes—so that it may assume its cosmic role in the sublime and tragic drama of the celestial bodies on high." Black art thus gained its fraudulent noble credentials via the folklore of mercantilist spirituality, *oye oye oye...*

But infinite are those who find inspiration in the Almighty, the One who never fails to honor His vows to those who are faithful! Thus it was that God wafted the idiot genius Shrobenius, who proclaimed his intuitions about the ancient civilization of the Nakem to all those who would listen: "These people are refined! They are civilized to the bone! Everywhere one goes, one encounters large avenues that are calm and peaceful, where one may literally breathe in the grandeur of a unique people, its human genius... It was only after white imperialism first made in-roads here, with all its violence and materialistic colonialism, that this highly civilized people fell from their majestic heights into a savage state, plagued by cannibalism and primitivism. But if one harkens back to the grandeur of the empires of the Middle Ages—for all one need to do is contemplate the splendor of the Nakem's art to grasp my point—one will come face to face with Africa as it really is: wise, beautiful, rich, ordained, non-violent, as powerful as it is humanistic. Why, the Nakem is quite possibly the cradle of Egyptian civilization!"

With drool running off his chin, Shrobenius doubled his profits upon returning home: on the one hand, he so mystified and enchanted his countrymen that they awarded him a prestigious professorial chair; and, on the other hand, he exploited the sentimentality of innumerable black idiots, who were only too happy to hear a white man say that, "Africa was the womb of the world and the cradle of civilization."

Consequently, the black-rabble gave away tons of masks and other artistic treasures to the acolytes of "Shrobenuisology," absolutely free of charge. Ah... God in Heaven! A sob for the childlike mentality of the black-rabble! Lord... for pity's sake! ... *Makari! makari!*

Secreting his own mythology, Shrobenius was ingenious but informal, malicious but pessimistic, anxious about his reputation– while he ceaselessly ridiculed the culture that had given him everything.

This fabricator and merchant of ideology took on all the allure of a sphinx as he imposed his intellectual rubbish, rationalizing his numerous contradictions and whims in a tone of solemn profundity. Ever the bogus ethnologist, he sold more than a thousand, three hundred artifacts that he and his disciplines collected free of charge in the Nakem to the Musée de l'Homme in Paris, as well as museums in London, Basel, Munich, Hamburg, and New York, pocketing the profits on hundreds of other artifacts through copyright and exhibition fees. "It is commonplace to speak of the 'universe of the Nakem,' or of this or that ethnic group," he ruminated in the magnificent chateau that he had purchased with black art, "but the universe of the Nakem should not be theorized in such terms. It is more accurate to say that the Nakem people carry a universe inside themselves, a resource from which they constantly draw their strength. Thus, the Nakem artist does not really possess what one might call a 'universe'. Or, rather, his universe, if that's what it is, must be construed as a vast solitude; no, a series of solitudes..." Should anyone draw attention to the obvious contradiction between this marvelous solitude and his prior affirmation of the Nakem's cosmological religiosity, the plethora of symbols from which Fritz cobbled together his image of the black artist, the ethnologist replied that his "true intentions had not been fully grasped," hastening to add that the cosmology of the Nakem took on many different forms...

Chasing after the nebulae of symbolism, occult religion, fabulous cosmology and myth, an Africanist School was born. It was so successful that in three years the numerous men who passed through its doors now poured into the Nakem. And what men they were! Entrepreneurs, adventurers, apprentice bankers, politicians, travelers, conspirators, philosopher—men who called themselves "scientists" but who were actually sentinels before the "Shrobeniusologic" monument of black pseudo-symbolism.

Already, the acquisition of ancient masks had become difficult since Shrobenius and the missionaries had first enjoyed the good fortune to acquire them in vast quantities. Saif therefore—and the practice is still common today—sunk hundreds of hastily executed masks that resembled those already sold into ponds, marches, pools, swamps, bogs, lakes, mud—left to be exhumed some time later, so that they might be sold to the curious and profane who were willing to pay in gold. These three-year old masks, it was said, *bore the weight of four centuries of civilization.* Before the credulous buyer, the vendors of these "ancient" artifacts lamented the ravages of time that had nearly corroded such irreplaceable masterpieces, imperiled from time immemorial, as was obvious from their poor condition. *Alif lam! Amba, koubo oumo agoum.*

6

Two days ago—*wassalam!*—Sankolo is let out of prison. Three years have passed since the last time he saw Saif. On the first day of February in the year of grace 1913, he happens upon the scholar Moise ibn Bez Toubaoui, whom he greets with the innocence of a savage beast and the complacency of a tree. But Sankolo can no longer deny the facts: Saif will not show him his face: he has retreated into his palace, forbidding him entry.

Sankolo, Kratonga, and Wampoulo are reunited. Words have been exchanged. They recognize each other in rare moments of peace and silence, known to all those who love the solitude of the bush.

For a week, they walk the same winding path along the shores of the Yame, cutting across the rocky embankments and the serpentine streams of flowing water. The sky rollicks above them, warming the land with sulfurous fumes—while, beneath it, three men walk the same path and make their plans, deadened by the sun's rays.

... And then one day, early in the morning, Sankolo died. He was buried the same evening.

The human masses multiplied. And, then one day, early in the morning, one hundred serfs died. They were buried the same evening. *Alif minpitjè!*

Order and calm reigned, wherever serfs, domestics, and manual laborers alike—the strong arms of common people—happened to die... A tear over their graves.

Six months later, on the evening before July 14, at eight o'clock, he showed up again at Vandame's doorstep, a weak excuse of a man, skinny, filthy, trembling in spasmodic fits, hiccupping as he spoke.

He told them that his name was Sankolo and that he had escaped. Vandame looked questioningly at his wife from the corner of his eyes but gestured for the stranger to stay. He secretly summoned his night-guard Kouyati, who identified this tattered scarecrow as Sankolo. So, he wasn't dead, after all! So they hadn't buried him!

"Yes, of course, they did."

"Then, what is this? Some kind of joke?"

Sankolo writhed to the beat of an inaudible rhythm, obviously "possessed." A few seconds later, he flayed about on the floor, growling and twitching like a fiend. Incessant and raucous howls issued from his throat. He asked them for a drink and was given a glass of water, which he emptied.

Then, as if by enchantment, he somehow was able to recover his balance, his reason apparently restored, but he remained awestruck. He explained to Vandame—with Karim Ba serving as his translator—that he had been buried alive and was later exhumed from his tomb. Then he was drugged and sent East to work under the supervision of a *Flencessi* named Dalbard Jean-Luc, who used women and drugs to gain mastery over him, forcing him to pass for a dead man and then sending him to the South, to the home of Tall Idriss, a friend of Saif, to whom was sent in return Tall's *living-dead*. Moreover, Sankolo claimed, all those who had "died" during the last six months had, like him, been turned into zombies: the *living-dead* who served and were used as free labor by Whites and Blacks, before they were finally sent to Arabia whenever there was a shortage of slaves:

"I am afflicted with an incurable disease. Nothing can save me now. Each time that I drink my drug, I succumb to its delicious torture. A feeling of sweetness washes over me, bringing me peace. My anguish causes my body to tremble like a cigarette on the lips of a man who is condemned to death. The movements of my face begin to torment me. I begin to howl. All listen to me in silence: each man seems lost in his own universe. We take part in the intermingling of races by way of music and drugs. Some are black. Some white. Some linger in the shadows. Some are day laborers, half-breeds, gamblers, a cock, and a sorcerer. The sorcerer lights the incense that fills our nostrils.

"My face twitches convulsively, contracting against my will, as the violent and sweet music permeates the night. We recognize each other in this music. Dalbard Jean-Luc, Huot-Marchand, Eugene Blanchard, Jean Martinon, and his friends try to imitate us. They are afraid. In this circle where sex is both sin and paradise, they seem to fear that they will be revealed as inferior. So, they turn everything into a joke when their anguish becomes intolerable. They clutch at the breasts of Black women. Their faces are both enflamed and disillusioned. They seem to have returned to an elementary state of being, where all is reduced to the pursuit of pleasure in its most basic form.

"My face stretches out. I can no longer see anything. I cry. I fall down. All listen to me in silence. I find myself in a trance. I clasp hold of the cock, devouring it alive, breaking its neck between my chattering teeth. I utter inaudible words. Unexpectedly, my body shrivels up. A strange and sweet sensation overwhelms me: I would like to flee from the noises inside me, noises from which I feel myself to be strangely detached. I long to escape into nothingness. But how? I lack the will. I love the numbness that little by little envelops me. The void triumphs over me. My body loses all weight. The earth, the room, the people in it and their faces turn towards me; their images penetrate me like rain over a freshly plowed field. My member follows its accustomed routine. A woman advances. She is black, beautiful, nude— and her breasts are two vast flowers that swell upon her chest, their stems overflowing with milky pap. Her belly, soft and voluptuous, undulates from atop of me. She lies back on a bed of smoking embers, and I take possession of her. Oblivious to the pain, she nibbles at me, watching me with flittering eyelashes. She pants. She toys with me, scratching my flesh, her voice raucous. She coils up on the ground, while I'm still hard inside her, as we gnaw upon snake bones and broken glass. The sound of our crunching is obscured by the clapping of feet and hands all around us. She disappears. Trances. I lift myself from the ground, a child born from the thrill of taunt skin, take a few steps and then stop in mid-stride, astonished by the very weight of my body upon the flattened earth. I must destroy without stopping to see whether I am despised or adored. I must kill without asking if it is resentment or love that compels me. Saif, I will smash your idol to pieces.

"Weariness. My wandering gaze rolls itself into a voluptuous ball over the void, a challenge for you and you alone. A voice inside my head speaks to me. The heavy music, drop by drop, resounds upon the leather drum. It hurtles on in the silence. Without thinking about it, my limbs move to the music, obeying the voice inside me that all can hear. My body enters the other room. It dissolves in this place of refuge, hurtling beyond all that is known, caressed by seaweed. My soul dreams of flamboyant silences, a green sun that sets over a violet ocean, drifting towards golden shores, hypnotized. At last, it is time to return to the others, whose faces, riveted by contractions, convulse in torment like mine, before they disappear in the next room. Nothing more to see. Ever again. There is only forgetting. Or deciding. But why?

"Slowly, my fingers feel the contours of my face; they lightly caress it, as if it were the body of woman. A shimmer of light now reaches the shadows of my face. It's fire from the burning wood. It's over. I go into the next room. The one next door. Cemetery of the hours of oblivion...

"Suddenly, a slamming door jolts me, causing me to turn my head. A beam of white light blinds me. Someone stoops over me. There is a buzzing voice in my head. I recall the anguish of the far corridors. The light flickers in quick clips. Darkness roils from my mouth and nostrils, a darkness that screams in agony.

"Far from the frail straw huts and smoking fires, my life begins anew: but I have depleted my energy in coping with my despair. Suddenly, I am born from the depths of my misery, turning over on my back, tearing out my hair, and then, rising to my feet and standing in place, I slowly run the rosary through my fingers, which gives me the strength to start anew… to begin again in the three days that follow. My life begins again. I fight in silence. The silence gnaws at me. Night. Silence. Then night.

"… Today, finally, the third night will come. The last night. I wait. I listen. I hear steps. Far off. Who approaches? Who's coming? Who is it? Clear spaces and shadows in the room. I do not move. The man approaches. I know what's next. I wait in silence. Wood is burned. A bull that is sculpted from wood is brought forth. There are now seven people in the room. The sorcerer holds the bull in his hands. The bull is God. The man approaches me. He cuts bloody gashes into my wrists and forearms with the sharpened point of one of its horns. At first, not much blood can be seen on my skin, but it soon appears in small beads. A vein is pierced. The blood spurts out, spurts… It dribbles into the purifying fires, crackling in the flames, exploding like a prayerful lamentation. My head throbs in pain. There is an irritating noise in my ears, relentlessly pounding my eardrums. The pain is concentrated at a single point, in the back of my head. I feel myself being dragged across the floor. My nostrils are drunk with the smell of my own blood that is singed in the fires. My hands flail about, fanning blood on my skin in the night air. I no longer suffer. Whispers flow, as everything flits and dances about me. The universe floats, vacillates, before it is suddenly illuminated like a bed of glowing embers. Then I am shipwrecked… My spirit flounders in the slime.

"It is at this precise moment that I realize I have the right to live—just like anyone else. Saif, I will smash your idol to pieces!"

"I undress. Using both hands, I splash water on my face. Trembling. Hollow. Hungry. I move slowly, almost calmly. At a certain moment, after you've spent enough time on the road, it's all the same whether you're dirty or clean. Still, I wash myself with water. According to rite. A man watches me. I know him without knowing how. I will stay here for an hour and then leave. It will be finished. The witnesses will swear to it. They will have been paid off. They will swear that they saw me die, and that they mourned my passing when death at last crushed my soul in its hands, after the ritual and orgiastic ceremony where I was honored. And for the second time I will be dead. Someone has to work for a cheap price. Sold without ever having been purchased. That was when I died. Now I will work without getting paid. Somewhere else. At the home of the friend of Saif, a man named Tall Idriss, who will bury his own *living dead* here, to work for Saif. We will be sold goods. It's an exchange, that's all. An exchange of services, which will finally plunge us into total madness, destroying us with obsessive music during the hours that we should be sleeping, filling us with the burning desire to work by day, so that we may do as we please at night. Satiating our flesh with sixty luscious women, drinking the millet drug that will deplete every ounce of our remaining strength… The guileless and naïve who tolerate and even justify the treachery of such men chalk it all up to fetishism. Voodoo. Or some other aberration. Crazy. Dead. I will disappear from the world. I've been sold.

"The water is tepid. I ask for soap with a gesture of my hand. I break it into small pieces. It's locally made soap; black, crumbly, made with indigenous by-products, big and fat. I smear myself with the soap. The water makes a mirror in the bucket of clear-iron, reflecting back my own image. Skinny. Badly shaved. Lips swollen. Less human than I can ever recall.

"I stir up the image, lifting the pail. Higher. Above my head. The water trickles down. The soap, the filth, the unctuous odor falls from me. The water streams over my body. My skin is alive, reborn. I wipe my limbs with my cupped fingers. I wait. The water dries. The sun drinks the last, sparse droplets from my body. For the moment, I am clean. I pull on the shirt of white linen that was given to me. I crack the joints of my toes. Walk. With nervous feet. No shoes. Cracked. Flat on the earth.

"I leave the clay knoll where I washed myself. I walk down towards the man. He doesn't move. He gives me an ax. A satchel. With crushed millet inside. Rope. A fine linen. White. Square. It's a handkerchief. Its purpose is to filter the water which I will drink in the course of my journey. The tissue will keep me from drinking too much dirt. I am not given a proper knife, but a penknife.

"The man recedes in the distance. He gives his orders. I am brought something to eat. I want to sit down and eat but am told to clear off. About a hundred meters. More to the south. I can eat then, but I have to leave the calabashes. A domestic will get them later. I am told next that I must start walking. Towards the south. Always towards the south. Following the river. In three nights I will arrive. They will wait for me...

"I think the word: sold. And the more I think about it, the more I don't want to admit it to myself. Sold... And what if I were to escape? No one will help me.

"At about a hundred meters, I sit down. I am feeble with hunger. I eat. Slowly. I do not want to give in, to lose my strength. I do not want to die. No... I swallow a mouthful. Catch myself doubting what has become of me. Drugged. Imprisoned. Me, myself. This is happening to me... There is no law. There is only money, and people will do whatever they can to get their hands on it. Saif, ah! My sarcastic rant is for you alone. My soul wallows in my hatred of you, filling up my nostrils with the stench of your crimes. I chew on the food they've given me. "*They've drugged it!*" I think aloud. The spices revive my appetite. My thirst. I drink. Eat, rolling the rice between my trembling and stiff fingers. My fingers resume their old habits. My belly digests the rice. A monkey watches me, letting out small shrieks. I cannot listen to it. I am still hungry. I stuff myself to regain my strength, to feel as if I'm reborn from hunger. My agile fingers nourish me. I drink a long gulp of palm wine. Stop. I begin drinking again. Then the gourd is empty. I rinse my gums with a gorge of water and my index finger. A second gorge of water, and my meal is finished. I get up. The domestic comes to take away the empty plates.

"The south. I hold the ax in my hand. I walk. Following the river...

"Always the same countryside appears before me, as if I recognize it, with its trunks of floating wood, its cries from wild beasts, its colors, its ever-changing light that bewilders me. I seek some tangible proof that I'm making progress but receive none from the depressing forest and its warm and humid vapors. The flowing water is a lullaby that hypnotizes me. During these long hours, my ax whacks away at the lianas. I walk. Blindly towards the south. As if stupefied, hypnotized.

"My meal has been drugged with *dabali*. But what does it matter? I see. I walk, that's all. I obey an interior mechanism, an imperial command. The south. The south. They're waiting for me. I'm thirsty. The earth spins. My tongue feels like dried leather. My thirst is intolerable. I will drink soon enough. I'll drink as much as I want, so long as I don't become waterlogged. There's plenty of water. I have the entire river to drink whenever I like. But I must keep walking. The wild fruits remind me of the color green, and green means water. The water quenches my thirst. I will drink soon enough. It's more important now that I walk. More than water, my body longs for my millet drug, the source of my inner calm. The south. I must do as they said. Soon enough, I'll allow myself to take a drink, after I've made my way through the lianas. There. That's where I'll go. It's not easy. There. I can finally take a drink. I bring out my handkerchief. I press it to my lips. I suck on the water, savoring it in small mouthfuls. I chew on my millet. Drink again... It's wonderful. It's fresh and sweet like the caress of a flower...

"I get up. The south. The south. My body floats. My legs move in a pedaling motion. My arms act on their own volition. But none of this has anything to do with me. As for myself, I'm quite all right. An angel carries me. I'm quite all right. The trees are blue. The water is mercury. I'm a jeweler. I make gems with the sun's rays. I offer them to the birds with white feathers and green eyes, casting them into the stars, and the birds follow me, making music to please my senses. At my feet, amid a retinue of sonorous drumming and amorous flutes, there are half-dressed women, veiled in silk shawls that hide their thighs. There are three brunettes clothed in virgin wool, two blonds with rings of gold on their hands, a redhead adorned in flowers, green leaves, and grapes, Black women in a circle, with neither robes nor gems nor sandals, Asiatic women with feline eyes and hair in ringlets–blacker than black–and mouths that are luscious and pink. They float around me, free and easy as feathers… Their smile provokes my member, which is their prey. It grows hard, veering off towards one of them, as my feet balance over the abyss. I possess them all. My arms flail about, speaking to the wind, as I rise up and then sail over a tapestry of auburn foliage, soft as down in the gentle breeze. Stars and planets fuse with my fingers. A gust of wind suddenly lifts me higher in the air, and I see many towns and villages below, all the peoples from the four quarters of the world extending outwards beyond measure, now sprouting the feet of storks and human faces, sculpted just for me. Suddenly, I see the white man who sold and drugged me, and I speak at last to my brothers and fellow slaves. They are small, black, with indiscernible traits. I speak to them, telling them that I must work without compensation, that I am dead to the civil state—a dog drugged by the parasites and maggots of the world– and I see that they now look towards Saif and slowly begin to weep. I suddenly hold a scepter in my hand. I bring the secret war for filthy lucre to an end. Saif is destroyed under the hot flow of lava. The reign of money is over. I bring it all to an end. I wash off my scepter, as lions approach me, shaking free their manes, in which all the women I've ever possessed and all the men I've ever dominated, luxuriate. The Blacks rise up again. The Jews rise up again. In their ascension, all those who are oppressed salvage their innermost essence. The wind acknowledges them. The silence listens to them. The sky is indigo black, and I emerge from the azure aftermath of the raging storms. I give orders. My word is at one with the power of the Word. At last, I descend back down to earth. I walk. I move forward. I smile without moving my lips. The river follows me. The waves follow me. Above me, the sun dances. My steps are light, flitting over the countryside and forming vast shadows, gothic arches, holy temples, enigmas that I alone decipher before the medusa-like forest. The trees stop to speak to me, and their branches jut out across my path. My ax is pitiless, lashing at the watchful trees and their limbs. A lion pants as he comes near me: he looms before me. He roars, showing me his tongue, backing away before finally disappearing on the horizon. He perches himself high in a tree, turning into a superb pink cat with fiery jaws, aglow like red flames:

"It's only the setting sun...

"My head...

"My head...

"My God, I am sick. I am tired. What is there in the south, anyway? My tongue weighs me down. It's a gigantic cube of ice. Reeling from the pain, I play with my deadened tongue of ice that excites my limbs with its blue coldness. My body is black. My body is a tomb harboring a frozen avalanche of cold shivers and all manner of tumultuous rubbish. Nature speaks. She is warm. I am king. I am entitled to a life of privilege. The crickets cry in the heat. I am an icicle of intense pleasure. I am sick. I do not want to be a victim of my own obsessions. I am a crippled field. My head rolls on the sperm drenched earth along the cusp of the lianas. My eyes do not give up the work of clearing out a path through the foliage. When you get deep enough into the countryside, some of the trees refuse to sit still: they lie in wait for you in a multitude of trenches, drifting along, sloping downward until the furthest point on the horizon where they suddenly stop, like a moth before the flame.

"My eyes see into infinity. The sun goes to sleep. It remains far away. It's afraid of falling. The sun is a timid pink cat, trembling behind the dunes and the blue dales. My headache is a farmyard. Wild. With its cries, its homely attractions, its rapid fluttering of wings, its endless squeals. Before this farmyard looms a green desert that desiccates the mucous in my throat. Suddenly, everything seems both strange and monotonous.

"I ask the earth to be still, so that I may rest without anguish, so that my body will not turn into a clenched fist in the gaping wound of the sunset. At each moment, I feel myself collapse into a heap of ruins, with every step, every movement, with the sun now inside my head, the waves of my body flowing one after another. After my downfall, I move on, silently, leg muscles weary, arms nervous. The footpath is transformed into an immense vagina. I disappear into its abyss; my body fends off the day so completely that I exist only in deferment, saved only by those sensations that never make themselves felt, that always come to my rescue. The forest looks like severed limbs. A rubber tree tears its roots out of the ground. I am a sniffling beast. I sense the presence of wine and a palm tree. I make a cut in the tree, drinking the palm sap and then chewing my drugged millet, which makes me thirsty. I drink more wine, as the effect of the drug begins to kick in. So I walk on in the blackness, hewing, striking, eyes dilated. I see nothing. Neither road nor footpath. It's nighttime. I do not like these trails; they are all the same; they lack character; guns in holsters, they march in their own manner, legs straight, torso like a plank, head tucked low, recently hewn. Silence sleeps but dreams of the sky, wherever storm clouds are jealous of the moon. I look only at the shore of the Yame River, with its black swells, its humidity. The river. The south. The south. I must go on. I am expected. Why sleep when I might already be there? I sprint forward to catch up with myself. I run like the wind. I stop, body upright, arms extended before me. I look like a lemon squeezed of its juices. I can no longer see myself. Neither my hands nor my limbs. To sleep. I am afraid of serpents.

To sleep. To dream. To sleep. I am afraid of red ants. I do not want to be eaten. I would like to become a beast and survive this menacing forest, its mosquitoes, its flies, its black things that crawl out from its belly in the black of night. Fire would help. I wish I had fire. I would fear nothing if I had fire. The serpents would flee from me. The rabbits too. But the monkeys, of course, would go on chattering. The beasts would all believe that I am armed. I would be saved. I wait for day break. That's when I'll finally sleep.

"The night completely crushes me with its procession of indefinable sensations. In the end, I *become* the wind, the silence of nature, its fears, its blackness, its expectations. I do my best to become better attuned to nature, to bask in it, to become one with it, to no longer fear its intolerable blackness. My fire crackles and sputters. Sparks fly around me in vacillating yellowness. Insects buzz around the fire, flickering, phosphorescent. They are fireflies, I think. Or maybe the eyes of cats. The tree branches speak to me, ululating, hiding behind my shoulder. I am afraid. I hold my ax in my hand. I stand up so I won't fall asleep. I walk around my fire of blazing wood, ax in hand. I turn. I take one hundred steps on supple legs. Spongy legs, my body floundering. It's difficult, but I work hard to break free. Under my claws, the earth now grows hard, cold, crumbly. My breath is raucous. My eyes are two onions. Tears well up without rolling down my cheeks. The insomnia is intolerable, but necessary. I want to live.

"The countryside dances before me. My eyelashes comb it, cut it into small pieces, grains, spurs eroded by the wind, an amass of greenery where it hides from me, towards the sky, now a mere vapor. Sparks flicker in a cascade of storms that somersault, wildly gesticulating, before at last dying of fatigue, rigor mortis.

"The moon is evil. Lack-luster. A trickster. I sense something. A living presence, hiding in the trees. Crackling the branches. No. It's nothing. Only the wind. Five minutes. A noise. In the blackness, a form, velvety, massive, concealed, somewhere over there, about three meters away. I howl, lash at it with my rope, jumping. The form lurks on my far side,

evading me, swearing. I hurl myself on it, gropingly reach
for my ax. A violent blow from behind knocks me over, and,
in a flash, a face surges before me: large, flat, brilliant. With
ferocious eyes under its shaggy visor, a mouth with jagged
teeth roars open. Sharp. Yellow fangs.

"The man, a Nakemian, has the same markings on his
face as me, regular and cut deep into his forehead. We're
from the same tribe. I speak to him. He speaks to me. He
tells me my name: Sankolo. Then his: Tandou. Silence.

"He sits near the fire. He also has an ax, rope, satchel,
just like me. But he travels towards the north. He chews
his millet drugged with *dabali*. He takes it in big quantities.
He asked for a handful of my own millet. For purposes of
comparison, he says. I protest and pretend to not have much
left. The man makes an offer. I agree to give him a little of
my millet, for information in return. About my future boss.
Work conditions. About life in the south, where he comes
from. "You will see," he explains to me, "they will ask you no
questions. You will work, eat, work some more. Don't speak
to them. Don't protest. Good morning, goodnight: that's it.
You'll have your women and your drugs."

"The man sneers, and then he cries. A long time, in
silence. It's as if, by his tears, he seeks to conquer his spiritual
exhaustion, this cerebral anesthesia which has turned him
into a beast. He needs to recover his own lost essence. He
speaks, as if in a dream. He explains things to me. He listens
to himself speaking:

"We won't get through it now."
"Through what?"
"The wall.
"What wall?
"The wall... over there... over there," he rambles, "Don't
you understand? A black man is worth nothing. He's a complete zero. A black woman is only good for fucking. We lack
the strength. We don't have the law on our side. There is Saif,
and a land with few witnesses; that's how we end up getting
sold. They sell us. It's terrible!" the man sobbed. And then he
added in a voice of gentle resignation, "But you will see how

it is. You will forget all of these things with the *dabali*. Yes... you too. You'll forget all right."

"I'll be alone. When you're alone, you have time to think. I could never forget... Never!"

"You're dead. *Dead*. Don't you understand? You have no proof, no civil state, nothing!"

"What about official inspections?"

"What inspections?"

"The census-takers, the police."

"What about them?"

"Then there's still hope."

"'You're *dead*. Get that through your head. You go to work in the south for two years. Two years and three months. When the census-takers and the police finally come, they'll bury you in the east. You'll be so drugged-up that you won't know what's happening to you. You'll howl like a beast, your eyes will get big with lust for women, and everyone you meet will flee from you. You'll have only two words in your head: *dabali*-work, work-*dabali*. From time to time, a whore will make love to you. And then... you will at last know madness... and death... Bah... You only die once. Give me a little of that millet.'"

"I give it to him. Should I just kill myself? What good would that do?... Maybe this is the way things are? This is the life of a black... A slave. Sold. Bought. Sold again. Disciplined. Cast on the four winds... There must be manual laborers at a cheap price.

"The man stands up. We extinguish the fire. In silence. Dawn breaks along the horizon. We walk in weariness along the edge of the river, a dirty mirror where we can see the shadows of our profiles grow larger. The man from my tribe heads towards the north. When he leaves, I feel a little of myself dying. I walk southwards without looking back."

As a security measure, Vandame guarded Sankolo in his own house, putting him in a room adjacent to his office, where he kept watch himself. When the translator Karim Ba returned from Vandame's house, he dined in haste and then headed straight towards Tillaberi-Bentia to inform Saif.

127

Eleven o'clock that night, Saif summoned Kratonga and Wampouolo. When they arrived, he turned to them and said, "Rough him up a bit."

Karim Ba was horrified, "But we made a deal," he protested.

"And if it's a trap?" said Saif in a flat voice.

Karim whimpered softly, his voice trembling in the silence of the wind, his eyes shining with tears. He croaked in his anguish and raised his hands to protect himself from the first blow, imagining that Kratonga would not be quick enough.

The attack still took Karim by surprise. Kratonga hit him with a speed and precision that was disconcerting. The translator collapsed but was lifted off the ground by a kick to the stomach. While Kratonga held Karim in place, Wampouolo assumed a crouched position, calculating the space he would need, and then launched into him with his right heel. The translator howled under the blow, his face ravaged with suffered, clutching at his belly with both hands. The two men beat him like a donkey, causing the blood to flow from his nose, mouth, and ears. Saif set his foot on Karim's forehead, as his agents stood aside: he acted as if he might crush the man with the weight of his whole body; and then, after sufficiently terrorizing the translator, he set down his foot:

"It's true that you didn't have any choice," Saif observed. "Vandame couldn't find out much without his dear translator, now could he? Of course, you didn't have to pay us a visit at all, Karim. But, your coming here tonight is proof of your concern for your family's well-being. So, for now, you should relax and have a good time, don't you think?" Said said. "After all, I'd like to see you smile and laugh a little. Go on, let's hear you laugh."

Karim slowly began to laugh, first in a crisp manner, hesitating, as if he was performing a difficult task for the first time. But when he saw the menacing look on Saif's face, he laughed harder, almost hysterically, until his chest heaved with deep, rollicking bellows. Saif smiled at the grotesque spectacle, paring his nails. Wampoulou and Kratonga alone maintained a serious air. Finally, Karim stopped to catch his breath. Clutching his knees to his chest, he breathed rapidly and unevenly. Saif's face turned cold and impassive—and then truth burst into the room, precisely as Saif knew it would. His spirit broken, Karim Ba collapsed at the sight of the dagger of Kratonga, who held him in place. He lowered his eyes to avoid looking at the gleaming knife.

"Go on," Saif ordered, "Tell us what Sankolo said to the governor."

"I beg you," wailed Karim Ba, "I implore you…"

Kratonga flicked his knife like a lightening bolt, cutting a glob of bloodly tissue from the corner of the translator's mouth.

"It's true! It's not a trap," Karim screamed hysterically, "It's true! Vandame's keeping watch over him in the office at his house. You must believe me! It's not a trap…"

His words ended in a sob. Then he vomited up his dinner.

"Then tell us what we must do."

The translator slowly lifted his head. As if awakening from a nightmare, he saw Saif smiling in satisfaction and Kratonga putting his knife back in its sheath. The vague thought came to him that he had just signed the death warrant of the governor.

"Take it!" Saif said, tossing him two wads of bank notes.

Wampouolo put the guard dog to sleep with drugged meat. The dog now snored at its post, some five hundred meters from the residence of the governor.

Kratonga picked up a handful of gravel and threw it against Vandame's window. The pebbles clattered against the glass, but nothing happened.

Wampoulo ran to join his accomplice, as both crouched in the shadows of the doorway. Still, nothing happened. Vandame was too clever.

So Kratonga got up again and, backing off, hid behind a tree. He aimed his flashlight at the window where Sankolo slept. The sound of chairs being moving around could be heard. In fear, Sankolo opened the door of his room to take refuge with Vandame in his office. Wampoulo grabbed him in the entryway, pushing the door ajar. Vadame came out, pistol in hand. He saw no one. He looked around outside the house. Something hit him on the back of the head: he lost consciousness.

When he came to a little later, he found that he was bound at the hands and feet, riding a horse on a trail not far from the Yame. The horses struggled as they skirted the rocky footpath, evading a waterfall that Vandame could feel but not see. Kratonga ordered Wampoulou to help Vandame from his horse. Then he tied the horse to a tree. Setting the governor's pistol on a rock, he took a seat.

The sound of the water falling in heavy waves of ivory surrounded them. Suddenly, they were thousands of years away from any form of civilized life. Bats flew in shadowy circles, a rumor of sound made all the more troubling by the moonlight, which covered the Yame in a milky tapestry.

Vandame felt something against the nape of his neck and grimaced. He wore Chinese slippers with thick felt soles, satin black pajamas, and an embroidered Chinese tunic–white on the front of his blouse. He held himself erect, crossing his knees. His maintained a military posture, his chin held high, and his teeth shiny between his lips. His eyes were wide open, and the dark, gray-slate color of his pupils seemed to swallow up his irises. There was a look of madness in his eyes. He seemed unconscious of his own actions, but he was nonetheless able to keep his head about him. His voice betrayed his nervousness. "I did not realize that Saif was so unworthy of France," Vandame said.

Kratonga forced a smile. "His Royal Lordship reigns in this land as God on High. His edicts are inscribed in the sky. Woe to all those who disobey. For one morning, they shall awaken only to be recalled to the Eternal Hereafter."

To his astonishment, Vandame discovered that Saif's agents spoke fluent French. Saif himself, he would soon learn, was also proficient in French, but he concealed his knowledge from the colonizers (thus taking advantage of their ignorance) and instead continued to rely on Karim Ba for translation. Wampoulo abruptly said, "I thought that you Whites were powerful. You'll have to forgive me."

"I don't understand," the governor said.

"Vandame, why don't you tell us what you don't understand," Wampoulo said, softly approaching the governor. His tongue protruded from his front teeth. Vandame made an effort to regain his self-possession. A smile spread across his face.

"I suppose that you work for money. You don't want what happened to your friend to happen to you…"

"What friend?"

"Sankolo."

"Then you know what happened to Sankolo, Vandame?"

"You know how it is…"

"No, I don't, Vandame. Why don't you tell us how it is?"

The governor fixed his gaze on the two men. "You're completely insane," he said in a soft voice, and then he added. "You're just resentful that we've colonized you. You can't stand that we've turned you and Saif into house boys to conduct our affairs in the Nakcm. That's why you commit these petty acts of revenge. (Kratonga now seemed fascinated.) You began as the sons of slaves, as captives that my country tried to liberate, to civilize– and this is how you repay us… You want this nonsense to go on forever because you're terrified of being shown for what you really are… which is worthless and mediocre!"

"Blame it on Dame Fortune," shrugged Wampoulo, trying to sound nonchalant. "She rarely performs her magic on our behalf. In our business, we must struggle to keep up with her, and we do as we like in spite of her decrees."

"You follow Saif because you want to," Vandame said softly. "This sort of life pleases you. You only pretend that it doesn't."

"Now that's not a very nice thing to say, old friend. How can you possibly mean it? Do you enjoy playing the moralist for the fun of it?"

"For the fun of it!"

"We're the best friends you're got, Vandame. You must treat your friends as they deserve."

"Okay, have it your way," he said with the air of taking his misadventure philosophically. "This can be a friendly chat, if you prefer."

For awhile now, he had been moving closer and closer to the rock where his pistol lay. Kratonga had noticed it, and Wampoulo too, no doubt. Suddenly, he pivoted and plunged head first for the rock to grab the gun. He picked it up, aimed it at the two men, and pressed the trigger—he pressed it again, three times in a row. Then his hand went limp and dropped to his side. He remained for a moment half-hidden behind the rock, as if exhausted. They could hear his heavy breathing. Then he slowly stood up with a somber look of despair. He gave the two men a smile that was difficult to look at.

"That wasn't very nice, governor," Kratonga said, picking up the pistol, and showing the cartridge clip to Vandame.

A hyena, far off in the bush, let loose a deafening howl. Vandame remained in the shadows, sweating profusely. The drama was about to run its course. It was Vandame himself who had set the final act in motion.

Kratonga walked off towards one of the horses, pulling a big bamboo stalk and a goatskin from his harness. The governor stepped from the shadows, fully cognizant of what awaited him. "We can forget about all this, if you like," he said without much conviction.

With a powerful thrust, Kratonga swept the bamboo stalk in a half-circle, spinning around in the moonlight, and striking it against the rock. There was an explosion of wood, as several rolled-up documents fell to the ground. It was the official report that Vandame had recently drawn up against Saif.

"I can give it to you in writing," Vandame said. "This way, you'll have proof of my intentions. I'll say that Sankolo escaped. My wife can sign as an eyewitness. We've seen nothing. We know nothing. (Vandame was now green, and his lips moved without ceasing.) I was only doing my duty. I can sign whatever you like."

Showing his contempt, Kratonga took the goatskin, opened it, and took a swig, offering the rest to Wampoulo.

"Give it to Vandame," Wampoulo said. "He's certainly a nervous one!"

"I'm not thirsty," the governor said in a feeble voice.

"Drink every drop, Papa! All the way to the bottom! Drink up, Papa. It's milk. It'll make you grow big and strong. Otherwise…"

Vandame looked at one man and then the other and then lifted the goatskin to his lips. He closed his eyes to better endure the torture. His soft throat gurgled as he drank. The goatskin was soon hollow. He had to drink it all, but his stomach was now nauseous. He staggered about and then fell to his knees. He dropped the goatskin. The milk expanded in his stomach. Vandame vomited on the dry sand. He slowly tried to pull himself together, lifting himself up on one elbow. His face had turned gray and sallow.

"You're out of shape," Kratonga observed. "You need a little something to regain your strength, Papa? Drink a little. Only a few sips more."

"I don't believe I can…"

"You're going to get yourself into trouble, Vandame. Come on, drink up."

Kratonga took a step towards him, so Vandame raised the goatskin once again to his mouth. He licked his lips and opened up. A black sticky fluid oozed from the goatskin and poured to the ground. Vandame did his best to force the milk down when suddenly he felt a cold breath upon his left calf. Lowering his eyes, he was horrified to see a poisonous asp. He stood perfectly still, turning crimson, as the reptile coiled itself around his foot. He quaked in terror, as Kratonga whispered, "Dafa…"

The snake uncoiled, moving off about a meter from Vandame. Wampoulo ordered the stupefied governor, who did not understand what he was being told to do, to lick the head of the snake. As Vandame wavered indecisively, Kratonga kicked him square in the behind. He fell over so quickly that he found himself sprawled on all fours, struggling to recover his equilibrium, as the snake hissed at his heels. Kratonga whispered and the snake remained in place, its scales rustling along the ground.

"Go ahead, lick it!"

The governor took a step towards the snake, momentarily recoiling in fear, but he at last approached it, fearing the worst, as he carefully licked its triangular, horned head. The forked tongue of Dafa, the off-spring of Tama, reciprocated by depositing quick, sticky markings on his cheek.

"Do that everyday and you'll enjoy a long life," Kratonga said. "You promise you'll do that everyday?"

"Yes, sir," Vandame said.

All resistance had left him. He had accepted the humiliation; nothing much remained to him now, other than the blind desire to please his torturers and thereby postpone the inevitable. The terror that Saif's agents had succeeded in awakening in him had rapidly accelerated from the moment that he realized his pistol had been emptied of bullets.

"I can sign an affidavit," Vandame said again.

This phrase became a sort of talisman for him, which he uttered like a prayer, without much hope.

"I can put it in writing."

All at once, Kratonga seized the snake and threw it at Vandame. The snake bounced off his chest and fell to the earth, where it coiled itself around the governor's legs.

"Untie him now, Vandame. Come on. This is perfect. I just adore you, Vandame. You are the picture of the righteous colonizer. Keep away from Wampoulo though. He's too honest for you. Further away. That's perfect, Papa. You're something else, Vandame. You're wonderful. I tell you what. We're going to play William Tell. It's one in the morning. The children of the fatherland are on the march. It is the 14th of July, Governor. Pick up your report about His Royal Highness. Come on, quicker than that, Papa. Roll it into a ball, Vandame. Put it on top of your

head, captain."

The eyes of Vandame seemed to pop out of his head:

"You can't do this to me..."

"Calm down, calm down. Don't get so excited! You'll see I'm a regular sharp shooter, man. Go on. Put the ball of paper right on top of your head! I tell you, Vandame, I adore you. You're a true humanist, Governor, a friend and liberator of the Blacks, civilizer of the Nakem, a republican and a family man to boot!"

Vandame stood with his eyes closed, arms dangling at his side. His body caved in... Against his knee, he felt Dafa.

Kratonga ground his teeth. The barrel of his automatic pistol precisely marked its target. Kratonga held the pistol at arm's length and took careful aim.

The pistol emitted a dry crackling sound, muted by the crashing of the waterfall. Vandame frantically jumped up, as it burst into flames. Kratonga blew out the fire and then placed the barrel against Vandame's head. He steadied his aim. The pistol rang out in the night. A small round hole appeared on the forehead of the governor, near his right eyebrow, along his nasal canal. He partially opened his eyes, as blood flowed from his head to the ground. He stepped forward to lift himself up, as if he wished to flee the scene. Then he softly slouched to the ground, stiffening for an instant and slobbering on the sand. At last, he collapsed on his belly. His feet scraped against the rock, as a rumbling of his bowels could be heard, a gurgling sound that escaped from his throat. Then his lungs let loose a long, uneven death rattle. He was a righteous man.

As Saif had instructed, Kratonga and Wampoulo brought the body of the governor to the office at his house, bringing Vandame's official report with them. Once there, they laid the body on the floor.

Kratonga and Wampoulo escorted Sankolo to Saif's palace. Sankolo knew that he was to be sacrificed. Threatening death (should he refuse or show the least sign of resistance) to his daughter Bineta, his natural child from his fiancé Awa, the serf reluctantly agreed to join Saif's choir, and so he returned to the residence of the governor.

The night-guard Kouyati pretended that he saw nothing: Kratonga and Wampoulo had paid him off in advance, threatening to kill his family if he betrayed their secret.

All went as planned. Sankolo pretended that he had broken in the the house to steal the governor's money, noisily ransacking Madame Vandame's private possessions and jewels until she at last awoke in terror and began screaming for help. Startled by her voice, Sankolo took flight, dropping his pistol to the floor. These events brought Madame Vandame from her bed, where she ran directly into Sanoko, who had fled the room, but in the wrong direction and so had doubled back upon his steps. A raucous fight ensued for possession of the gun. He smashed her face with his fist, and Madame Vandame collapsed to the floor. Pistol in hand, Sankolo fled the scene, not without knocking over various items in Vandame's office to give greater plausibility to the governor's murder. Then he broke the window and made his escape. Kouyati fired his gun at Sankolo, shattering his skull into multiple pieces. Vandame's pistol fell to the earth as evidence against the assassin, who was no longer recognizable.

Captain Mosse, his wife, their son Jean, Lieutenant Huygue, his wife, and the bulk of the soldiers awoke, running in alarm from all quarters.

As for Kouyati, he was able to prove that "he had not failed in his duty as night watchman, that he had not fallen asleep, for he had shot at the unknown thief, whom the governor himself had put up for the night in an act of kindness..." Forgive us, Lord. *Atchou hackè*!

The lying in state of the body of Vandame and his wife went on for three days amid great pomp and ceremony. Eighty thousand people filed before their mortal remains to render their final homage to the righteous colonizers, whose purity was celebrated by all, for they had lived entirely in the margins of Nakem politics, winning for themselves a reputation of impeccable virtue among the liberated natives and the colonial administration.

The silver ornamented caskets of the couple were splendid: finely chiseled angels adorned the borders of each coffin, bathed in the golden light of candles. At the base, there was an engraved marble plaque that read: *Honor and Fatherland.*

The burial at the cemetery of Mount Katsena was the most ostentatious that had ever been seen in the Nakem. There were twenty-eight cartons of flowers, half of which were donated by Saif ibn Issac al Heit. *Wakoul rabbi zidni ilman*!

When he returned to his house, Saif learned that the family of Lieutenant Huygue, whose daughter had been committed to the Sainte-Anne Asylum in France, had decided to leave the Nakem forever, carrying the hatred of Africa in their hearts.

Saif said: "Our Father who art in Heaven," and the little birds cheeped in response.

7

The Whites set up camp amid the troops of *tirailleurs* and the duplicity of their lamentations. This was accomplished by way of harsh disciplinary measures, corporeal punishment, and the shrill threats of the *Flencessi* officers. In the disorder that broke out in the year 1914, many *tirailleurs* deserted or were reported missing. Some were simply executed. Many lives, as well as personal belongings and wealth, were also lost in the universal disarray of the Great War, as chaos danced its way across an angry world.

In despair at the clear loss of his authority, not so much weakened, but disarmed, Mosse, the appointed successor to Vandame, conducted a number of private interviews with Saif ibn Issac al Heit, during which he demonstrated his great esteem and utmost respect for him. His Royal Lordship was shortly afterwards granted favors and concessions previously unimagined. In return, he promised to win the black-rabble to the army's cause.

When popular acclaim for him therefore reached its peak– *Ya atrash!*–Saif ibn Issac al Heit, flanked by Madoubou and followed by his sorcerers, appeared before the crowd, proclaiming that he had at last transcended his own body, and that his own voice had now grown utterly still before the decrees of God, whose Spirit alone issued from his mouth. In a celestial tone, he announced to the *tirailleurs* that they–who must understand that they were little more than playthings of the Invisible Master of all worlds– must now submit to His inscrutable wisdom. Should they die in battle, they would surely live in the hereafter amid their tribal kinsmen, "with souls seven times purer than dawn at the time of the morning prayer."

And so their cries resounded throughout the woods, their chants and drums proclaimed their somber message, hawks soared with missives in their talons, and Saif the Wise, whose words flew from his lips like holy papal bulls, only to settle amid the ranks of the ecstatic black-rabble like seraphim, obtained from the Whites the concession that not a single hair of the sons of the nobility–all of whom were exempted from military draft—would be touched.

To better entice the *tirailleurs,* connoisseurs of the splendors of Holy Paradise, the nobility worked assiduously for the salvation of the souls of the military men: soldiers, guards, infantry, and combatants, kissing their sobbing wives goodbye, decked out with talismans on their arms, rows upon rows of gris-gris dangling from their necks–all which brought golden smiles to their faces as they rushed off to war. Grave troubles and seditious plots broke out, fomented by lucid spirits here and there, as well as a few rabble-rousers–whose punished was impalement!– who protested, "Aren't these *tirailleurs* just like the early Christian martyrs fed to the lions, declaring their faith in the eternal resurrection?"

But, Saif, the Commander of the Believers, helped his illuminated people to see the poverty of mere human reason when compared to faith: so, he succeeded in sending to Mosse the most arrogant and mean-spirited of the *tirailleurs,* recruiting a multitude of robust young men, carrying knifes, hoes, iron-rods, sling-shots, or, more rarely, fire-arms, all of whom were hypnotized by the sorcerers, rushing to their deaths with gaiety in their hearts and brandishing bullwhips in their left hands, confident of their eternal resurrection.

More than one disappeared, "sold to Mecca," as the chronicle reports, spirited away in the commotion of the ecstatic masses when some were observed (Heaven protect us!) rushing before canon fire, killed without so much as a hurried adieu, in their haste to be seated on the right hand of the Eternal Father, for whom the earth is golden dust and the river an ever-lasting blessing; others were seen thrusting their arms deep into the iron barrels to pack in the canon balls. The French officers at last ceded their authority and disbanded, impotent, asking for help from Saif, who was able to appease the black-rabble, preserving order and respect for the military authorities, forbidding all pillaging, all excess, "under penalty of being refused entry into the Eternal Kingdom on High." "Might it not happen," he intoned in pious litanies, "that we will one day be reunited in the shadow of the throne of Our Gentle Lord in the province of Eden? This divine grace is my daily prayer. *Amina yarabi!*"

It had once been easy for Saif to preach counter-revolution in Nakem, to encourage his subjects to draw blood against "these white macaques in their cages." But, in the meantime, the black-rabble had been emancipated, and the nobility had been well compensated for their losses; these developments led Saif to remark that fighting against the Whites as they were mired in a world war was too problematic: any attempt to return to a feudal society based upon slavery, the source of the notables' prosperity, might lead to civil war.

Thus Saif, who profited from nearly as many miracles as he dispensed, came to be decorated as a grand officer in the Legion of Honor and dubbed "savior of France in Nakem," as well as obtaining a royal pension for himself and for his faithful. In ostentatious contrition, the notables loudly prayed for the *tirailleurs*, for the resurrection of the saints and appointed themselves "guardians of their souls and of the souls of their spouses whom they had left behind."

"Do not be in such a hurry to take your place with the Almighty on High," Saif said to them, "for He may punish you for your haste. Immortality should not be desired for its own sake. First, you must perform your earthly duty as soldiers. Fight, but be patient for your eternal reward. You cannot force Heaven to come down to earth, but you must instead wait in a spirit of humility for God to bestow His blessings and salvation upon you. Let us sing praises to the Lord, my gentle lambs, for his abundant favors and for the blessings that He in His mercy showers upon us in order to increase our devotion to Him and to deliver us from evil. *Allahou Akbar! wakoul rabbi zidin ilman!"*

Then Saif walked in measured steps, preceded by the music of drums, balafons, tom-toms, lambis, and trumpets, as his sorcerers sang that he was invulnerable. His guards carried long bullwhips, which, it was said, possessed the power to deter bullets. Kratonga and Wampouolo, who were covered with as many fetishes as Yafole, and who held cocks by the necks in their clenched fists, walked next to Madoubo, behind His Royal Lordship, who ceaselessly murmured sacrificial prayers.

... And so the soldiers reported to Mosse, organized in clans, to fight the Germans, dividing themselves into tribes that were led by their sorcerers and the emblems of their superstitions, some worn on their arms, some on their skulls, as they chewed "prepared" tobacco—that is, tobacco prepared by the Great Spirit. Their rifles too, it was said, served as talismans. Let it be so. Let us ask the Master of all worlds for health and protection, both now and for life everlasting. *Allaneou.*

And tradition tells us:

"Man, lower your voice. Don't you know that His Royal Lordship Saif ibn Isaac al Heit is present wherever his praises are not recited?"

And so it happened:

The tenacious and courageous Germans held out against the troops who had been fanaticized by Saif, retreating to the towns of Ruande and Gnoundere, where they were not defeated until 1916 by the Franco-British troops that were led by the Generals Dobell and Aymerich; which is why the military cemeteries even today mark the old paths through the jungles, between Buanda Fele and Ruande, and bear witness to the horror and obstinacy of a war without hope; which is how Taruatt surrendered in June 1915, Gnoundere not long afterwards, and Ruande in January 1916; and how at the last post before Fousseri at Zora in eastern Nakem Major Von Rabben, who had commanded his besieged troops for eighteen months at last surrendered, but only after he learned that Governor Ebermayer had already evacuated the territory; which is why he was later so highly decorated; and how Colonel Zimmermann succeeded in breaking through the French lines in southern Nakem and in escaping with the remnants of his army to Spanish Guinea; which is why in this merciless war the army of the adversary was often less dangerous than the forest, the fevers, the climate, and the isolation: all of which are themes that are of almost no interest today.

Throughout this period, the hunchbacked Father Henry—as humbly beautiful as the despair that percolates in the Christian soul and driven to the point of madness by the duty of love— journeyed forth in his obsession for the plight of the blacks, from village to village, case to case, a suffering servant and priest, tilling the earth of the peasants, lavishing attentions and medications upon them, while reading the *Acts of the Apostles* by night.

During four years of war, years of panic and terror, years of joys that brought laughter and laughter that brought fear, he sowed the Good Word of the Gentle Lord Jesus among the panic-stricken natives who were daily traumatized by the explosions of shells and grenades, as, not far away, the notables greeted the outbreak of hostilities with joy, singing hymns to Saif the invulnerable.

The bombs set fire to the forest as bloody dawn lit up the sky, and the gray facades of the huts.

For the first time in African memory, the ardent sun of April was almost unable to pierce the thick smoke of the forest fires, set ablaze through the folly of men. All was black within a ten kilometer radius of Tillaberi-Bentia: It seemed that the apocalypse was near at hand...

Wrenching himself free from the sobs and regrets of families afflicted by this catastrophe, the tireless Henry came to the people's aid, begging his way across the Nakem. He brought diverse medicines, bandages, and the cast-off garments of the colonizers and *tirailleurs* to Krebbi-Katsena, carrying them on a donkey and distributing them to those who had suffered the most because of the war.

He shook the hands of soldiers he met along the trails, genuflected whenever he met a farmer, or stood immobile before the enclosed plots of land, ready at a moment's notice to be put to work. His face was so worn, his humpbacked body so misshapen, that alms were never refused him.

Despite his poverty, he charitably gave away everything that he had been given to the widows and orphans, grinding millet for the elderly, and, in some instances, assuming the role of a sick school teacher or repatriated missionary.

One night, during a vigil in the village of Toula, he confessed in humility that he had left Sankolo to die, and that he was also responsible for the death of Barou; hence, everyone began to believe that he was crazy and fled from his presence, swearing their loyalty to Saif. In villages that he had already visited, as soon he was recognized, the children ran to their mothers, who bolted the doors of their huts against him, loudly cursing him. The least vicious among them set a bowl of gruel on the threshold of their dwellings, and then locked their doors shut against him.

Repulsed everywhere, he continued to give away free medications, which no native would accept, if it came from his hands; thus, Henry fed himself with yams, sweet potatoes, fruits fallen to the earth, diverse roots, and food items abandoned by the military troops. He traveled further and further into the remoter regions of the Nakem.

Then, one of the sons of Savadogo, village chief of Toula, fell ill. None of the herbs of the sorcerers, nor the remedies of the magicians, nor the prayers of the notables brought any relief to the child, who was afflicted with a tropical disease. By applying the appropriate aseptic, Henry was able to save him, and the wall of antipathy against him crumbled.

Thus it was that a host of red-eyed adults and children, their faces ravaged by leprosy, others with yellow sores and snotencrusted noses, thrust out their black hands with leopard-like pink spots and missing digits towards Henry, pouring in from the regions surrounding Toula, sheep-like images of despair, with fetishes dangling from their necks, wearing multi-hued cotton fabrics with naïve designs of palm-trees, portraits of Saif, masks, rhinoceros, or sea-vessels, crowding along the stony pathways with friends and relatives in tow, where they stumbled and tripped into the ditches of stagnant brown water: Some of the lepers begged for food in clay pots that were also used to feed the ducks, scraping together enough food to provide them with a meager meal. Those with small pox ate millet with *dabali*, their lips swollen from the drug, which made them all the more frightening to behold. Enormous black women with heavy lips and golden rings in their ears had no more than a thread-bare pagne to cover them, wearing a melancholy but dignified face, whispering to him that they suffered from syphilis. Others who claimed to be bewitched by sorcerers and sorceresses threatening to kill them from a distance threw themselves on the ground, slobbering at Henry's knees, while still more who were afflicted with tuberculosis spit up blood in his presence, trying to make their words understood between racking coughs.

Henry made a hair shirt for himself with iron-spikes. He crawled on both knees before every house with more than four grain-bins and before the compounds of the polygamous notables. He obtained food stocks and used garments from them, with which he clothed the ragged and fed the starving. He washed the feet of the disinherited little people of Nakem, whose skin was covered with scaly pustules, colder to the touch than the scales of a serpent and rough as lemon peelings.

Then, setting them upon the backs of mules that had been donated by the wealthy, he provided the sick with first aid, also stopping at the infirmaries en route to the hospital at Krebbi-Katsena.

His own face was so ravaged, his appearance so lamentable, that all pitied him at first sight. They prayed and wept for him, as he piously carried on amid the terrors of the all-encompassing war.

At night, they slept huddled together in some abandoned hut that radiated a nauseating stench as thick as fog. Henry shared their bed, attending to their every need. Meanwhile, Saif, whose pension was irregularly delivered due to the war, began selling slaves to Kartum, Zanzibar, and the Arab world to augment his income.

The Libyan Desert, which was only sporadically policed by the Italians who preferred to concentrate on the coasts, served as a thoroughfare for many of Saif's acolytes who now preached holy *habbo*[1] against the English and the French.

... But the wars of men often have consequences that are unforeseen at the time that they erupt: with the hindsight of historical perspective, it becomes easier in time to comprehend them.

One of these consequences was this:

"According to the Treaty of Paris of September 8, 1919," the chronicle reports, "as well as the London Agreement, nearly all of East-Nakem, beginning from Fousseri, was placed under the authority of England, whereas France added another two hundred kilometers to its borders. The Ziukio–annexed to Nakem, included Taria, Souia in the South, and Riboa in the North—, fleshing out the definitive borders of the future African Republic of Nakem-Ziuko."

From that time on, the schoolchildren of Nakem-Ziuko, including the children of the Gondaites, Fulani, N'godos, Radingues, and Zobos, learned to sing the Marseillaise (so be it), in addition to commemorating Jaurès's assassination (God be merciful upon him!), the Marne (and grant it so!), Verdun (the Eternal), Europe in its fury (grant to it salvation!), the Italian defeat at Caporetto (*amen*), the retreat, the victory (glory to the Most High), and thirteen million dead (God refresh their couch), among whom must be counted the anonymous black-rabble imported from a distance of twenty-nine thousand kilometers, and killed for no good reason. Forgive us, Lord. May Your holy protection save us from such a calamity! *Amina yarabi.*

8

Amid the wreckage of the war, Kassoumi took leisurely strolls to his banana tree, daydreaming from under its gray leaves of burgeoning fruit. Casting his impoverished gaze across the Yame River, his reveries were occasionally disturbed by the foul odor of the rotting carcasses that the fishermen caught in their nets and dragged into shore, the decomposed body of a German in uniform, killed from the blow of a lance or saber, his head crushed by a rock, or drowned from being thrown off a bridge. The sludge of the river concealed these obscure acts of vengeance, unknown feats of heroism, muted assaults, more perilous than the greatest battles of the era, and that took place without the trappings of glory.

The pious notions of his youth—the appeased ardor of his first flickerings of religious faith—begin to gently simmer in Kassoumi's heart. Teachings that had once provided him with a refuge from the misery of slavery now seemed an honorable means for his own children to possibly escape from his own precarious and torturous lot in life.

Remembering how Henry had instilled in the school-aged children the habits of prayer and study, he swallowed his sorrow and immediately got up, walking past the Yame to the gloomy church where, at the foot of the choir, he kneeled before the arched flame of an oil lamp, sacred guardian of God's presence.

He confessed his sins to Henry, confiding in him all his sorrows and miseries. He asked him for advice, for pity, and for help. In the days that followed, he ceaselessly repeated his prayers with growing fervor and emotional intensity. His desiccated heart, shriveled by so many anxieties, thirsted for the waters of white culture, so that his own children might have a better future among Blacks than his own; little by little, as his pious habits grew more fortified, as he indulged in secret conversations with the devoted followers of the Savior who brings consolation and comfort to the miserable, he received a blessing for his spiritual efforts: Henry recommended that all five of his children be admitted to the French and missionary schools: Anne-Kadidia, his daughter, who was svelte and who leaped about like a rabbit; Raymond-Spartacus, who was the first born, and who was small with a flat nose that beaded over with tiny drops of sweat; Jean-san-terre, who walked with the careful gait of a homeless cat; René-Descartes, who was famous for his broad forehead;

and René-Caillé, the spookiest looking of Kassoumi's kids, who had the eyes of a lynx.

Each child wore an amulet around his neck, except for Kadidia, who wore hers around her waist. When the time came for them to attend school, the sister's experience did not amount to much more than an enjoyable but brief holiday, for she was dismissed after the first year; for René-Caillé, school was a brisk romp through the lianas; and for René-Descartes, school became a prolonged means of rest and relaxation (the boy sat vacantly at his desk during his lessons, immersed in his daydreams). Only Raymond-Spartacus made a fanatical cult of his studies, transforming his education into a weapon of emancipation: He surpassed everyone's expectations.

... From the earliest days of his childhood, his lucky star followed him throughout his studies, a consequence, it was said, of the amulet he wore which was not black, like those of his siblings, but made from bright red leather (his by right, since he was the eldest), which gleamed like fire and could serve as an aphrodisiac in a pinch; "It might not bring the dead back to life," Saif remarked, offering his assurances, "but there's no wound or sickness that it can't cure."

From day till night Raymond-Spartacus caressed the amulet with his little fingers and then pressed it against his lips.

Throughout the years, at the moment when nighttime gave way to daybreak, Tambira–with fingernails as delicate as the wings of a locust—prepared special meals for her children, who rarely got enough to eat in the servants' quarters. They barely finished two slices of bread and butter before their plates were already scraped clean.

"Don't worry, mother," said her sons. "We will go to school and work hard. We will bring honor to Father and you, and you'll be very happy in your old age."

Their father Kassoumi replied, "It's certain you'll go to school. What worries me is that you may never come back."

Still dull with sleepiness, the children ate at daybreak and then went back to their beds, until the rest of the household woke up.

Sometimes in the early mornings, they went to the shores of the Yame with their slingshots, bringing back turtledoves, partridges, or wood pidgins, which Tambira coated in mud and then cooked upon the glowing embers. After awhile, when the mud coating had hardened, she would break the mold open, and the feathers of the bird would fall off, exposing the tender flesh– so juicy and savory!—of the baked fowl.

Dressed in a simple pagne, their mother took pleasure in watching them eat. On her face, the suns laughed, and, on her breasts, the moons shone. But, finally, it was time for them to go to school, and Tambira, who was seven times more beautiful in her maternal pride, climbed on her step-ladder to watch her sons walk across the courtyard on their way to school.

Their father Kassoumi stood behind her. They formed a couple as harmonious as the sun and the moon in the eastern sky.

Such was their lives over the days, weeks, months, and years; but in 1920, on the last Monday of the dry season, when Tambira thought about the coming exam period for her sons, she began to feel worried, and so she said to her husband, "It's not right that I sit around here and do nothing. I must speak once again with the sorcerer Dougouli and offer a sacrifice for the success of my children."

"If you can manage it, you should go see him right away," Kassoumi responded. "I feel as useless as you do."

After her travel preparations were completed, Tambira yanked three silky hairs from her scalp and cast them upon the winds. Then she departed for the house of Dougouli, while her husband worked the fields along the Yame.

Eight hundred meters from the Place of the Flames, on the opposite side of the river, Tambira at last came to the house of Dougouli. She was so lost in her thoughts that she completely overlooked him.

"Shame on you!" said the sorcerer. "Don't you recognize me? For more than a year, I prayed for the well-being of the fruits of your womb."

Tambira realized that it was Dougouli who stood before her.

"Woman," he shouted in a shrill voice. "Woman!"

She stared at the sorcerer and was surprised to see unmistakable signs of religious delirium on his face. Her small black eyes did not reveal any indignation; she not have the right to be indignant. Tambira forced a humble smile, as if the obvious signs of weakness in the sorcerer granted to him a certain license that he had formerly lacked. As a result, she cast all caution aside and began chattering with him at once.

"By God, Tambira, I know why you're here. Come inside. Don't act like a stranger. Be good to Dougouli."

They went inside his somber hut, which was lit by a small hole in the ceiling. The man's frail mumblings echoed off the mud walls of his hut. She smiled humbly, as he gestured with his hands for her to be silent.

"Sun of suns and radiant splendor in the sky! Oh, Tambira, your beauty is a bright light in a dark world! I've waited for you to come for so long ... Tell me your troubles. What has happened?"

"How could I not have troubles? My sons are preparing for their exams just to make me happy, and I am powerless to help them."

"It's me who will help them," Dougouli said, "but only if you are good to me."

"Why wouldn't I be good to you, when it is a question of my sons?" replied Tambira.

Dougouli extended his right arm, and Tambira was immediately fascinated. He struck the earth with the end of his amulet, and, from it, a mortar brimming with grain transmogrified in the air, along with a stout peasant woman, who was as strong as a man, her hands gripped upon a pillar.

"Stretch out your hand, woman!"

Tambira extended her hand, and the sorcerer touched it: from it gushed forth a flood of grain that slowly drained the mortar of its contents.

Dougouli struck the earth with the end of his amulet: a white lamb surged forth, surprised and innocent.

"Hold out your hand, if you are a woman!"

Tambira extended her hand, and the sorcerer touched it: from it sprang six hyenas that chased around the lamb, before ripping it to pieces and carrying its mangled body before Saif.

Dougouli struck the earth with the end of his amulet, and one hundred serfs caught on fire. He said to Tambira:

"You must save them."

"I'm too afraid," she stammered. "You do it."

"Look," murmured the sorcerer.

He struck the earth with the end of his amulet, and, the faces of Tambira's sons arose from the ground; the serfs, petrified in their ecstasy, prostrated themselves before her sons, singing hymns of devotion to them. Then they turned into white doves.

Meanwhile, a calabash poured forth water over the dry ground, as Tambira, who was completely hypnotized now, saw her sons at a distance, busy taking their exams. Praise be to God Almighty! *Aouyo yéwa!*

"Sit on the floor and take off your pagne," the sorcerer ordered.

A horrible combination of repulsion and terror choked Tambira. She was a fool, a fool worn out by mother love. She thought now of her husband's love for her and his years of misery, as she attempted to drive from her mind the sorcerer's kisses on her neck, the tenderness of his caresses, the fire of his lips, the saliva from his mouth, the heat of his body, his loins, his armpits, his belly, the engorgement of his member, his undisguised lust, the quaking of his legs: she removed her pagne and squatted over the puddle of water in the dirt.

They stared across the puddle at one another, their eyes filled with loathing and desire, lips swollen, hands trembling. The nude thighs of Tambira gleamed back at them in the puddle.

But now the sorcerer stammered out his prayers, drawing signs in the dirt, as if listening to the sound of quiet whispers in the distance. In his delirium, he suddenly cried out, "Hee hee! Look, Tambira! Sit completely still! Look at the hairy lips of your twat! Go ahead! Take a look! It's red like the tuft of the cock. See, how it opens up? It's yawning at us, dancing, waggling over the abyss! Hee hee! Tell me what you see inside there?"

The puddle moved in gentle waves before Tambira's fascinated eyes. Enthralled, she furiously bit at her drunken lips, as murky forms swirled about in the water. Softened by the violence and excess of the moment, her indignation seemed insignificant to her. Suddenly, a white cock surged out of the puddle, then ten white sheep with black heads. The cock crowed in a loud shriek, and the sheep bleated. The puddle began to swirl about, lifting it from the earth. The water became heavy with hundreds of feathers from cocks with gashed throats as well as the gory heads of sacrificed sheep. And then there was nothing. All she could see was the reflection of her partially opened vagina in the puddle. Then, the puddle itself disappeared into the dry earth.

"Get up, woman! Hee hee! A white cock, oh my! Two white sheep, hee hee! Offered to me by way of sacrifice, oh yes! Then all your sons will pass their exams," prophesized Dougouli.

Tambira flattened her pagne, which she unrolled like a sheaf over her thighs and legs. She was happy at the news but also terrified at the price: one cock and two sheep! ...

"One month from now, before the morning star arises, happiness will be yours, Tambira. One cock and two sheep! Then all your sons will pass their exams. Unless... "

She let out an instinctive cry from her heart, "Unless what?"

The eyes of the sorcerer glowed with desire, and the slave woman felt herself to be caught in his spell, against her will. The man wanted her. She detested this sorcerer with his snake eyes, his heavy lips, his gangly legs, his head that trembled like a mule's, his stench of blood and amulets cut from sloppily tanned leather. Trying to regain her strength, she closed her eyes: whatever fascination the sorcerer had formerly held for her now vanished. He had no power over her, so long as she avoided looking in his eyes.

"You will not leave this place until I am satisfied, Tambira. The cock and two sheep. Or, I will do as I please with you right now. No, I'll do as I please with you, anyway. Later, we can talk about the cock and the sheep."

Dougouli closed the window and approached the woman, who stopped him with a slap across the face.

"Woe unto you and your household!" shouted the sorcerer. "Perhaps I won't taste the sweetness of your flesh in this life, but how will you escape me when all your sons are dead? Crooked be your path, Tambira!"

Enfuriated, but dreading occult vengeance and the black magic of the sorcerer, the woman sobbed in her misery. Like a faithful dog, she at last removed her pagne and lay down in the dirt.

When she left the sorcerer's hovel, her head low and her shoulders high, she saw Kratonga and Wampoulo waiting for her outside. They threatened to tell her husband what they had seen. The time had come to avenge the assassin Sankolo, their old friend whom Kassoumi had reported to the authorities.

They ordered Tambira to follow them, and the woman did as they instructed. She was indignant but frightened. She was afraid of her husband, who was such a good man, and whom she had now deceived. She feared for his safety too, as well as her own.

Wampoulo and Kratonga led her behind the waterfalls of the Yame to a bushy spot overgrown with weeds. Then they took her. They took her again and again during the course of the day, terrifying her for their amusement.

Her head low and her shoulders high, she was then escorted to the house of Saif. All that night, Kassoumi and her children waited for her to return, and, when she never came back, they went out the next morning to look for her. All their efforts were in vain.

Two days later, Kassoumi trembled when Wampouolo and Kratonga showed up at his doorstep.

The body of Tambira had been discovered. Behind Saif's courtyard, latrines had been set up that were used by his domestic servants. They were neatly arranged over a gaping, rectangular trough that brimmed with muddy feces and teamed with caterpillars and worms of all shapes and colors.

Over the trough lay long planks upon which the domestics would squat to perform their natural functions. It was in this latrine that the corpse had been discovered.

Tambira sat in the trough of feces, as if stranded. Her perpendicular body was fully dressed, but worms crawled from her nostrils. Her head was held in place by a knotted rope that was tied to a plank above the trough. Tambira–was she a suicide or murder victim?—held a crucifix in her right hand, which had been given to her children by Henry as an award for their hard work in school.

The domestic servants did not dare to name any possible suspects, nor to even affirm that Tambira had been murdered. So, Kassoumi silently untied the rope from the plank and, without showing any signs of disgust, hoisted the filthy body of his beloved from the trough and then gently washed the feces from her body. While cleaning the deceased, he was compelled to suck the worms from her nose and spit them onto the ground. He did not complain but was resigned to the decrees of Heaven. He lacked even the strength to weep. Her arms dangled as he carried her towards the Yame, followed by the servants from Saif's house. He brought her to his banana tree near the river where he had first seen her on a warm afternoon. Tambira had truly loved her family. May God Almighty elevate her to His Celestial Realm!

Amina Yarabi!

And the sky grew bloody when the evening prayers were recited that night, as we prostrated ourselves upon the ground:

In June 1920, all the sons of Kassoumi and Tambira were awarded their diplomas.

"Come, my sons, do not give in to despair and mourning. The Savior who watches over our souls is among us. Study, my gentle lambs, study... May peace and happiness be yours," Kassoumi said and then burst into tears. "May the milk that nourished you sustain you throughout your lives. And you, Raymond, my first born, may you be so brilliant and so wise that your mere presence will transform the black night into luminous day. May your success at school prove sharper than the finest sword and more penetrating than the swiftest arrow. I have spoken."

And so, the sons studied, and the father busied himself with his duties as a domestic servant. But one day, Raymond came home from school in tears, throwing himself so furiously on the sofa that its four legs collapsed from underneath him.

"What has happened, my son?" his father asked. "Has someone insulted you? Are you sick or have you been expelled from school?"

"It's not fair that I must study so hard and be an orphan too! All day long at school, a boy named Rokia made fun of me because I have no mother, and because I'm at the head of the class. He and some other kids laughed at me and hit me with rocks from his slingshot, without even letting me speak in my defense. How can I go back to school after receiving such an insult?"

"Calm down, my son. Tell me what he said to you," asked Kassoumi.

"*Dog! Son of a dog who died in the shit of slaves! There is still milk on your chin, and you think you're as good as me? You damned imposter! It's time that you knew your place.* Oh, father, how will I ever show my face again?"

"The embarrassment that one feels from such incidents does not linger as long as you imagine. Two days at the most. Besides, I know a way to make them forget. Climb on the back of my donkey, with your back facing its head, and walk the donkey three times in front of all your friends. Observe how they respond and then come back and tell me what happens."

Raymond climbed up backwards on his father's donkey and walked it three times in front of the school kids. The big kids as well as the small ones, the serious students as well as the troublemakers, shook with so much laughter that they nearly rolled on the ground.

When he passed a second time, the laughter died on their lips. "There's more to this than meets the eye," they said. "He must be riding his father's donkey like that for some good reason…"

When Raymond returned to his house, his father gently asked him, "Well? Tell me what happened?"

"When I passed by them the first time, they shook with so much laughter that they could hardly stand up. The second time, a few of them laughed, but most of them did not laugh. Some were bothered to see me, a model student, acting as if he'd lost his mind. The third time, not a single one of them laughed anymore. 'He is not crazy,' they said. 'There is some reason why he's sitting backwards on his father's donkey…'"

"Very good. That is exactly how things will turn out for us," Kassoumi said. "At first they will laugh. Then they'll be worried. Later, they'll forget the whole thing."

… In effect, that is what happened: When Raymond's classmates saw that he still made the highest marks in the class, and that his father had not remarried, they laughed at him, but eventually no one gave the matter further thought. And the Kassoumi family was finally able to live in peace. Praise be to God the Most-High. He is powerful in all things and can grant to us all our wishes. Let us humble ourselves before Him: *Amîna Yarabi.*

The least gifted of Tambira's sons gained employment from their school diplomas as officers in the colonial administration at Krebbi-Katsena, where they were paid two times over, first by France and then by Saif.

Only Raymond pursued his studies beyond his first degree, which he received in 1924. From that time forward, he was no longer required to perform household chores, by order of Saif.

The vacation that followed that year was the most terrible that he had ever experienced.

He took refuge under the banana-tree of his father; his face was sallow and gray, and the big whites of his eyes were as raw as hemp. He nonetheless remained impassive before the taunts of the bullies who assailed him from afar, calling him a "lazy, good-for-nothing." In truth, the field slaves did not really welcome his academic successes, for they viewed those who spent their time scribbling on paper as dangerous weaklings who–like the runts of the litter–should be killed for the common good.

Leaving the Yame, Raymond walked to the courtyard of the palace where he sat before Saif's door, leaning against the date tree in the courtyard. He sat without making any bodily gestures or movements. Every now and then, his eyelids would blink over the two white spots of his eyes, but that was all. Did he have a clear understanding of the facts of his life, torn as he was between Africa and France?

He returned to his place in the courtyard for the next few weeks, but his inability to help with the chores, as well as his hours of sitting without moving, began to wear on the nerves of Saif's slaves, for whom he had become a nuisance, as well as a buffoon and martyr–free game for the local bullies who enjoyed tormenting him.

Kratonga imagined all sorts of cruel farces for him. Because he ate with a fork like the Whites, his mealtimes became a constant source of diversion for Saif's domestics Soon, the serfs from neighboring houses showed up to watch Raymond eat, as news spread from door to door of his outlandish eating habits. Sometimes, a puppy would be set on a stool close to his mahogany eating-bowl filled with millet. The dog smelled its way to the food, softly approaching his dish, stealing a quick bite, and then just missing the sharp end of Raymond's fork in its snout. Closely packed inside the smoky walls of the kitchen, the spectators laughed, jibbed, and danced. Raymond's father was never present during these incidents, sent away on an errand by Kratonga to the other end of the village. Without saying a word, Raymond resumed eating, holding his fork in one hand and slapping the puppy with the other. To the amusement of all, the puppy ran off with a yelp.

Sometimes, they pretended that Saif had asked for him, or that his father needed him; and the young man, when he arose to answer the summons, was unexpectedly knocked backwards against a cluster of sooty pots and pans.

Finally, the domestics grew bored with these pranks. Enraged that the boy's education promised a better future than his own, Wampoulo took to slapping Raymond every chance he got, ridiculing him in front of the other servants. All his efforts to ward off Wampoulo's blows were useless. Then a new game was invented: the game of the eyelids. The domestics, the servants who worked in the kitchen, began thrusting their hands in his face to make him blink. He did not know who to turn to for help, and so he simply covered his head in his arms whenever he was approached by one of these black devils, who then took to shouting insults in his ears, laughing like jackals. Ridiculing his appearance, they fixed their eyes upon him, ready to pounce on his every gesture or movement. Sometimes, they invented girlfriends for him, claiming that he had been promised to Tata, a heavy girl with big hands and chubby cheeks, who brought him his food on a wide platter. Her warm eyes registered her disapproval of the torture that was inflicted upon him.

Before long, Kadidia returned from the market where she sold bundles of wood. When she saw how they treated her brother, she stammered to the servants, "*Yourou mendè.* For God's sake, have some pity!"

They lowered their heads and pretended that they had only meant to tease her brother, and, masking their hatred, made a few lame jokes at Tata's expense. Then they returned to their daily chores.

They were not mistaken about Tata. She lavished her tenderness and affection on Raymond, as if compensating for the endless miseries of his daily life as a serf, following him from afar at all hours, through the gravel alleyways and footpaths of Tillaberi-Bentia, and at the Place at the Acacias on the Yame. She watched him at a distance, as he walked with grave steps, his hands behind his back and his forehead facing the ground. Sometimes, he stopped and returned her smile, as if they shared a special secret with one another–and as if thanking her for understanding matters that were far beyond her years.

At last, they sat together in the green millet fields along the shores of the river, for she was afraid to go beyond her accustomed limits. She chatted freely with Raymond, in ignorance of the world beyond the trees marking the boundaries of her line of vision. And, when the serfs, who soon tired of seeing them together after every meal, cried out to her, "*Han! yérago pili bara!* Why don't you run off to the house of the *Flencessi* with your black white-man and become a lazy bum like him? *Bédéguéi gombo oumo héyé hein!*"—she did not respond, but withdrew with him deeper into the millet, seized with a vague terror of the unknown, dreading the strange world of the student, the faces of the Whites, the appraising stares of the strangers whom they happened to encounter, and the glances of the gendarmes who passed by, two-by-two, along the length of the road through Krebbi-Katsena, where they instinctively hid behind the shrubs and rock heaps lining the road.

When she spotted the Whites coming from afar, their boots shiny under the hot sun, she became as agile as a beast, searching for a quick hiding spot in the brush. She slumped down along the embankments, letting herself fall like a limp rag and then rolled herself into a ball, so she might become invisible, like a rabbit in its hole, camouflaged against the brown earth. Not that she ever had any doings with them, but she carried the terror of the Whites in her blood, as if she had inherited it from her parents–who died performing forced labor in the service of the colonizers.

Encouraged by Saif, Raymond asked her to marry him. *Oum ibem min imbè: ama yéguéré!*

Early one morning in August 1924, during the thick of the rainy season, Saif was summoned to the Mosses' home. When he returned at noon, he announced to the assembly of notables that Raymond Kassoumi had been granted permission to pursue his studies in Paris and would be sent there in one month, a few days before the opening of the school year, so that he might earn his baccalaureate. Saif, who considered Raymond as his own personal property due to his birth, his education, his heredity, and his future–an instrument of Saif 's future politics–now required the serfs to show Raymond proper respect, heaping copious favors on him, opening his palms so wide that it seemed they would never be emptied of gifts. Raymond's brothers were married to the domestics of the scholar Akbar ibn Bez Toubaoui, and his father was also lavished with generous gifts *wassalam!* As an amusement during the festivities following this announcement, Saif showed his favoritism to Raymond by ordering on account of the merits of his ancestors—May Allah honor their faces!–an arena of sand to be poured amid the debris of millet, kapok, and corn at the far end of the palace courtyard, so a *tchiprigol*, or wrestling match, might take place in Raymond's honor.

On Saif's order, two nude men– Toucouleurs–whose sex was hidden in a leather thong, lunged at one another. They carried panther claws in their hands, attacking one another and doing their best to make the other fall to the dirt. Their weapons lacerated the flesh of their opponent with deep, bloody gashes.

The fighters fixed their eyes on one another, leaning into one another with trembling limbs. Suddenly, they were entangled in a sinewy embrace, before one of them lifted the body of the other high in the air. His body was held in a headlock and then pummeled with the knee of his opponent, before he collapsed to the ground like a lump of soft paste. In the midst of the ferocious and passionate shouts of joy, the crowd of spectators unconsciously imitated the movements of the wrestlers, as their war began anew, the two men locked in mortal struggle. Blood pouring from their flesh, they became living and breathing wounds, as they ceaselessly lacerated one another with the panther claws. The right cheek of the smaller one was ripped to shreds, while the ear of the other was split in three separate places.

"Hit him! Come on, hit back, *karmadjo! warmo!*," the crowd cursed and insulted them. The big one was knocked unconscious and slumped lifelessly to the ground. He was carried off amid the jubilant shouts of the crowd, "*Naguè! naguè! hockèmo naguè!* A cow to the victor!"

Then, the spectators turned away with a long sigh of regret. Sad that the match was already over, each returned to his own house.

Raymond's days from then on were like all those of all the members of his generation–the first generation of the

African bureaucrats who lived a life of gilded prostitution under the power of the nobility–rare commodities, somber geniuses to be manipulated behind the scenes, tossed into the maelstrom of colonial politics amid the warm smells of carnival and compromise– deadly games where it was easy to lose one's equilibrium, where the master fell to the level of the slave who oversaw the other slaves, but believed himself to be the unrepentant equal of the white master, and where the slave thought that he was now the master of the master who was in fact merely the slave who oversaw the other slaves...

Thus, the betrothal of Raymond and Tata was made official to insure the return of the fraudulent black white-man upon his departure for France, smitten as he was with the big, strong, fat blackberry of a woman, whose warm and mysterious beauty disturbed the dreams of many. A blossoming life illuminated by the promise of ever greater happiness–interrupted by the student's departure.

He was accompanied by many to the boat, a wheezing and vibrant old caldron: his family members, his fiancée, Saif, the assembly of notables, Kratonga, Wampoulo, Yafolè, Henry, a host of turbaned beggars, and a few employees of the colonial administration. Then it was time to go. The ship's horns bellowed, as it slowly withdrew from the port amidst the blur of colors, cotton and silk fabrics, old pagnes and boubous, cries of farewell, songs in praise of Saif that broke through the chaotic noise of the docks, last minute advice shouted to him, smiles and tears, laundry lists of items to bring back, the voices of rowdy urchins who skipped about their somber parents like so many black chicks. *Djoulè: homoh andi djitingal? djoulè! Amina yarabi...*

9

But it was too early and too late. Dazzled by Europe, Raymond had already discovered another shadow of himself, and the reason for Saif's anxieties.

Because the white man had infiltrated him so deeply, the mere fact of his presence precluded every move that he–the child of violence–might make against him. Scorning Africa, he did everything in his power to propel himself over the abyss separating him from the crowning achievements of white civilization. But the overwhelming evidence of twenty centuries of History, or what remained of it, could not simply be dismissed: rather than probe into the reasons for historical differences between the two—may the Evil One be kept at bay!—he submitted to them.

And so, taking shelter under the dead tree of academic insularity, a learned sage without roof or hearth, scraping by amid the husks of dead words, Raymond Kassoumi, now having lost his way, aping the accent of a street-smart Parisian, at last became an expert of literary jargon, turning himself into a ventriloquist's dummy who expounded upon the "facts" of his own culture, only to become engulfed by his own inanities.

Months of failures, false starts, bewilderments, bumbling mistakes, pointless debates in which he sought to justify himself before Saif: he could no more rid himself of Africa than a plant of its roots.

But France fascinated him, his professors, his fellow students, the white man in general. How different they were from the people of Nakem, who all seemed to him now like thick-witted gendarmes, other than Henry.

The son of Tambira redoubled his efforts at school, humiliated to find himself by far the oldest student at the Lycée Hugo. He was awestruck, however, by distant rumblings from the underbelly of Paris, its women, big blond girls, raven-headed girls, redheads, and brunettes, titillating him from the other side of the iron grill of the courtyard of his pension, first with their long and refined throats and then their shapely rumps, their arresting eyes and red lips, wafting him with the intoxicating smells of their perfume and rice powder...

His life went on, sedentary and as bleak as his first winter, which was long and brutal. Then spring came, turning the lycée green once again; and the students, slogging away at their homework like diligent ants, wiling away their hours in revising new drafts of their essays, drudging in isolated cubicles of the study halls, were whipped into submission by their own ambitions, cracking open books of all shapes and sizes that begat knowledge in the prospective graduates and amazement in their parents, who dropped by to behold these larva of culture in the visiting room, ushered in by the school attendant.

The year was going well, or so the professors said, those merchants of language, who deepened their influence on their students by the warmth and urgency of their advice, by the scrupulous performance of their duties, by inculcating time-honored precepts in the minds of the students, by their make-shift religiosity, and their true devotion to a profession that alleviated the anguish of their spiritual poverty.

They listened to their students in the same way that a conductor listens to an orchestra of musicians, suddenly rapping at the podium to lay down the law: "Monsieur Bertrand, Monsieur Bertrand, is that a solecism?

What is the function of x, Monsieur Kassoumi? You must enter into the spirit of a language, my boys "

The concert was not in vain. For suddenly, after a month of tests, an immense cry of joy burst from the mouths of the young men. They swore, cried, coughed, spit out their plans for the future, discussing the results of their exams as the son of a painter or poet might discuss a painting or poem at ten or twelve years old: all of them, Kassoumi included, were admitted as bachelors, with the exception of three country bumpkins from Charente who looked more like sheep herders than students.

Sending a telegram to Henry and Saif, Raymond at last felt justified in the eyes of Nakem, the lycée, and himself, after many long months of silence in which, believing that all was lost, his career hopes shattered, he had ceased communicating with his family. Intoxicated with his success, he agreed to accompany some friends that night for an evening of pleasure.

At last evening came. Pigalle blazed with light. It was a warm Saturday night in spring, as Raymond and five other boys from school swaggered over the sidewalks, two-by-two, leisurely strolling in procession.

They skirted the alleyways that bordered the hotels, on fire with an appetite for women, of whom they had been dreaming through the last months before their exams. Pierre Duval and Philippe Bourdeau walked ahead of him, led by Lamotte, who was known as "Dédé, The Shyster," an intelligent rascal, shrewd and hardworking, who served as their negotiator each time that a girl called to them. It was his job to figure out which ones were actual prostitutes, to approach them and bargain with them, his fly half-open like the curtains at the door of a pub.

After sauntering down the somber roads leading to the Place Blanche, where a spirit of pleasure imbued the night, Dédé settled upon an obscure alleyway where neon-lights with sonorous and colorful names glimmered above the doorways, flickering in the darkness... On the pavement, sellers of fried food, who wore aprons like the local gendarmes, pushed their carts along the alleyway, hailing passersby to hawk their stale grub, already three-days old.

Here and there were placards of nude photographs of women, whose virtues were sung by the uniformed doormen; and, further away, at the threshold of one of the establishments, a swarm of girls displayed their goods behind a glass door, wearing sheer dresses revealing their heavy, rose-colored breasts, veiling thighs of varying shapes and sizes. They smiled luridly, as the boys passed by. Down the alley, another woman flaunted a green silk dress that accentuated the contrast between her round body and thin face, which was long, desiccated, and ruddy, topped off by a beehive and framed by wavy locks that fell along the length of her temples, forming a veritable living sandwich, a human head that was a slab of ham between the two buns of her blond hair. The creature, an old frog wasting away in her miserable retirement, called out, "Hey, boys, you wanna get sucked?" She latched onto Kassoumi, calling him her Doudou, caressing his neck, fondling him in word and gesture, lavishing upon him all the energy that an indebted, ruined, and desperate woman could muster, clinging to him as a usurer might cling to his debtor. Raymond, bewildered and acutely aware that he was the only Black in the group, feebly repelled the woman's advances as his friends looked on, uncertain whether to make further inquires about the costs of her services or to take their quest for bawdy adventures further down the road. The woman at last grew annoyed, thereby annoying her clients in turn, and Dédé, who was initiated into the ways of Pigalle, told them it was time to move on.

And so they sauntered down the road amid the insults of the now infuriated prostitute, while more women inside the hotels before them rapped upon the windowpanes of the doors, sending them alluring looks to entice them inside. They continued on their journey, growing ever more aroused. The porters cajoled them from one side, while those women whose aging bodies had been scorned cursed them from the other. Now and then, mixed clusters of soldiers, sailors, confirmed bachelors, lecherous old men, beardless youths, and impious family men passed them from the opposite direction, a sparkle of ferocious joy in their eyes.

They continued on their way. Everywhere, within the fissures of unknown alleyways, along the torturously narrow paths aglow in the neon lights, the odor of women's flesh oozed from the dampened walls.

As last, Dédé, with a wave of his hand, brought their march to a halt before an elegant building, not far from the Moulin Rouge.

The orgy was total! Four months of savings were depleted. Ordering a single room to more fully stir up their excitement, they ravaged their dark-eyed partners for three hours, reveling in the extravagance of their desires, their faces aglow with passion; their open lips and teeth, even their smiles, exuded an uncanny and ferocious sensuality; and the girls' hardened breasts, elongated and firm, sharpened at the tips of their porous flesh, seemed to be elastic, as if made from steel springs. In the wild extravagance of their caresses, reflected to infinity in the mirrors framing the silk-curtained walls, a truly animalistic quality emanated from the girls, transforming them into superb cows, who had been created solely for the purpose of unrestrained copulation.

Every now and then, all six boys caught a glimpse of the eyes of their companions in the mirrors and grew ever more inflamed by the relentlessness of their coupling and the full-throated moans of the women who embraced them, the grinding of their teeth, their involuntary convulsions and moistened bites, followed by a feeling of physical exhaustion that was as profound as death. But suddenly someone sneezed or coughed, and all twelve awoke once again, ready to begin copulating anew, to kiss the swollen throats of their exhausted partners. The spirit of their adventure was as simple as one and one makes two: a raucous groan of pleasure took the place of thought.

Proud of their bodies by instinct, the girls did not hesitate to adopt, propose, and demand a variety of erotic positions to enhance the inexhaustible richness of their flesh: lying back on their flanks, their shoulders, upon the foot of the bed, propped up doggy-style or their two legs V-shaped, their knees spread wide apart, they let themselves be taken with a laugh, rump in the air and hands flat on the floor; then they rotated partners, making a mad dash around the room, hurling themselves upon their partners with wanton abandon. When the desires of all were satiated, they collapsed in exhaustion, nibbling upon Danish biscuits and drinking champagne. Microscopic beads of sweat glowed upon their skin, as the powerful odor of sex filled the room, a salty and frightful odor that emanated from the deepest crevices of their flesh.

When all the champagne bottles were empty, one of the girls peeked her head out the door and ordered another six bottles, along with three more packages of Danish biscuits and caviar.

Each boy wrapped his limbs around those of his companion, who would then rotate partners. The carved wooden beds, which were large and surprisingly tall, were pushed together to make one large platform. And, after the last glasses of champagne were emptied, the sextuple coupling began again on the now moistened sheets, reflected in the mirrors upon all four walls, as the sour music of the phonograph droned on from the bartop.

At last, they stopped again to eat and drink; then they began coupling all over again; later eating and drinking once more.

Everything had grown blurry and pleasant. Each boy, with his partner pressed against him, sang or wailed, screeched like a cat and threw kisses out into space, pouring champagne down his throat, liberating the human beast. In their midst, Kassoumi stroked a rotund black girl who sat astraddle on his lap. He contemplated her with passion. Less drunk than the others, though not because he had drunk less, he felt overwhelmed by vague notions that seemed to come to him from nowhere. More tender in his disposition than the other boys, he was in the mood for conversation. His ideas taunted him, dimly fading away and then returning with a flourish, so that he could not exactly put into words the thoughts that swirled in his mind. He chuckled to himself, stuttering, "Hey... hey there... uh... so have you been here long?"

"Two months," responded the girl.

He appeared satisfied with the answer. He began to hum, wagging his finger in the air to the sounds of the phonograph. At last, he ventured, "You like living this sort of life, do you?"

She became quiet and then sighed, "You get used to it. Things could be worse. Slave or whore, it's pretty much the same thing, right?"

He was sympathetic. Then suddenly, "You're not from Martinique?" he hazarded.

She shook her head "no," remaining silent.

"You were born in France then... Huh?"

She shook her head again.

"Then you come from far away?"

She nodded in agreement.

"Where then?"

She appeared to hesitate, thinking for a moment, and then she breathlessly said: "From Nakem-Zuiko."

He smiled again, content, and hungrily kissed the girl. "That's good. I'm happy to hear it... um... yeah..."

She in turn hazarded: "You're a *tirailleur*?"

"No, my dear, I'm a student."

"You come from far away?"

"Oh, yes, sure! I've worked my way here. You know, school, exams, universities."

"You've been lucky."

"It was hardly luck. It was a matter of survival."

Suddenly she seemed tense, fearful, doubtful about something, then after a moment, setting her glass to the floor: "You haven't met any students from Tillaberi-Bentia, by any chance?"

He slapped his thighs, shaking with laughter, "Why, I saw one this very day!"

She shuddered, now rapidly setting down her champagne bottle, "Honestly? You really mean it?"

"Isn't that what I just said!"

"You're not making it up?"

He raised the hand, "On the head of my father! I swear it."

"Then, do you know if Raymond-Spartacus Kassoumi is still a student?"

He was instantly sober, disturbed, worried, even terrified; but, before responding, he wanted to know what this was all about. "You know him?"

Distrustful, she avoided a direct response.

"Well, no, you see," she pretended, "There was someone who was asking about him."

"A White?"

"No."

"Who then?"

"Well, someone."

"From here?"

"No, from over there."

"Where over there?"

"It was just someone... Someone like me, a woman."

"But what does she want from him, this woman?"

"I dunno."

The two stared at each other, ill at ease, choked with anguish, sensing that something terrible was about to happen. He began again. "Can I meet this woman?"

"What would you say to her?"

""Well, I would say… I would say… that I saw Raymond-Spartacus Kassoumi.""

"He has a dry roof over his head?"

"He's fine."

"He's not hungry? He's doing well in school?"

"Yes, yes."

She became quiet again, avoiding his eyes, searching for words.

"Where do the students from Tillaberi-Bentia live?"

"They're right here in Paris, of course!"

She could not repress a feeble cry: "What?"

"Yes, of course…"

"You know him then? You know Raymond-Spartacus Kassoumi?"

"Didn't I just say that I did!"

She hesitated, fidgeting with her fingerprint stained glass. "Listen, will you tell him… No, never mind!"

He stared at her, horribly anguished. Finally, the suspense was too much for him. "What do you want from him?"

"Me? Nothing. I don't want anything from him! I assure you…"

Then suddenly making a decision, she climbed off his lap, still naked, and began gathering up Kassoumi's underwear, pants, shirt, and vest, as well as her own dress and undergarments, bringing them back to where he sat. "Get dressed."

"Why? I've paid my money."

"Put these on, and I'll tell you."

He obediently dressed himself, watching her slide her bra beneath her lovely breasts, slip on her underwear and then her dress. At last they sat down on the bed across from one another, as the others continued with their lovemaking.

"Good, now I'm listening."

"Wait. First you have to swear to me that you won't tell him you've seen me. Nor to tell him that you know I'm a prostitute. Swear it."

"I swear it."

"On your father?"

"On my father."

"Good. Then, you must tell him that his fiancée Tata, who was condemned by Saif for knowing too much and for refusing to betray Raymond, has been killed, that his father was sold and sent away with three hundred serfs, to the south, to the home of a French man named Dalbard, that two of his brothers, Jean and René, who worked for the colonial administration would not submit to the notables, so two years ago they were drugged by Saif, and driven to the point of madness."

He felt as if he had fallen off a cliff. For a long time, he remained in shock, at a complete loss for words. Then, disbelieving, he hazarded, "You're raving!"

"I'm telling you the truth."

"Who told you these things?"

She put her right hand on the back of his neck, and looked him directly in the eyes: "Do you swear to keep your mouth shut?"

"I swear it."

"I'm his sister!"

"Kadidia?" he said, reflexively.

She looked at him anew, fixing her big, round eyes upon him in horrified terror. In a low voice, she stammered with her fingers raised to her lips "What…. What? … Is that you, Raymond?"

They sat immobile, their eyes riveted upon one another. All around them, the other five couples softly moaned in their lovemaking. The noise of their moist thighs, the palpitations of their bodies, the heaving of their respirations, and the raucous din of their kisses were intermingled with the creaking sound of the phonograph. She came closer to him, and it now dawned on him that he had possessed his own sister, that they–brother and sister—had been physically intoxicated with one another! Then, in a low voice, afraid that one of his friends might overhear their conversation, Kassoumi moaned, "Lord… Lord…. Oh Lord…"

For a moment, her eyes as well were filled with remorse, as she stammered, "It's my fault, isn't it?"

But Kassoumi said rapidly: "So, she's dead, they were drugged, he was sold!"

"Yes."

"My fiancée, my brothers, my father!"

"All four in three months. In the coldest part of winter, I was left alone with nothing but my camisole and my pagne. So I followed father to the place where they took him. He didn't want me to come. He was afraid for me."

"I became a servant in the house of Dalbard Jean-Luc, a French merchant of rare wood, among more disreputable professions. Father worked six months there, without getting paid. This man got his *dabali* from the house of Saif and from the house of Tall Idriss. He mixed all sorts of garbage in the food to dope it for the workers, so these poor kids would work like slaves, just for their drugs and women, recruited in part by Wampouolo. To get rid of the boys when the census-takers came around, these crooks would send them away, pawning them off on others who were traveling to Mecca. Off to take the hajj, they said! But here's the thing: while the notables always returned from their bogus pilgrimages, the drugged workers never came back. They'd already been sold two times over.

"And then, one morning, I awoke and Father was no longer at work. He had been whipped because he refused to sleep with their women. He was cut to pieces. I guessed that he'd fled, and that he didn't want to bring me with him. Maybe they killed him… Or, maybe he was captured in flight. I don't know. I went further south, and another White, a pharmacist named Polin, misled me. I made some foolish mistakes. Then I went to work in the house of an old coffee farmer, who seduced me and drove me to this hovel in Grosso because he had gotten me pregnant. After awhile, he never came back, the fool. I spent four days without anything to eat. Since I wasn't able to work anymore, I became a whore, like so many others. The next month, I got an abortion and hit the road. I've traveled to a lot of places! Africa, the Mediterranean, Tangiers, Gibraltar, Toulon, Marseilles, Le Havre, Paris, and now here I am!"

Tears rolled from his eyes onto his nose, flowing down his cheeks and into his mouth. She spoke again, "I thought you were dead. You never wrote, my poor, poor Raymond."

"I didn't recognize you!" he said. "You're so different. You've gotten so heavy now. You've completely changed! But why didn't you recognize me?"

"I see so many *tirailleurs*," she said in despair, "And you're different now too. You're grown up...."

He looked deep into her eyes, crushed by an impotent despair that was so poignant that he felt the need to eat his own fist. He still held her on his knees, hugging her neck, and he was now struck by her clear resemblance to the Kadidia he had once left behind in his own country, along with all the others who had now been killed, sold, or driven to madness. Now, holding her like a sister, he leaned into her as sobs of anguish, prolonged like nausea, issued from his throat in random hiccups. He stammered: "It's really you. It's really you, my little Kadidia."

Then suddenly, he stiffened, jumping to his feet, shouting in a loud voice, knocking his head against the mirrored wall, and shattering it to pieces. Then, taking two steps, he collapsed in a heap, his face flat against the ground. He rolled around in convulsions, cursing, slamming his body and teeth against the hard, wooden floor, wailing so piteously that he seemed to be mortally wounded. The others stared at him, the girls snickering with laugher.

"He's drunk as a black skunk," a blond said, ironically.

"Better get him to lie down," another suggested. "If he goes outside like this, the cops will lock him up for sure."

So Kadidia paid for him, the Madame offered a spare room, and his friends, bleary eyed and stumbling, hoisted him into bed, as his sister stayed at his side, sobbing through the night.

Eight days later, taking advantage of a Sunday to visit his sister, Raymond learned that a sadistic client had inserted a razor blade into a cake of soap at her bidet, and Kadidia, while washing herself, was so badly wounded that the hemorrhage, which was impossible to stop, had caused her to bleed to death before help arrived.

The brother of Kadidia lived alone, all alone. He no longer had the heart for his schoolwork and barely passed the exams for his second baccalaureate degree. During the two semesters of the year that he took his competitive exams to gain admittance to the School of Architecture, his poor grades led to the suspension of his scholarship, but the surprises that his new life brought distracted him from worrying too much.

He resumed the habits of his old life in Tillaberi-Bentia, waking early in the morning, taking long walks, eating later in the day. Having refused to return to Africa, his needs were few. In order to survive, he got a job addressing hundreds of envelopes, trying his hand at bookkeeping, or working night-jobs at Les Halles. But, at the memory of his academic failure, of his sold or vanished family members, of Henry still back in the Nakem, his heart would soon began to beat–Kassoumi gave up his job the next morning, searching out one of his school books, hoping to "pick up where he had left off" from the previous session.

But when he found that he was unable to concentrate on his studies, he got up from his wicker chair and threw himself on his bed, where for hours upon hours, days upon days, he would contemplate his misery. It was not so much anguish that he felt but a nervous, physical need to kneel down and drink deeply from the well of his own narcissism, to glut himself upon his own despair. Then, hounded by physical appetite, the student finally left his room.

He walked along the length of the sidewalks that were strewn with rust-colored leaves, beneath the streetlamps teeming with fat moths; then, deliberately closing his eyes, as if he was watched by a thousand invisible notables, he drank in the night air. Shivers reverberated throughout his body, and he at last realized that it was time to circle back in the opposite direction. Endless questions surged from nowhere as he walked through the long corridors of tree-branches, along the roadways, between the cracks of the stone walls. They arose in the surrounding silence, emanating from the bowels of the earth, falling amidst the leaves, clinging to the backs of his growing fears, darting about, folding in upon themselves, becoming intertwined before disappearing and then return-

ing in circles, wrapping around him until they became fully
entangled with his body, imperceptibly crumbling to human
dust, thick, somber, and infinitesimal, then returning to his
body like an obsession—which at last respected his bastions
of legend, God dawdling behind the blurry halo of his rising
tears, smelling of road and moldy pavement.

... When he was finally worn out from fatigue, singing
the serfs' hymn of praises to Saif in the twilight—it was then
that his heart, like the despairing rain, drove him towards
other human beings, towards the jostling sidewalks of the
Latin Quarter.

So he took up the habit of the brasserie, with its close contact among drinkers, the thick smoke of pipes, heavy beer, a
lifestyle that weighed down his spirit but calmed his heart.

He lived there. As soon as he awoke, he went off to seek
his neighbors who always gave him something new to see
and think about.

"It's sheer cowardice."

"Conviction."

"Cowardice," he repeated.

It was against himself that he fought, seated at *Chez
François*, smoking his slow-burning cigarette, which kept
him stupefied for a good quarter hour. Then, he peered down
at his beer glass.

A tremor arose, first in his face, causing his cheeks to
nervously twitch, his lips to part, his nostrils to dilate, as he
opened up the cavity of his mouth, the clear saliva of his
gums flowing as it came into contact with the yellow fluid
that he poured down his bobbing throat; a cascade of living
gestures like the quiet trill of a bird, whose final, contempla-
tive note fell warm and soft in his stomach.

When he heard the sour sound the phonograph music,
Kassoumi grew sleepy, awaking an hour or so later. It was the
middle of the afternoon. He quickly clasped his hand to the
beer-glass that the barmaid had set before him while he was
asleep; then, savoring its taste, he retied his tie, smoothed
down the pleats of his pants, the collar of his vest and the

cuffs of his shirt, slouching before the same newspaper that he had already read that morning.

He read every single line of the paper, headlines, announcements, advertisements, comics, public notices, stock exchange tables, and the coming weekly spectacles. Between four and six o'clock, he took a stroll in the Luxembourg Gardens, for fresh air, he said; then returning to take his seat at the table that had been saved for him, he asked for another beer and chatted with the regulars with whom he had struck up an acquaintance. They commented on various news events and political developments: all of this filled the minutes before dinner hour at last arrived. He rapped his saucer against his glass, and the barmaid brought him a plate, a glass, a napkin, and the menu of the day.

As soon as he had finished eating, he hastened to rejoin a group of conversationalists two meters from his table, who rolled away the evening, as easily as they had rolled away the afternoon, taking him all the way to closing time—the dreaded moment when he was forced to return to his student's quarters, not to study, but to contemplate the miseries of his life. This had been his life for more than a year now.

Thus, knowing that closing time was in a half-hour, but wishing to stay where he was in order to forget his troubles, Kassoumi could not make up his mind whether or not to order another beer. In pity, irritation, and contempt, the barmaid, who wanted him to leave, reproached him for his unhealthy lifestyle, for living like a night-owl, for the simplicity of his daily pleasures, his tastes, his appearance, his habits, the meagerness of his tips, and the placid sound of his voice.

Kassoumi pretended not to hear. He murmured: "I'm fine, I'm fine." Then he walked off towards the men's room.

As soon as he was there, he bolted the door shut, so he could be alone, completely alone. Of late, the barmaid had given him so many dirty looks that he only felt completely at ease when the door was locked. He no longer allowed himself to think, reflect, or reason with himself, unless he had first locked the door against all the noises and incriminations outside.

Sitting heavily on the toilet seat to relieve himself, he dreamed that he would sooner or later find a way to resolve his financial troubles and, at last, be able to pursue his studies in peace.

The idea of finding some immoral way to earn money seemed to him so dreadful that he did not even dare to think about it. To work in a factory or on a newspaper was equally impossible; but in less than a month his situation would become desperate.

He stayed seated on the toilet, his arms dangling, seeking confusedly a means of solving his problems, but could think of nothing… "Fortunately, I have my degrees," he said aloud. "Without them, I would truly be in a fix."

The idea came to him to write to Henry in Nakem; he resolved to do so; but, almost at once, the memory of the hostility that existed between the man of the Church and Saif made him fear that the notables might consider him a lackey of the colonizers; so he was once again lost in anguish and uncertainty.

The barmaid knocked on the door. He jumped up. Someone outside was waiting to use the toilet, and he had not yet relieved himself! Thus, in bewilderment and feeling rattled, Kassoumi quickly splashed water on his face, as if he had been summoned into the bistro for an important event. Then he calmly walked out, frustrated but calm, telling himself that he had nothing to fear. He cast a glance at his newspaper, went to ferret among the oysters that were for sell at the window in the corner, returned to take his seat; but a door swung open, and the barmaid approached him.

He ordered another beer, feeling dispirited and distressed. Then, suddenly, the blood in his temples clamored, beat, rumbled, gelling with warmth and irritation, and he sensed, not far from where he sat, that the eyes of someone from the street were fixed upon him. He looked up.

Someone was indeed there, staring at him, a respectable middle-aged man, handsome and friendly, gray streaks in his beard, the ends of which fell on the collar of his overcoat. He smoked a cigar, watching Kassoumi seated on the other side of the glass. Following his smallest gestures with love, as if throwing kisses to his frizzy hair, he now stared into his eyes, then at his cheeks, mouth, hands, and, moving lower, Kassoumi's crotch, where he concentrated all his attention, revealing his embarrassed but tender desire.

Momentarily taken aback, Kassoumi tried to concentrate on his beer. He did not despise the man for his preference but was afraid of the barmaid (who had not seen the exchange), terrified of what might happen. Even a few seconds of misunderstanding would suffice to cause a catastrophe: voices shouting about homosexuality, curses shot at him like bullets, he and the barmaid face-to-face, looking one another directly in the eyes, wild gestures, a rapid-fire interrogation, withering remarks, which would cause his heart to pound, his mouth to grow dry, later turning him limp as a rag, exhausted from the confrontation.

The telephone rang. Someone, the manager, cried: "Gilberte! It's for you!"

The barmaid picked up the phone. When she returned, she no longer seemed exasperated, but filled with a cold and terrible resolution. She did not give Kassoumi a chance to speak, coming straight at him:

"Monsieur," she said to him, "This is not a hotel. We will close in a quarter of an hour. You need to place an order or leave. That's how it is."

"Yes, of course, Mademoiselle."

"Then what will you have, Monsieur?"

"The same thing."

She brought him another beer. He paid for it, leaving a big tip, with his last centimes. It was midnight.

When she walked off, the unknown man approached Kassoumi:

"Good evening," he murmured. "Nice weather, isn't it? Hmm…. Permit me?"

He pulled over a chair, and, in the same instant, caressed the neck of Kassoumi. The student sunk down in his chair, staring at the White in bewilderment. He no longer understood anything; he felt himself grow numb, his senses dulled, then deranged, as if he had fallen and hit his head; he struggled to remember the many horrible thoughts that had, only a second ago, run through his mind. Then, little by little, his mind, like troubled waters, grew calm and became clear; and an abomination took root in his heart. He, a Black. What hope is there when you're black? The man had touched him, looking at him with such forcefulness, with such self-assurance, with such troubling frankness, that his fears were temporarily assuaged, but he had his doubts about his own powers of perception, now subjecting his five seconds of complicity with the man to a rigorous self-examination, analyzing each gesture, the overheated memory of his anguish; and, every new discovery wounded him like the sting of a wasp.

Something strange awoke within him, an atrocious, poignant, and cold sensation, the memory of his misery, his mother who was murdered in the feces of serfs. A shivering broke out through his entire body, as well as his bones, which were suddenly icy.

He lifted his gaze, frantically looking the stranger in the eyes; his thoughts became unhinged like a crazy man's; the White's face was transformed when he saw the look upon his face, taking on a bizarre and sinister hue.

But Kassoumi kept his prayers to himself. He had no choice. The man wanted him, and this was a matter of survival.

His temples throbbed in irregular beats, his blood boiled over, a jolt of nausea shot through him, and then a feeling of gratitude, all taking place before the penetrating gaze of the man, a salt as good as balm and warm like his breath. The student stood up: he had decided to sell himself.

His head felt like it would explode, as if the world's order had at last revealed its inherent delirium. Humbly bolstered by his own shadow, at once dead and triumphant, Kassoumi recognized in this tired portrait, not so much a secret likeness with himself, as much as an inchoate meaning, the inarticulate fraternity of his innermost essence and his displeased moral sensibility when confronted with his gigantic thirst for self-affirmation.

"Come," the White murmured to him. "Don't be afraid. I know what it means to be a man without a woman, what it means to believe in a woman, to be with a woman but not possess her, to live days of long silences, and thus, instead of love, to know the call of an unnamable thirst. Come, come, I have looked for you for a long time, in every body imaginable, my love. Before I even knew of your existence, I knew of you. Before knowing the others whom I have met… With your love and mine, I will have known a desire without anguish for at least one day. A single day. Wouldn't that be good for you too? A day that will save us both. You and me. Me and You. You are firm, healthy … You and me, together, even if you know nothing about me, my friend. I will teach you how to immerse yourself in the quicksand of love, our love, my little one. Black body, I no longer wish to sleep on a pillow of stone, but to know peace—which you will whisper in my ear. You alone can save me. You alone can destroy me. My only desire is that you may need me, that you will always need me, at the very moment, at the very instant when I am no longer with you, and my absence will then spark a calm warmth in the depths of your heart. I love you. Don't flee from me. I have suffered too much already. My regrets. I want to dissolve them in the clear look of your eyes. Come. I know that when I press my hands upon your arm, you will desire only me, my love! My sweet refuge that I will ravish with adoring caresses! Come. We're here. This is my house, where we will reel in the rosy taste of the soft-footed dew that will wash over us, my little one. Come, my garden."

And so they walked together, beneath the streetlamps, their steps impeded by the obscure bond that brought them together, zigzagging a little.

The wind was loud. The airy sound of its blowing caressed his ears and intermingled with the whisperings of the man, whose words calmed Kassoumi's spirit; then, as if exhausted, they were dispersed in frescos where silence wove yet more silence, dreaming of calm and sentimental solitude. It was a moment of fullness in which their hearts became engorged with blood, nearly ecstatic. Extraordinarily suave, they gazed at one another with languishing eyes. They walked on; their voices were low, infused with tones that caused the sweetness of their despair to gush forth, their solitude too, decked out in all the richness of a single prolonged note, evoking a beauty without fault, the voluptuousness of their shared anguish and introspection. They were under the hypnotic charm of a felicity that longs for nothing other than itself, savoring and seeking its own essence.

Suddenly, they came to a stop. The man brought a key from his pocket, opening his door. He felt around on the inside of the room, triggering the light-switch.

The apartment was respectable, even luxurious. The man made Kassoumi something to eat, after having him take a bath. They did not take long before going to bed.

He made one or two remarks about the color of the room's light, then, all was silent. Both of them breathed in the apartment's relaxing atmosphere, which slowly filled them with a sense of wellbeing. The leisurely pace of time was diluted in a mass of soft sensations, melting into drunkenness, palpitating with the loss of reason. Their latent need for one another, little by little, was made manifest, as if in answer to their prayers. The sharp mirage of the pale drapes, which he saw with half-closed eyes, revealed the desire of the White for the form that lay by his side. In his intoxicating desire, he felt the effluvial warmth emanating from Kassoumi's neck, his reclined body, his thighs…

Kassoumi longed to sleep.

He succeeded in keeping his eyes closed for a longtime, but the man was not shy about imposing himself upon him. He opened his eyes. The other watched him with a gleam in his eye, gazing at the curve of his shoulders, diffusing a fluttering warmth upon his vague feeling of well-being. At last, he rose up on one elbow, as Kassoumi dozed at his side, half undressed. Their desire sucked the air straight out of the room. Hesitating, the man lightly stroked Kassoumi's foot with his toe, drawing curved lines upon his flesh with his caresses… Timidly, Kassoumi embraced his partner, enflaming him with a kiss upon the mouth. They drew closer to one another.

The sheets were silky, rustling against their skin; giddy for a taste that they now already knew, they were only able to breathe with great difficulty; Kassoumi came closer still and found himself sprawled against the smooth body of his partner. Quietly hugging, their undulating bodies shivered with impatience, as their softened and feeble hearts faltered in this dream in which time was suspended...

Their bodies became intertwined, softly falling into one another as they savored–in their indolent languor–the delicious sound of their own hearts, beating in unison. A soft moan of pleasure, the delicate joy of their mutual fondling, escaped from their throats, as they breathed in the odor of horses, of fungus, of soft skin upon skin, intoxicating them to the point of insensibility... Every now and then, they shivered, a convulsive movement that spurred them out of their torpor–and then they opened their eyes. All quietly faded and disappeared...

They were no longer man and man, lover and lover, but one single creature, issued from some strange power of life. They formed the apogee of the natural order of love, an immense ocean rollicking in the confines of their shared hammock, in which they didn't speak, but shivered. Pressed against the length of the other, luxuriating in the wealth of their warm bodies, they satiated their lungs with the good odors of their flesh, intensely aroused by the sound of their own coupling.

Every now and then, they exchanged a gentle word. And neither of them could behold the lips of the other without being deeply stirred, without striving to affirm that he had never in his life made love without seeking to escape from his own anguish.

The tender timidity of these moments awoke in each of them an affluence of gratitude. Wordlessly, they joined hands and hugged for a long time. Kassoumi, with the miserable look of a beaten dog, drank the irregular secrets of their love in slow sips, whispering confidences, imbibing them as if they were flowers, roses in his airy fingers, savoring their sweet taste against his palate and tongue. He loved this taste of rose petals that emanated from the man whenever he kissed him, the delicate aroma of roses that filled his nostrils. And it seemed that each breath was an imperceptible bounty, a thick and endlessly recreated harvest; and whatever it was that was born in him, whatever it was that had also died, now flowed like sap drenching their two bodies in mutual culpability: it was, of course, none other than himself, Kassoumi, the son of a slave, the Black brought to heel, alienated, who was struggling to be born. He surged into the world of the living from the boiling depths of an abyss. He germinated like the earth, and his anguish was an arid dune of sand that spoke to the dry winds, silently, as if according to rite; as if by remaining it would affirm his eternal solitude, shout aloud that all was well, unalterable, and that he had never had any other desire than to experience true serenity at the conclusion of this single instant, now, as the very breath left his body, at his own furthest limits... And, as if at peace with what had happened to him, the strange thing that had taken place inside himself, the student inhaled the fragile shivers of time, breathing through the smooth silk sheets that were pressed against his cheek...

Thus it was that the next morning, under the weight of the calm trembling of his being, Kassoumi forgot how long he had slept, finding himself seated upright next to the other, serenely irrational, replaying the drama that had brought him to this unexpected moment, how he had come to lie down in this place, his thoughts turning upon a single reverie, which, little by little, diluted the benumbed remnants of his will.

Inexplicably, fixing his vacant eyes upon the body of the other, which was pressed against his own, he recalled the school at Nakem, the glory of Europe that shone upon the entire planet, and he heard the oceans rolling within him: there was a ship, there were slaves going to work in the azure pits, women who were sold, children thrown into the water, priests, armed soldiers, men in chains, and rowers; there was also the slave merchant and his black-rabble, and, suspended ceaselessly in the wind and odor of the world, the crimes of the notables with their deranged cult of human dignity.

And it was here, at the dawn of oblivion, amid the faces that were reborn before his very eyes, the symbols too, faintly perceptible at first, then criminally obscured, impalpable, hazy, gray ash falling on his eyelashes,—his misery was suddenly concretized, a familiar object, recognizable, then giddy, a solemn dance, moist and fecund, delirious, clamoring with a debauchery of images of clear faces and screams that surged from the surface of this troubled water where his memory of celebrated names and places that were well known, appreciated, and comprehensible appeared before him. All were transfigured, Saif, the Nakem, the blemished face of this white man, who came from a totally different world, and yet was so close that he looked upon him in disapproval, under the intolerable weight where a glimmer of truth surprised him, illuminating him in this long march towards the memory of the wretched land where he had first seen the light of day: and he did not so much seek delirium as the profound meaning of his own destruction, the hideous scar upon his face that proclaimed his name: Spartacus!

Kassoumi underwent a slow usury of the flesh, a usury born of chaos, irrevocably binding him and opposing him to the White; and then, whenever he kissed the lips of the man, in wretched tenderness, the house grew calm and the sky blue, but the sun still burned with the lurid gleam of its hidden gaze, hinting at a mystery that he hoped to solve. He smiled at the other, as before, but soon he demanded to be paid. *Alif lam!*

He came back the next day and the day after that, for eight days; then, three weeks, and finally six months, always in the nights. And each time after they coupled, it was only when he was by himself in the bathtub, where he sat immobile for long moments, staring into space with half-closed eyelids, body upright as if against a headboard, that he finally took full stock of his own existence, horrified beyond measure.

While the other murmured words of love to him, he remained behind to wash himself, until he no longer knew who or what he was, or until he no longer knew how long he had gazed into the immense emptiness and lost silence of his anxieties... Then, the next day, his steps carried him back to his own identity: the anguish, the problem of his body and his skin, as well as the body and money of his partner, whose life was also a failure.

Finally, during another afternoon of his despair, when he had motionlessly drawn the shutters inside himself, anticipating his own avid thirst to see and experience too many sensations, a soft and humming feeling of vertigo overwhelmed him, and he knew how much he now needed the White, how much he needed to lose himself in the other, in his warmth and solitude.

He allowed himself to be kept by his lover, a rich investor from the Rue Danton: Lambert, the natural son of a woman from Strasbourg, "the only woman," he swore to Kassoumi, "whom he had ever desired, a woman who troubled him, seduced him, worried him, attracted him, frightened him, and excited him like a courtesan but also like a virgin."

This man was the providence of the student. Born for the nocturnal life, indefatigable though he always seemed exhausted, vigorous though pale, very elegant, his curled mustache, supple and graying in streaks, light hair, fine lips, he was one of those men of the night, whose time in the gym, fencing, playing golf, taking the waters and saunas, had infused him with nervous energy and deceptive agility. Like other Parisians, he was energetic and irresolute, indifferent and passionate, torn by contrary instincts, assuming all those whom he met should serve his every whim, a true, wide-eyed lover of life, buffeted in every direction by the changing winds. In exchange for two nights a week, he agreed to let Kassoumi keep his modest room on the Rue Mouffetard, giving him enough money so he could lodge, cloth, and feed himself, as well as hire a private tutor.

Their liaison lasted eighteen months, during which the student was just able to gain admittance to the School of Architecture; his scholarship was reinstated. And then there was an unexpected drama: Lambert's mother in Strausbourg fell gravely ill and called her son to be with her. He flew to her side, followed by Kassoumi, who, after taking up residence at a nearby hotel, sketched out his first architectural designs and studied various related disciplines: mathematics, statistics, mechanics, physics, chemistry of building materials, construction, the application of architectural theory, law, the history of art: the investor spent most of his time at the sick woman's bedside.

She was slow to recover from her illness—decalcification of the spinal column. One day as Raymond waited in his room at the hotel, he noticed upon his lover's return that his eyes were strangely bloodshot and timid, less hardy and blue than normal, with pupils so black that they seemed unreal. He leaned against the door to regain his composure.

Kassoumi devoured him with a look of savage lust in his eyes, biting his lower lip. He stood before the gaze of the investor, his throat rising and falling with each breath. Sheepishly, Lambert said, "At times, you look like a cat ready to pounce on my neck."

Then he sat down, as did the student in turn. He spoke to him about his mother, recounting to him gentle banalities with the magical voice that had always intoxicated Kassoumi. But, looking into his eyes, he seemed to communicate something that contradicted the words that came out of his mouth. Kassoumi, masking his irritation, pressed his lips upon the base of his lover's neck, upon the tufts of the hair that grew there, in the very place that he had longed to kiss. Lambert moved slightly to increase the gap between them. Miserable at being rejected, Raymond murmured, "You have forgotten."

"What did I forget?"

"That I love you."

"You're satisfied with this life?"

"Stop toying with me. You know very well what I mean."

"What a joke!"

"I made a promise to you."

"What did you promise? I forgot."

"You?"

"Me."

"You weren't so forgetful last night."

The man let out a burst of laughter. Suddenly indulging an obscure need to avenge himself, to wound his black lover, he announced, "I've decided to get married, my little one. My mother has arranged everything. Better get used to it. There's no help for it."

They were seated face to face, their eyes locked. Kassoumi remained immobile for a few seconds, as if he failed to comprehend the meaning of these words; then, all at once, his whole body trembled. His face suddenly convulsed, from his chin to his forehead, his ears turning violet, as he shouted: "You lied to me!" He hastily gathered his meager belongings, his books and clothes, stuffing them randomly into his valise and running towards the stairwell, delirious, crushed, unnerved, tumbling down the stairs to the receptionist's bureau, in his haste paying too much for his room, sprinting for the front door as fast as he could, like a man about to throw himself in the river to be drowned, before he was at last swallowed up by a taxi—as Lambert looked on, petrified.

For three years, during which he followed a new course of study each month, and after winning ten "commendations" in each discipline for a total of fifty credits (not counting his practicum as an architectural assistant), Kassoumi worked extremely hard and thus ascended to the rank of "first in his class"– an honor that had never before been bestowed upon an African. He therefore gained for himself a haloed name back in Nakem-Ziuko, winning the sort of glory that flatters to the black imagination, elevating him above the rest of humanity, transforming him into a mythical genius of science, culture, and intellect; at last, Raymond submitted his thesis on architecture.

Four years passed, during which his life, obscure and without further upheavals, was relatively uninteresting; then suddenly, in 1933, exploding like the burst of a loud thunderclap, the news came of the definitive success of his thesis at the School of Architecture, where he was dubbed "the black pearl of French culture." At the same time, defying all the calculations of Saif, he married a French woman, whose mother, an old ironing-woman from Strasbourg, tended to the dead and dying of his quarter, sewing up her clients in smoky sheets that they would henceforth never leave, and then setting her iron to the task of pressing the laundry of the living. As wrinkled as the posterior of a she-ass, bawling, a tireless worker, extraordinarily greedy, she was a widow who gossiped without cease, singing the songs of Musette at the top of her lungs, constantly fighting with the coal-dealer, revealing to the concierge the intimate details of her daughter Suzanne's relationship with "a handsome Black with a future," confiding for the benefit of the neighbor on the floor above the secrets from the alcoves of the neighbors below, filled with ridiculous stories, idiotic beliefs, grotesque opinions, stooped over as she walked along the balconies, as if the eternal motions from her ironing had finally caused her kidneys to burst, as she cynically babbled on about the neighborhood's various agonies and romances.

As the notables of Nakem-Zuiko remarked—at least those who deigned to entertain rumors about his new life—it was probably her lower social class that had attracted Kassoumi to the girl, his certainty that the milieu of his mother in law was well suited for someone only recently "evolved" to the point where he felt comfortable living among Whites.

The mother of Suzanne, Madame Teyssedou, endowed with udders like a buffalo cow, was mean-spirited and obstinate, one of those shrews who go through life without ever grasping its ironies, nuances, subtleties, who, never suspect anything and so never perceive anything, who deform everything, and who refuse to admit that the possibility that anyone might think, judge, believe, or act in a manner different from herself.

Kassoumi first saw the mother and her daughter, his neighbors, because they lived on the same floor; he spoke to Suzanne, held her against him, felt her fat and ardent breasts, her big haunches that were shaped like a lyre; and he proceeded to caress the undulating and divine curves of flesh that ran from her throat to her feet. Her spirit as simple as two plus two makes four, she readily agreed to take him for her lawfully wedded husband. For six months, Kassoumi remained in Strasbourg, toiling in the offices of various architects, paying off a small house that he had built for his mother-in-law, attending to domestic matters, the education and support of his three children, for his wife did not work.

He succeeded in paying it all off, in leading the life of a respectable, black-white member of the middle class. Outside of his family, he was attached only to Henry and his mistress from a local cabaret, a girl to whom he turned whenever his wife was indisposed from childbearing.

But no one suspected that war was at hand, and that it would soon–an explosion of furors and grievances eternally professing the same litany–traverse the entire world, waking up nationalist sentiments even in Tillaberi-Bentia, his terrible homeland, manipulated, of course, by the hand of Saif. *Houlmoh! Waar rèoudè!*

10

The nightmare that Raymond-Spartacus Kassoumi lived—*wallahi!* –was the same as that of untold millions, his contemporaries. The towns quaked in terror at the brilliance of the exploding bombs that wafted the corpses with the stench of eternity. Many townsfolk grew vigilant against the invisible enemy, fearing him like an evil wind that blows upon a desert of salt, an expanse that only the great caravans ever venture to cross.

Soldiers fallen in the empty hollows of the trenches–with flies at the corners of their mouths and puss in their nostrils, gnashing their teeth in despair over their impending deaths– skirted along the borders of an unknown land, their muscles now slack, eyes vacant, throats desiccated, at one with this war that they did not understand, and which splintered their skulls in a relentless dream, amid the raucous music of the assault vehicles that filled the air, the insanity and confusion that reigned on every side...

Throwing body and soul into the defense of France, as if coming to the aid of an endangered friend, Kassoumi found himself carried from the shore of the Rhine to Italy, fighting at Cassino, then in Provence.

Left for dead near Mehun-sur-Yèvre, where he was buried beneath the wreckage of a house, he succeeded after countless efforts in wrenching himself free of the debris, his face swollen, his body aching. He waited until nightfall, and then, after three delirious hours of struggling to keep his legs moving, one agonizing step after another, he found himself along the shore of a river, at the foot of a weeping willow, in a vast and hairy patch of frail weeds that glimmered in the dull moonlight. He kneeled down, bending forward, to drink the somber water, which quietly flowed along the length of his throat, like an icy, delicious caress,—the scintillating lights of the river danced before his eyes, as the skeletal trees encircled him in the night. L'Yèvre. L'Yèvre. Mehun-sur-Yèvre. Where was he? He must run, or at least walk. Hide himself. But he was hungry. By God, he was hungry! He wanted to live. He must run. Breath. Survive. His gums. How they ached! His ankles too. He must walk all the same, through the tall weeds, through the rotting leaves. There were berries in the bramble-bushes. He could eat the berries. How to find his division now? Suddenly, a crossroads. He was on the road to Châteauroux now. He must sleep. High up in the trees.

He awoke with a howl, strangling something that burrowed at his side, something that terrified him, a vague, fleeting form. It was a squirrel.

A riot of shivers rollicked through his body, flaying his already taut nerves, followed by hallucinations in which he became detached from his limbs. He imagined that he heard small row boats every time he breathed.

Towards dawn, he continued his long walk among the bramble-bushes and the nettles, reflecting back upon the truest moments of his life: and, when he forgot how to hope, when he forgot to hope for his own survival, an unspeakable hope came to him nonetheless, stealing upon him like death itself. He decided to wait and see what would finally happen to him. He too was a part of everything that surrounded him, and he could certainly count on this much. It was a thought that sustained him, as he slept in some somber copse, even in those moments when his anguish was at its most intense.

…Kassoumi lived on leaves and wild fruits, rats and tree roots; reduced to bestiality, he ceaselessly struck his forehead with his own fists, struggling for many long hours, nights, and

months, to convince himself of the absurdity of the temptation of suicide. He lived this life, anxiously puzzling over his
destiny, for eighteen months—which appeared to him like a
vast connecting road that led nowhere, hopeless and agonizing; yet he was constantly tormented by his extreme terror
of the German, whom he dreaded to see swarming over an
occupied France.

....When the myopic egoism of such fears finally left him,
Kassoumi dared to come within five kilometers of the towns.
But suddenly afraid that he might be thought a "collaborator," he sprinted back towards the copse, hiding himself like
a burrowing animal.

In October, however, he was sick and crushed by the
crises of Autumn 1945. The preceding winter, when he had
dressed himself in the skins of rabbits that he had snared,
his health was seriously undermined, so he at last decided to
walk into Paris on foot, where he could lose himself in the
crowds and possibly regain his strength.

For a longtime, his ears had forgotten the sound of bombs
and human lamentations; and so, wearing a tattered uniform,
he entered a bistro in Orleans, saying that he was a sailor in
search of employment. He was surprised at the calm of the
streets and the heavy happiness that he saw upon the faces
of those he met. Filled with a passionate and gentle love, a
sickly love that was pregnant with the memory of death, he
was struck, after so many nightmares, as if by a miracle: Paris,
since August 23, had been liberated.

So he ran off to declare himself at the police station,
informing them of his rank, his long travails, his educational
background, his ceaseless miseries: Notified immediately, his
wife came from Strasbourg to meet him the next day. Two of
his children were dead. His mother-in-law had died too.

In the same bistro, where he was already installed as
dishwasher and hero, he embraced Suzanne at last, kneel-
ing before her, as she caressed the back of his neck with
her fine, soft fingers, murmuring words to him that were as
life-restoring as the fresh waters of an oasis: and it was here
that the son of Tambira learned the vanity of all things—of
the ruin of his house, which along with many of the town's

neighborhoods, had been bombed to rubble by the occupier: Saif, the Other, the evil White, the Hun.

Born in the colonies overseas, he was not himself French: as the translator Karim Ba had unceremoniously scrawled on his passport back in Tillaberi-Bentia. Even now, Raymond-Spartacus Kassoumi remained a *French subject...*

Orphaned by this world that had turned him into the formula of a man that was incompatible with normal conceptions of what it means to be human, the husband of Suzanne felt like a leprous witness, blindly groping, like the fanatic who joyfully murders as a gesture of self-affirmation.

This caused him to become enraged, to long to crush his unhappiness. Abandoning his measureless thirst, he blinked his eyelids for a long time upon the vision of what his life might someday be, once he was delivered from the unknown... And he knew once again the savor of Suzanne's moist lips, which he ravished with his tongue...

But, back in Nakem-Ziuko, the winds of reform and change had brought in a new current, the desire for emancipation.

Mosse had been recalled to Indochina, but his successor Renard summoned Saif ibn Issac al Heit, informing him that Paris now desired a more fitting relation with its overseas populations, allowing them to freely pursue their own interests, and leaving the indigenous to choose their own elected representatives.

Upon his return to Tillaberi-Bentia, where he convened his council of notables, Saif explained to his dignitaries that France's principle concern was to keep pace with the rapid political evolution of its colonies. What it all came down to–in practical terms– was the French's attempt to come to terms with the birth of the United Nations and to rebuild their destroyed economy. France was increasingly mired in the bloody rice-fields of Indochina, and its current legislative efforts to preserve the French Union could be summed up in the slogan, which was famous at that time: "Leave Asia, but keep Africa!"

He thus sent Prince Madoubou to the traditional chiefs of the Nakem Empire to pressure local powers, who now harvested the bitter fruits of their political scheming since 1900. Pretending to cooperate with the *Flencessi,* whose civilization they had actually scorned, they had only allowed the sons of serfs to be educated at the Christian and missionary school. Now it was these very same serfs who would be called upon to defend the notable's interests before the National Assembly at Paris, and through whom they now hoped to govern. *Amoul bop toubab makou fallé!*

Slowly, in the midst of their debates, of their silences, and arbitrary decrees, a name of a candidate would be launched, but to little avail, for the very sound of the name would get stuck in their desiccated throats–ventured by some noble whose somber calculation did not necessarily betray him, but made the others grow more alert. A notable who had been so sanguine and amiable only moments ago suddenly became alarmed. A notable whose only horizon of justice was the inviolable desert of Saif– who sat through these proceedings with rock-like immobility– was suddenly defeated, agitated, cornered, or made irrelevant; he would now propose to Saif and the other dignitaries the names of a hundred other badly whitened blacks, the sons of their house slaves, who, still beardless, could barely hold a pen in their hands. If they happened to be present, these young men who were deemed suitable by virtue of their grammar school diplomas proclaimed to all those assembled that they would gain twice as many votes as their rivals; others who boasted that they had been granted a primary school teaching certificate, that they were, as a matter of fact—miracle of miracles!–full-fledged holders of a bachelor's degree, swore that they would not return to their homes, oye!, until they were formally named as candidates.

The turbaned heads in the room nodded in approval, but each secretly harbored the same timid thought: the man of the hour was Raymond-Spartacus Kassoumi, whose university success in the land of the *Flencessi* was widely known among the people, who whispered that he was, by God, more highly educated than the most educated among the Whites: *o djangui koié!*

Was it not true that, in homage to his prodigious learning, a White woman now enjoyed the ecstatic pleasure of taking the famous architect Raymond to bed, a man to whom no Black woman could lay claim, for–*tjok!*–it was well known that Raymond could solve the problems of math and physics as easily as his mother had once shelled peanuts ...

Assuredly, this was not a man who wiped his ass with the back of his foot! Lord, a tear for the black-rabble–for pity's sake!...

From the time of the great wars in which the black *tirailleurs* had undertaken the duty of violence on behalf of France, many of Saif's councilors had learned to appreciate how the drooling Shrobenuisologic literature, with its mixed hucksterism of racial ideology and mercantile opportunism, celebrating the splendors of Black civilization, had created a religion of the "Good Black Child," an irresponsible and philistine negrophilia that offered no critique of the popular Messianisms, and that catered to the banana-mania of the white soul, with its fixation on the black-rabble.

For Raymond-Spartacus Kassoumi to make a choice under such conditions was to both exalt the people's narcissism as they gazed into the watering trough of their prodigious destinies and to flatter the Whites who now squawked about how they had civilized the underdeveloped: *Wahoom! gollè wari!*

There followed six months of courtesies, scraping and bowing, palavering and correspondences, during which many griots– narrating the political evolution of Gentle Nakem-Zuiko–sung that al Hajj Hassan, after having once plotted against Saif with the help of the Bishop Thomas de Saignac, was now determined in his jealousy to discredit not only Saif, but the most highly educated man in the land, Raymond.

Saif therefore launched a vast campaign that led, two days before the arrival of Raymond at Nakem, to the outbreak of civil war at Tillaberi-Bentia, which was quickly repressed by France and Saif.

Imprisoned for undermining the security of the colony, al Hajj Hassan, it was said, finally smashed his own skull against the walls of his prison cell, unable to bear the shame of his public humiliation. In tears, his domestic servants confessed what had really happened to their bishop Henry, whispering that Saif, with the help of Kratonga, had bought off the prison guard–David Bouremi, the adopted son of Saif–and the warden of the prison, both of whom had disguised his assassination as a suicide...

Poisoned by this death and by the outbreak of tribal warfare, local separatism was nonetheless forgotten the next day when Raymond the architect was officially welcomed at the newly constructed airport, accompanied by his wife Suzanne, who held their son Pierre by the hand. He was met by the governor and his high functionaries, Saif, the former dissidents who had been paid off by Madoubou and won to Saif's camp, the impassive notables, and the ever delirious people.

How happy was the son of Tambira to see on the eve of the elections how he was celebrated by all! Young and old, clerks and dignitaries, spoke to him respectfully with true affection in their eyes, offering gifts of two sheep, three cows, twenty chickens, and more than thirty robes for his wife and son; for himself, they gave him Turkish slippers with red leather, finely embroidered with gold and silver stitching.

The same morning, Renard made a speech in his honor; Raymond echoed the words that he had heard spoken, and then Saif responded in his turn; the people kneeled down, and the army, in the midst of this fanfare, flanked by dozens of rolling tanks, shot off a series of rifles in honor of his victory—in an election where he was the only candidate...

Held up, promenaded, adulated at Tllaberi-Bentia, at Krebbi-Katsena, where the governor lodged him in his own palace, he quietly savored his revenge when French and indigenous personalities alike came to pay him their respects and offer him assurances of their loyalty throughout the afternoon.

For Saif ibn Issac al Heit, the work of subjugating the educated black-rabble was complete. But the master of Tillaberi-Bentia knew that it was easier to subjugate a people than to keep them subjugated. He therefore summoned that same night a delegation of sages, elders, and marabouts, whom he met at the cemetery to mourn for al Hajj Hassan, gratifying the family of Raymond's murdered rival with a royal gift of a thousand cattle.

Kassoumi, who was a shrewd calculator, had nonetheless failed in his calculations: armed with his degrees and the support of France, he had imagined that he was the master of the ancient master, only to find that the torch of Saif, after flickering for a brief instant, burned brighter than ever. He realized that he had won the election only because Saif had fixed it in advance. *Yérété! aou yo yédè?*

Often, it is true, the human heart rages when it sees its native land floundering in desperation, searching blindly for its own identity. On the night of July 17, 1947, the dawn of the elections and also the seven-hundred and forty-fifth anniversary of the founding of the Nakem Empire, Kassoumi thought with melancholy of the legend of the Saifs, a legend in which the future seemed to look for itself in the night of the past: prehistory in frockcoat–the true image of the African.

Not that Raymond, at this splendid turning point of African civilization, incarnated a mere ideological position. But he knew that his entire existence would henceforth be transformed, in spite of his defiance of Saif, into an antithetical posture: the scandal of his success that would henceforth accompany him remained "unclassifiable."

But the nobility here–like the bourgeoisie elsewhere–was ready to recuperate all his rebuttals–drawing them up, labeling them, wrapping them up, playing down the scandalous. The political man that the son of Tambira wanted to be in the Nakem, a land that had assassinated his entire family, remained in the eyes of traditional society a kind of con-artist, a free agent, for he was himself an enigmatic figure, a living contradiction.

Certainly, Raymond-Spartacus Kassoumi found in his alienation a pathway to revolt: it was actually his duty for him–for all Africans—to be revolutionary. But how?...

While he chaffed in impotent bitterness, Suzanne was dazzled by everything that had happened, deeply flattered at

the high destiny that awaited them; and the architect realized in horror that, by the mere fact of his presence, or by the
mere fact of his death, he would ceaselessly bestow honors
upon Saif, who stood the most to gain by all his efforts.

Far from such thoughts, Suzanne's eyes gleamed with all
the greed of a venal woman; her husband detested her for
loving him in this way, adoring in him the figure of a puppet-
bureaucrat: he approached her, enflamed with mute anger.

The mouth of Suzanne. The lips of the woman are curved
and surrounded by honey colored flesh. Her tongue is moist
and pink, a beacon in the gaping abyss of her mouth. He
bites it, sucking on its tip, savoring its flavor. He unfastens
his pants and forces the cavern of her mouth upon the apple-
shaped head of his penis. Suzanne feebly resists. She tries
to lift herself, but he falls between her breasts with his erect
member. Immobile, passive, but without releasing the neck
of the White woman whom he grips with his two hands, he
empties himself of his hatred upon the woman, whose hair
falls down along her eyebrows, as she works on him with open
mouth, sliding off his pants with trembling hands. A ball of
brown flesh slaps against her tongue like a fabulous fist. She
works her way down to the somber velvet of two swollen
protrusions perched beneath his brown shaft. Her clitoris is
as hard as the pit of a date, polished and smooth. She lifts her
thighs, pressing the cudgel of her vulva against him now. The
man tastes it, harvesting its rich bounty, lapping it up, glean-
ing its wet delights. His long brown legs held upright, toes
curled in pleasure, are the only tokens of satisfaction that are
given by the serf's son.

The woman, arching her chest, returns to bestow more of
her sticky juices upon him, taking him off guard, until she is
finally out of breath and collapses—in defeat—to the floor.

With a serene heart, Raymond visited Henry, who was
making preparations to travel to Tillaberi-Bentia–to see
Saif.

"I'm going to be late," began the bishop, "and Saif is a
man of protocol... Would you prefer that I come to your
house tomorrow morning?"

"That would be fine," murmured Kassoumi.

There was a new intonation in his voice, a sort of weariness and detachment that caused the bishop to prick up his ears:

"What's the matter, my friend?" he asked, regarding him with a perplexed air.

"Oh! It is nothing."

Henry detained him:

"Sit down. Will you take something to drink?"

"No, thank you. I prefer to walk with you."

Holding his bicycle by the handlebars, the bishop at last broke the crushing silence of the Nakem night, speaking as if he knew the reason for the strange mood of his former pupil.

"The Chinese have a game: 'the tie that binds.' They capture two birds, which they bind together. Not too closely, thanks to a thin but solid, long line. The line is so long that the birds, once they are thrown up in the air, fly away, soaring up towards the sky. Believing themselves free, they revel in of the beatings of their wings, making great turns, but suddenly: crack! They are snapped backwards by the line. They fly crazily in all directions, turning and twisting about, blood dripping from their fluttering wings that trickles down, along with feathers and bird down, upon those who have come to watch the spectacle. The Chinese find this funny, highly comical and refined. They shake with laughter! Sometimes, the string gets wrapped up in some tree branch or around the birds themselves, and they struggle against one another, pecking out each other's eyes, beaks, and claws; or, when Providence doesn't impale them on the branches, having reached the end of the game, one of them dies. Alone. Or with the other. Sometimes they both die. Together. Strangled. Eyes pecked out.

"The human race is a bird of this type. We are all victims of this game; separated from one another, but forcibly bound. All, without exception."

"But, but…" stammered Raymond.

"Yes?"

"You… Why did you tell me this story?"

'Because I know how Saif assassinates his enemies with vipers. And this is a matter that concerns you. Let's walk further, shall we?

"As you're certainly aware, Saif is surrounded by sorcerers and seasoned botanists, who study, preferably in the dry season, the natural landscapes where one may find many useful herbs and ivy, as well as the hidden nests where quails and partridges lay their eggs. The snakes that live in the grass are never far from such places. 'So what?' you may ask. But it's quite simple: the snakes take their nourishment from these eggs.

"This is how the sorcerer discovers the dens of the grass-snakes. Climbing up towards the more rocky places, he can, if he is patient, discover the hiding place of an asp. The only thing that remains to be done is to smoke it out and then tie up the scrip to keep it from getting away. The rest is a matter of nerves. You soon go back to the scrip, re-tying it so that the tail sticks out. This is a matter of simple prudence. This is how you avoid getting bit as it twists and turns inside the scrip, after you open it. The next step is to procure some *dabali*.

"Take note that this is the same *dabali* that the Zobos of Yame use for fishing. They sprinkle the water with *dabali*, both upstream and down stream, along an isolated crook of the river. When it gets warm and the waters are still, the drugged fish begin to float to the top, and then you only need to lower your nets to bring them in by the hundreds. You wash them off, and they're perfectly harmless, ready to eat. But let's come back to our vipers.

"You put *dabali* in the scrip, which is partially filled with water, to put the viper to sleep, and before long you can pull it out. The snake is now asleep.

"You measure its length and circumference. The criminal who does all this now brings out a bamboo rod, putting the viper into the cylinder trunk, leaving a few centimeters of empty space. Then he closes up the end with a round piece of wood. The other end is stuffed with an item of the future victim's personal clothing, stolen at an earlier time.

"Reflect for a moment, my friend, upon all the early crimes that were committed against the administration, after 1902 but before the death of Chevalier. It's true that you could not have known about these things, they all happened so long ago. But that's not what's important. What's important is that the vipers have always done what they were trained to do.

"The criminals who do this inevitably seek out the most filthy laundry of the victim that they can find, something that is saturated with the odors of the person to be assassinated. When the viper wakes up and wants to escape, they immediately bring out the dirty laundry of the future victim, bottling up the opening. Then they slide a needle into a small hole that is cut into the cylinder of wood. When the viper tries to crawl towards the exit, it is jabbed in the tail. The asp writhes about, thumps its tail, hisses, bites into the clothing. This operation is repeated until the snake is conditioned by reflex to bite into the clothing. The viper ends by being able to identify the specific odor of the clothing.

"You follow what I'm saying? There comes a moment when it is no longer necessary to jab the viper; the odor alone makes it bite into the clothing, the *clothing with its prescribed odor that it recognizes*.

"Now they steal a second item of clothing that belongs to the future victim. I am not mad, I assure you. The blacksmith Jean Barou explained all this to me before he killed Doumbouya and then was killed himself in turn. After the murder of Hassan, I myself have lost two items of…"

"Hassan was murdered?"

"That's right. And because I knew it, I myself was nearly killed. You know very well by who. But let's not talk about me.

"As I was saying, they seek out a second item of clothing from the same victim. At nightfall, he drags it along the ground towards the bed of the 'nuisance' who is marked for assassination. They move back, opening the scrip, and the serpent crawls out, slithering towards the bed. It bites the victim and then disappears. Where? In the direction that was already marked out for it: guided by the scent of the victim's clothes, it returns to its original point of departure, where it is tied inside the scrip. This is the form of assassination that has been practiced against the administration and the missionaries, and so now I'm telling you about it. They make sure the serpent crawls some place where it is certain to be discovered, some where obvious enough that a fellow con-spirator, who is paid off by the killer, cries out, 'It's a snake! A snake!' The rest is pure comedy. The reptile is killed in the presence of the petrified on-lookers, who deplore the negli-gence of the victim…

"So you see, my poor Raymond, you have no choice. You didn't have any choice from the first day when you sat down upon the riverbank of the school.

"I've told you all this so you can take the proper precau-tions in all your dealings with Saif, for tomorrow you are certain to be elected. Don't forget that after forty-five years of patient efforts, I've not succeeded in accumulating a single scrap of evidence against him. That's another story. It'd take too long to tell it tonight, and I must go now to Tillaberi-Bentia.

"To the house of Saif?"

"Yes."

"But that's suicide," protested Raymond.

"I'm going to the house of Machiavelli. Or Judas. Don't forget: tomorrow you will be elected. Tomorrow is your day, my child. Good night."

IV

DAWN

"Yesterday, I went out for a walk," Bishop Henry began after a moment. "Five minutes. To see the movies, a film, *Zamba*, that was inspired by the history of Nakem-Ziuko. I go into the theater. The movie has already started. I sit down right in the middle of a scene with a lot of killing. There's an explosion of gunfire on the screen. No. They haven't killed him, after all. He's the film's hero.

"I don't understand. I'm trying to figure out what's going on in the film. While I can see that the story involves an intrigue of some sort, there's also a lot of butchery. Off in the distance, someone is pulling all the strings. When he pulls too hard, everyone can smell the true villain of the melodrama, and a howl can be heard from the audience. I look up at the screen: nothing is left to chance—anything that keeps the secret political war going is pressed into service. But for all parties involved, the driving force is the will to experiment, not so much to express a bloody vision of the world as to establish an immanent relation between the world and life itself. In this sense, what really matters is that violence itself, the vibrant and unconditional submission to the will to power, becomes a prophetic illumination, a means to interrogate and respond, an on-going dialogue, a tension, an oscillation that, from murder to murder, creates further possibilities of response, fulfillment, and contradiction—but also further uncertainties and conflicts between the denial of decadence and the nostalgia for a privileged experience, a situation in which our anxiety over our ambiguous morality provides us with a glimpse of false happiness: The golden age is always a day away, when all the filthy bastards will finally die off. The furor is a part of us all. It can be seen in the glimmer of light that escapes from a keyhole, heard just within earshot, the killing that is without respite. Then it disappears, once again. Frenzy vibrates in the images that appear, preserving our nostalgia for the days of splendor, and for secrecy. The one who was hidden away was a cornered God, a free-agent who, with every explosion, was pounded into nothingness, inhabiting a world of his own choosing, peopled with reprobates of his own choosing, as well as the pure of heart. Then, suddenly, wham! Liberty is restored against a backdrop of adventure and legend…"

"When you lose your cold-bloodedness, you become vulnerable," Saif said ironically. He suspected the bishop of disguising the true meaning of these words. "It's not necessary to imagine," he continued, laughing softly, "that the sun will never rise again. We stumble in the midst of disaster, that's true; but we fall down and are humbled. We gargle poison from the bloody chalice of violence, from the chipped glass of our own heroic deeds; we are sick, degraded; but, let's face it, the world is strange. "It overflows with the strangest sentiments that are churned out by God amid the chaos of His blessings! I am tempted to render a verdict on Him, as you can see, a verdict that Satan himself might wager was proclaimed by a kindred spirit."

Then, with a high-pitched voice:

"You see, old friend, there's a tale that we like to tell in Nakem: 'On the subject of men and their folly, Destiny once remarked, *"I should forgive them all, for humanity is so young!"* And so, he waited. And he still waits, as patiently as a monument.' Now, I find this tale to be provocative… And suddenly unpredictable! It upsets the established rules of the game: 'What is it that breaks down?' All our human machinery is ready to explode, and explode it does! But Destiny always stands ready to offer its fatal pardon, a pardon that is officially signed — ratified and signed with a formal date and place, before it is affixed with a seal. The document inside is what is called a stay-of-execution; when it expires, humanity begins anew, in malice; and Destiny assists this re-birth with its untiring pardon. And how could it not offer its pardon, not without succumbing to Boredom, the empty awareness of a time without content? The boring innocence of one who has himself never sinned! And we are all sinners. Thus God pardons us because He is constrained — or, perhaps, He does so out of love."

"Constraint, for the metal of a good soul, is like the blow that is struck against flint rock: the spark that glows is called Love."

"Who cares about a love that is merely a spark?"

"Man."

"Hold on a minute, my dear bishop. Now why is that?"

"Because life, as soon as one lives it, becomes faith in the love of life… Life is presented to us as if it were a plethora of man's interests, and then we're told that, if we hope to understand life, we must learn to walk in the shoes of the other. Fair enough. But I do not understand a life of love that is not also a priestly life, and I cannot understand any priest who does not want to be an apostle."

"And your point is…"

"My point is that I dreamed about Nakem and its entire history. I prayed for it."

"And what did you learn?"

"That we may know God but we will never understand Him."

"Is that so important?"

"Men kill each other because they don't know how to keep a conversation going."

"But they only love each other because, after they go their separate ways, each realizes that he has spoken only about himself. Haven't you ever failed to connect with those you love?"

"Yes, for too long. By trying to force them, rather than letting them be who they are…"

"You mean the people of Nakem."

"I wanted to be alone, pure."

"But solitude goes hand in hand with a feeling of guilt, of complicity…"

"Excuse me," retorted the bishop, "of solidarity."

"Man is in history and history is in politics. We are torn apart by politics. There is no place for solidarity or purity in politics."

"What matters is to despair of purity and to believe that it's right to despair of it. That's the essence of love. Politics does not know the goal, so the politicians forge a pretext. It is because they are clumsy forgers that so many regimes collapse."

"But these botched jobs are necessary, since so little in politics is honestly expressed, or since there is so little honesty in politics to begin with."

The bishop laughed heartily:

"That's true enough," he conceded, "though I detect a tone of sarcasm in your voice… You see (he now set his elbows on the table, crossed his fingers, and stared at his interlocutor with an indulgent and complicit smile), that's why I've been able to understand the Nakem and its history," he began again, smiling gently at Saif, who was put off, vaguely ill at ease. Then casually shrugging his shoulders, Henry asked, "Do you have a chessboard in your house?"

Saif hesitated for a moment, looking at him in puzzlement. He was obviously disappointed.

"I thought that you understood me," he said. "I was convinced of it."

Henry's gaze was firm and penetrating. Their eyes met, and Saif felt anew a feeling of terror and vague complicity.

"In any event, that doesn't matter so much, does it?"

"Absolutely."

"How long have you had this conviction?"

The bishop reflected:

"I believe," he said, "that I was born with it. To know, as you and I know, that we cling to the impossible, and that this is probably a form of love, or folly. Without this, we would quickly lose our bearing on reality."

"Yes…"

There was a moment of silence. Saif stroked his lips to hide his smile, and then he arose to get his chessboard. He brought it back along with a bamboo flute that he sat on the floor. As if trying to justify himself, he remarked, "I warn you. I don't know how to play."

"You've got that right."

"What do you mean?"

"It's simple, you see. You just play the game. You play it without being played upon. But you must constantly keep your eye on the moves of your opponent," Henry insisted, smiling conspiratorially at Saif. "You must figure him out. You must want to know how to figure him out. So you say to yourself, in both a literal and figurative sense, *I want to play the game in such a way that they don't see me playing*, entering into it without drawing attention to yourself, encouraging your opponent to imagine that you agree with him, misleading him without letting on or forcing it, nor of deviating from the rules of the game, untangling its knots, but cautiously, never laying a finger upon it until you've first figured out how it works. Without being cautious, my dear friend, can you succeed in killing your opponent... in the game?"

Saif understood. He knew that Henry knew. But the bishop remained imperturbable:

"The strong player is the one who manages to hold his ground but without tipping his hand." And, lifting his eyebrows as if surprised, he politely remarked, "That's the nature of diplomacy: *to replace force by ruse...*"

Veiling himself in all the splendor of his high position, Saif remarked: "You know, my friend, one never really solves a problem of civilization; instead one dedicates oneself to it—and, from the beginning, carefully studies it. The law of justice and love is the only profound bond that can unite men from above, despite our irreducible differences. Here on earth, amid the strange fauna of human passions, men thirst for power and glory. But this is the true source of our wealth, as well as the reason for our bond. It's how we complement one another."

The flute softly rolled towards Henry, who could tell from the look on Saif's face that, at this very instant, as they listened to the quiet hissing that came from the flute, his life, as well as Saif's, was at stake. However, both of them pretended that nothing was amiss, their eyes locking in a moment of inexpressible strangeness.

"In any case, you know I don't know how ruse works," laughed Saif.

"You are wrong," admitted Henry, smiling. "Man... umm... is a political animal, is he not? Ruse is the truth of force and right, the art of dialoguing with life."

"Man is evil," Saif said softly.

Both of them burst into laughter.

"You are wrong to reject ruse," repeated the bishop.

The eyes of the old man were clear, lit up by a peaceful expression. On his lips, there was a detached smile. Saif, in trusting the look on his face, felt that this was a man who knew how to keep secrets—that they were the only true conspirators in Nakem-Ziuko. Both of them had confronted the ultimate lie or the ultimate truth of existence.

"Ruse?" Saif repeated with circumspection, nearly with fear, as if he sensed in his interlocutor's calm smile a mysterious and supernatural power. He looked at the Bishop with an expression that was at once ambiguous, affectionate, and fearful.

"In other words, freedom," responded Henry. "The idea of liberty is not a simple one. It takes many forms. Like the structure of the game. The same idea has a multitude of moments. At the moment when an idea reveals itself, it is finally inseparable from its definition. Men believe themselves free at the moment that the law is recognized and articulated. Play! I will teach you the rules. You will exist."

"*Amen.* Existence can be made to conform to the law, but it cannot be deduced from it. Play! We are responsible for the success of the stratagems we adopt."

Both of them waited to see who would begin. And the bishop, tactless but respectful:

"If you do not decide, it's because you do not want to know what you secretly desire, and because you refuse to take responsibility for what you are."

(The flute pitched about on the floor, rolling between them.) "It's necessary to know the art of intelligently making mistakes and then covering one's tracks," Henry said.

"And why is that?" smiled Saif; there was a trace of self-complacency in the harmonious curve of his lips.

"But look, the squares, the line of pawns that are decked out like foot-soldiers of the Nakem night, the two bishops, not unlike Chevalier and Vandame, the two knights, Kratonga and Wampouolo, the two rooks, Kassoumi and Bouremi. Now look again! It's the queen! She's the most powerful piece of all; she can move in every direction, while the others can only move in one direction. And all of this, all this activity, happens solely to save the head of the king–your conscience–the piece that remains stationary. You see? All this ... is to defend the king. You confront life in a brotherly confrontation of all your forces, and you play, you calculate, play some more, adapt, make mistakes, yes, no, careful, no movement is without meaning, so you calculate....

"Devil or God: — you restore the equilibrium of your own boat. And you learn to see. You look beyond the limitations of your own life."

Saif's eyes shot off sparks. The flute rolled away from Henry towards Saif and then back to Henry, who joked: "Should I be afraid?"

"Afraid? Of who? Of what? You? Me? Us? *That*? I tell you now... you have nothing to fear!"

"Unless?" the bishop said, rising to the challenge.

"Unless you are forced to curse yourself for underestimating your own strength. And, of course, your own importance! Play! Each piece is a functional object that is played by the player but also a thing in its own right. You must try to draw the other player into a trap."

"And if he refuses?

"Refuses what?"

"To play the game."

"He doesn't; he will not refuse. He is a fellow player. He must be trapped in an act of aggression, suspended, as each tension gives rise to another, as each player evades the snare of his opponent."

"And if none of it makes any sense, if it's all absurd?"

"Something that's absurd isn't necessarily senseless. Nature doesn't make sense, but it's not absurd. It is. The absurd comes from things that ceaselessly perpetuate themselves and self-destruct at the same time. It is this notion of absurdity that becomes clear in the face of the unjustifiable." The bishop was both flattered and embarrassed by this homage to his ingenuity. "The flute is dancing. It rolls towards me. Go ahead and kill, Saif!" he ordered, revealing that he knew the flute hid a viper.

A sudden tremor broke out over Saif's face. The bishop felt the shock that had been set in motion within the breast of the other. It was followed by a series of nearly rhythmic trembles. It wasn't fear that he saw, Henry was sure, nor was it remorse, but exhilaration over what might happen next. Saif thoughtfully rubbed his jaw:

"I have no right," he said, after a moment, fixing his anguished, gray eyes upon the bishop.

HENRY: "You mean you don't have the power," he gently replied.

SAIF: "No. I have no right," he insisted.

HENRY: "Right without force is caricature. Force without right is misery. Swear it!"

SAIF: "There's nothing to swear. The triumph of right is the triumph of might. As for... your game..."

HENRY: "The game."

SAIF: "... The game and all that, it's too exhausting." (*Then after a moment, as if illuminated by grace.*) "The opponent," he acknowledged, "is so constituted that one imagines him to be the embodiment of evil. This is inescapable."

HENRY: "From the moment we come into the world, we are caught in the game. You can't avoid getting drawn into it. So, go ahead and kill me!" insisted the bishop.

(*Saif looked at the flute as if it had magically materialized between his hands.*)

SAIF: "You want me to kill you?" he asked Henry with a stupefied air.

HENRY: "Why shouldn't you?" (*And without saying another word, Saif suddenly, before the amused smile of the bishop, picked up the flute and tossed it in the fire. Then he returned and sat down across from*

Henry.)

SAIF: "You see... there are too many constraints upon us."

HENRY: "It's a game, " he said, forcing a smile. Then he added in a different voice, "It's game that has its rules."

SAIF: "That's because there's no choice."

HENRY: "Oh yes there is! You are free because you don't have any choice."

(*The two men looked into one another's eyes, smiling, and, for the first time, they agreed to speak the same language.*)

SAIF: "Symbols never die," he said, as the viper crackled in the fire nearby. "Generations in the Nakem have come and gone, and it has only been in the last fifteen minutes that anyone has known how to discuss its health."

HENRY: "But the king will not die."

SAIF: "Play! The queen."

HENRY: "As for love, in any case ... The knight."

SAIF: "But there is always one who loves and another who turns the other cheek. The pawn."

HENRY: "Well, you have to know how to forgive. Play! The king."

SAIF: "The impossible thing about forgiveness is that, once you forgive someone, you have to go on forgiving them, day after day. Play! The queen."

HENRY: "Life is like that. Play! Happy are the peacemakers, for they shall see God. And praise Him!"

SAIF: "Play! Happy are the politicians for they understand life. And Eternity."

HENRY: "Play! And the troubadors of Nakem sing the history of Judaism. The king."

SAIF: "And praised be. Play! Saif Moché Gabbai de Honaine. The queen."

HENRY: "The Eternal. Play! Saif Issac al Heit."

SAIF: "*Amen.* Play! Saif al Hilal."

HENRY: "The Nakem of the Empires is inscribed in our souls! Play! Saif al Haram. The king."

SAIF: "Glory be. Play! Saif Ali. The queen."

HENRY: "The Eternal. Play! Saif Youssoufi. The bishop."

SAIF: "*Yallah Al'allah!* Play! Saif Medioni of Mostaganem. The bishop."

HENRY: "So be it. Play! Saif Ezechiel. The pawn."

SAIF: "Glory be. Play! Saif Ismael. The knight."

HENRY: "The Eternal. Play! Saif Benguigui of Saida."

SAIF: "*Amen.* Play! Saif Rabban Yohanan ben Zaccai."

HENRY: "So be it. Play! Saif Tsevi. The king."

SAIF: "*Maschallah! Wa bismillah!* Play! Saif ibn Issac al Heit. The queen."

Often, it happens, the soul dreams that it can hear an echo of happiness from days long ago. But, once cast into the world, one cannot fail to grasp that Saif, mourned three millions times, is ceaselessly reborn to History, under the warm cinders of more than thirty African Republics...

That night, they probed one another's thoughts until the balcony became engulfed in the blackest moment of dawn, and a thin sheen of dust settled over the chessboard; but, at that very instant, as the eyes of Nakem sought refuge in the memories of days past, the bush and coast alike were fertile and aflame with pity. For men and the world that they inhabit, wind, water, and fire are indispensable: all else is but a game...

Translated by Christopher Wise

Note

1. War [author's note].

A BLACK
GHOSTWRITER'S
LETTER TO FRANCE

BY
YAMBO
OUOLOGUEM

OPEN LETTER TO ALL VICTIMS OF ANTI-RACISM

Dear Truly Caring Consciences,

Allow a Negro[1] to dare utter what your social conventions forbid you to articulate...

I say *dare* because we are all aware of the sensitivity of some individuals and authorities whenever one ventures to speak on the subject of black people. And if the racist himself denies the fact that he is racist, so too does the non-racist who is hypersensitive whenever he broaches the well-publicized *Black Issue*...

...Both being the victims of official anti-racism, they are subjected to the anger of Negroes, forced to "respect" the dignity of those merchants of anguish, those champions of misery. So, any attempt to foster dialogue is doomed in advance to failure because of a philistine negrophilia that is obliged to no one or nothing—a right leftism.

Of course, it may seem strange to some that a Negro would censor his fellow Negroes, just as it would be incomprehensible for a Jew to denounce Jewishness... But that is not my concern.

It is my contention that Negroes have lived up till now like slaves, since they have always defined themselves (not in relation to themselves) but first and foremost in relation to Whites. Hence, mimicry and reverse racism, conspiracy theories whispered on the silk of black skin... As a matter of fact, France finally has become an alibi for Blacks. This alibi prevents us from thinking about the real problems of both Africa and France.

While Biafra is currently a great concern for us all, we tend to forget what has been going on in Vietnam for more than twenty years now, a Biafra for Yellow people...

In point of fact, this means that there is no Black Issue, only human issues, to which the black man brings a certain color.

The day Negroes will agree to hear unpleasant truths will mark their awakening to the world around them.

...For, the Negro France of General de Gaulle is entering a political era. But there are more Negroes in France than there are Blacks in Africa or in the Americas: the slave-laborers, the hoard of people haunted by the S.M.I.G.,[2] anonymous inhabitants of this French desert, which is also a miniature Africa.

Of course, none of this is news to anyone.

"We wish we could say what you've dared to say in your book," some French observers have remarked to me, "only we would then be labeled as racists."

I have therefore taken it upon myself to speak out. At what risk, I wonder? Has a Negro ever before turned red with anger? ...

Hence, don't expect to find any concessions in this *Black Ghostwriter's Letter to France.* I have deliberately opted for the satiric genre of the pamphlet. I hope that it will be ferocious enough that it will put an end to the comedy of the whimpering Negro, who is nonetheless untouchable—and that it will also cause both Blacks and Whites to at last stop wallowing in bad conscience, especially those who are audacious enough to love one another, but who endlessly complain of not knowing how to express it.

I know that France is neither the America of Black Power, nor South Africa under Apartheid. But France has been inhabited by Africa, and Africa haunted by France.

Therefore...

LETTER TO THE PRESIDENT OF THE FRENCH REPUBLIC

To the left, to the right! My dear General,

Before I abandoned my own prehistory to flee to your country, every night, from sunset to sunrise, the troubadours in Africa would sing to me your praises, telling me how privileged I was to be allowed to sit upon your knees, and to suck on a gaullipop, which you lavishly bestowed upon me.

Then my head became like a world map and I ran off to school, blessing you in my serene intellectuality. Abandoning my boubou for your manner of dress, I no longer looked like a lit-up Christmas tree.

At school, I learned that France belonged to Negroes like me, who were welcomed there with open arms. (Plus, they were allowed to marry French women.) Thus I came to be highly regarded in my village, thanks to this demagogy, which instilled in me the hope that I could someday shed my own black soul. Indeed, I came to believe that my education would not only purify me, it would also confer complete immunity upon me.

That wicked and wet little girl who is inside of me—but where exactly? My tongue?—loyally embraced your regal bearing and tall stature, all the while blaming colonialism on the people you sent here. In a perverted game of instinct, I nurtured in myself a faith as fragile as a wisp of straw.

Is that called alienation?

The more I recall (along with the President of my own local Republic) having been powerless, the more I feel like asking for the impossible from you and for squandering your money. The more disappointed I feel at having been singled out, the more the malicious world pushes me to my own ruin... That must end, my General, because I don't want you to lend yourself to the fantasies of the obsessed, the coprophiles, the sadists...

Not long ago, many of my fellows, uprooted and oppressed by the honorable occupation that was the means of their séduction, succumbed to the temptations of seducers of all kinds.

These seducers have created thousands of *l'Afric*[3] problems, which they would solve, from time to time only to give themselves greater confidence. Later, they would create new and more ingenious problems that left my fellows at their mercy. The claptrap about civilization was merely a distraction. Cooperation, assistance to underdeveloped countries, and the billions that vanish into Swiss bank accounts—I don't need yet more examples to know whether or not I want to cash in on your paternity...

The sensual pleasure of depriving you, even if I am threatened with hunger, Biafra and countless possible Congos, helps me to overcome the shame I feel for once having allowed you to caress me. Beware, my General! Beware of Africa and Latin America! Beware of your marriage to the Third World! In all monogamous civilizations, the great hetaera has always enjoyed the privileged role of vengefully precipitating the ruin of her man...

If France is turning black by virtue of all the Africans that you have now baptized, Africa is a woman who loathes the idea of being bought off by her own husband, and who finds herself saddled with a man before whom she feels frigid and unsatisfied. She likes her lovers (the Russians, the Chinese, and the Americans, to mention only the most powerful ones) because her pleasures are nothing short of infantile and brutal, and she is only satisfied with the sexually perverse: She is a woman who is open to the highest bidder.

Marriage being a sort of legalized tolerance—an indispensable concession to the flesh—results from that curious state of mind wherein any violation of indissoluble monogamy is condemned as a crime. And if, because of you, Africa is now the woman who will bring about the ruin of France (and this, dating from the era of 'our ancestors the Gauls'), it suffices here to recall that the French are Republicans, and that the Church wants to banish all forms of prejudice, to grasp that it won't be long before the banks too will be compelled to open their coffers and let the cash flow in a southwards directions…

౿ళ౿

The Church never ceased condemning infidelity in marriage and, not content with violating the male's polygamous instinct, it had the effrontery to seek to delimit his pleasure in matrimonial sexuality. In the hidden chambers of the Church of the Cooperation, France remains African and Africa remains French. This is so, no doubt, since human animals share with primates the instinctive albeit irrational urge to make love.

You have created in Negro France and in French Africa a distinguished patriarchy, built upon the discrete principle of familial slavery, my General. But, you may rest assured that not all those who belong to this patriarchy share identical sentiments regarding its virtues.

Haunted by the illusory and ephemeral nature of this possession they are offered, there are some who turn away from it in disgust since they cannot find in it, from the time of the Negro's "independence," the sentimental gratification that comes from asserting one's own power.

But the majority of them, enjoying above all the power that their financial resources give them over the black-rabble, who are prostituted in all civilizations, find in the latter a powerful and erotic pleasure, one that is absolutely impossible to find in their homes. Paris and the French desert are validated by the commitment to provide assistance to hunger-stricken countries, where dramas that differ very little from what is now happening in Biafra are silently played out…

In fact, all men have one of two psychological reactions to the Negro France you have created: on the one hand, he may respond like a humble little White man who secretly feels in his heart of hearts that he too is a poor little Negro, and so discovers in himself the tender longing to tend to the ills of all the oppressed peoples of the earth; on the other hand, he may respond as a fast-talking imperialist, who finds in this situation opportunities for personal gain. In this case, he takes advantage of what is now happening to further enslave and dominate others, but in his own sadistic manner, making a killing as a professional weeper.

Sometimes, both of these possible reactions will be brought together in the same man: indiscriminately. Often the word contempt will be prominent in his vocabulary, and noticeable from behind his eyeglasses —there where the true battle between the races plays itself out. If part of him longs to be a suffering servant, the other part does not hesitate to rape and pillage...

Dear Charlilitch Gaulléline! Beware! In your own country, spectacle is giving way to testimony. And it is even possible that, if everything falls apart here, you will be obliged in coming centuries–for I know you are immortal: symbols never die–to imitate your colleagues in Great Britain, where the devil himself would have a hard time immigrating.

But your black grandsons take refuge under your roof to learn a few things, to earn just enough cash to survive, and then return to their own homes where they sing your praises. So, for now, the time has not yet come for you to take on the responsibility of crushing these snakes that you see encoiling themselves in the tender heart of the Republic. For the time being, you are only vaguely aware of this succession of pathetic wretches nipping at your heels. You see only a hoard of wretched beggars who keep knocking on your door, gurgling from their throats, to inform you of their endless problems and hidden riches.

I know that it is no accident that you have gray hair, which reveals your intelligence and wisdom—and that you know what you are doing. Your diplomatic policies are informed by twenty centuries of History, or, at least, this is what you've told me...

In establishing my affiliation with you by virtue of a contract that I have entered of my own free will, I can delude myself, at least in theory, about your so-called liberal nature. In fact, you have continued to foster a liberal attitude, a gauloiserie, which I was obliged to accept in order to simply exist, both in a social and even physiological sense. As a child of the General, my efforts for emancipation were limited to the moral sphere and did not, at any rate, improve my material conditions in the slightest...

In feeling that you were the more powerful between the two of us (since I, of course, recognized my own weakness), I turned myself into a crass masochist. This brought to me the satisfaction that one gets from submitting to a superior partner, or, to put it in slightly different terms, I came to believe that the partner to whom I submitted was superior to all potential suitors. In any event, they finally amount to the same thing...

This pathological masochism turned certain political leaders from my own country into France's whores: guilt and desire, the tendency to punish others in order to escape guilt... My need for expiation, because it could find no redeeming outlet in the world of human labor, became mere prostitution.

That's why, my General, you need not furrow your brows whenever you hear the braying of your lost sheep in far-away colonies, their railing at your brothers...

In fact, by bestowing respect and dignity upon these black sheep, gaining independence obviated the possibility that their better nature might fully develop. In effect, no consideration was ever given to the virtues that result from hard work and the exercise of creativity. As a result, your little sheep have now lost their way, and so they busy themselves delivering inflammatory homilies against the evils of colonialism. As they chug down their Bentley whiskey, they dig themselves into deeper and deeper holes, plummeting the depths of the most sibylline ideologies, even in their own workplaces, where these moderns that you've created now vent their spleen, ranting and railing against the state... And they blame you for creating this situation!

You once read to me the fable of The Cicada and the Ant.

> *The cicada having sung,*
> *During the entire Summer,*
> *Found itself destitute*
> *At the first frost...*

Decked out in bright colors and chirping happily, how is it that the cicada, a worthless insect with any number of detestable traits, came to be so celebrated in your perversely nationalistic music, your boisterous and grating national anthem, which sounds about as pleasant as a sledge hammer on a rock, and which seduces your willful children like a television image that is aired ad nauseum? Tell me, my General, why? ...

༺༻

As for my suffering, "you live it, you're upset about it, you pale at its sight, which troubles your frantic soul... *Oh Lord, how all this pains you!*"

Beware, my General! As the firstborn of the Francophone community, which announces itself without bothering to change its form before disappearing without a trace, I am concerned above all about saving face. Accustomed to intermingling blood and roses in my politics, I have no qualms about groveling beneath the immense arcade where the prestige of French culture is in vogue, taking shelter under shady rocks where the lions roar, where hippopotamuses frolic, where ministers deliver speeches to each other, debating the value of the French franc, not far from the censers, the heavenly host, holy sacraments, holy *gauloseries*, holy liberties, *agnus dei*, as well as tales of Jesus, where the consistory members and missionaries of the Church of the Cooperation thrive... Whether they are secular or religious, they are all Gaullists to the core, who fix their eyes upon the heavens above, beyond the furthest reaches of the starry cosmos, where they finally deposit their souls before the Eternal Father, who is decked out like a translucent Pope, and, behind whom, at a respectful distance, the two members of the Holy Trinity offer their salutations, not to mention Holy Mary, Mother of God, upon whom He also bestows a sense of historical grandeur–cleverly cobbled together nonsense, and how!

… With executive precision, I drift out of your orbit, dear General, I myself who–when I am away from my Africa, which has been transformed into a miserably blackened France–feel just like a Negro Christ dangling upon the perch of a white birdcage.

…Holding white lilies in your hands, you guide my every step, as one might guide the steps of a fragile child, upon the shimmering clouds of your liberalizing efforts on behalf of the black-rabble…

My destitution and my current drama are the bodily remains of what was, perhaps–at least viewed from the outside— a religion that is built on the personage of Jesus Christ. You carefully guide me over your minefields, into the secret museum where your desk looms like a throne. And there, you show me the photographs, engravings, and landscape paintings of your various mascots, as well as planks of worm-eaten houses, lead gables, pink tiled roofs, the sea, and a small corner of the blue sky. And not far off, there is a green shadow that reflects scenes beneath sculpted clouds, tumultuous and billowy shapes that form little angels or seagulls…

"My grandson," you say to me, "this is what Africa will look like after it is fully developed."

But then, you suddenly stop speaking to me. Do you believe now that the Negroes who are supposed to complete this rosy picture are too bedraggled and unworthy for you to give them the time of day? … Do the fingers of the black women, with their nails painted in red cow's blood, seem too grimy to you, as they scratch and claw for the banknotes issued by international Cooperation….

Oh yes, my General, we understand one another very well...

We both know what France is. We understand perfectly well that it will never consent to becoming Negro! To do so will not improve its image in the slightest, and it will drive away all the tourists...

I understand very well, dear narrator of Universal History (since you yourself told me as much one night at a wake), that you were doing your utmost to become the powerful arbitrator of the world's most obscure nations. This is why you chose to base the Church in France, and not in Africa, so that the Africans who showed up on your doorstep would forever remain obsequious Negroes!

Up till now, I have been entirely mistaken ... No surprise there. A primitive mentality like mine must do what it can to preserve its reputation for being underdeveloped. Given that I'm such a slow and hopelessly stupid bastard, I had failed to grasp that France wasn't Negro because, first and foremost, the French have two servants: their money and their Negroes! But if you lose your money, beware! .... The worst that could happen is that you'll end up becoming just like those chauffeurs at the consular services of the young African Republics: You'll end up as a negro who has to serve other Negroes...

Wisdom therefore dictates that, rather than allowing your African laborers to migrate to France, they should all be repatriated along with their Ambassadors...

❧

And so, my General, if you want to avoid having Black problems in France, you should first set up a *Reflection Commission*, an anti-May 68 movement, that lends itself to "any means necessary" in order to achieve its political aims. Wasn't it the journal *France-Soir* that printed the following headlines: "Thirty Thousand Black Workers Enter France in a Two-Tiered Truck"? ...

Given the gravity of the problem, it is therefore essential for the French public not to reveal its inherent vengefulness during any ecstatic moments of trance...

And if, due to your own traditions, you are compelled to propose a referendum, you will ascend to hitherto untrammeled heights, my General. Newspapers will write of your work, "A Gaullist Triumph in France. More than a Hundred Percent of the Population Enthusiastically Unite in Affirming the President's Mandates Not To Lynch Blacks..." Now, tell me, is that what you call an official anti-racism: a right leftism?

And of course, all of this follows an already established protocol. In fact, from the time of the XIVth century, there has always been a clearly established procedure to guarantee cooperation, calm, and order. This is why the Whites agreed among themselves not to insult Uncle Tom's many fathers, and why every art object and other impressive sculptures will eventually be returned to Africa. Everything that you see happening today adheres to a clearly established pattern...

White merchants of primitive arts! — General, help me on this one–you shouldn't confuse the platitudes of Mao Tse-Tung with the Third World's raging hunger for ideology. Go ahead and sell these bits of wood to the fishermen of the Seine! They make excellent buoys, and they are already filled with worms and spiders, which also make good bait...

Merchants, go ahead and sell off, or toss into the water, these prehistoric knick-knacks, or I guarantee that they'll become cumbersome tar-babies that will turn your hands black. You too will soon smell of tar, and your nose will then fail to guide you in the struggle for life where you are both everyone and no one, just another face in the crowd...

Oh Lord, what a strange fate! ... Here, I stand, condemned in my turn to monkey tricks and apery, like the Negro kings of old! This is your civilization in all its insanity...

What did I just say? ... Fortunately, my cultural hybridity with France is not deep enough for your hideous scars to be visible on my skin...

May Heaven turn me into a cannibal forever if I am lying! It is said that you speak eloquently on television. But it is also said that you swear behind closed doors, even while you are at your prayers.

Swear, my General! Swear in the name of a Negro's head!

The grandson that you did not father!

LETTER TO MIXED COUPLES

Dear Romantic Fools,

The teeth of History have bit into the raw flesh of the imprisoned soul, my friends! And, centuries ago, in a style that is more spectacular than our own, men who were loaded down with cheap junk arrived on the shores of Negro civilization–but, in those days, the Negro didn't have a soul, only working appendages...

Thousands of exemplary bodies without souls, stolen in the African night from a neighboring tribe–through the duplicity of the black notables and their courtiers, all of whom had black souls as well–were traded for Western nick-knacks: junk jewelry, alcohol, socks, combs, and other vanity items...

And the Negroes were shipped off to the Americas as slaves, destined for a life of forced labor... Bought, traded, taught a few things, and then sold all over again, these children were not recognized by their own fathers. They were children whom the masters bred with black women, hand-picked because they were least chimpanzee-like in appearance. As a consequence, the world became peopled by a miserable assortment of half-breeds, mulattos, quadroons–the *café au lait* negroes. But, let's face it: You are a black man. Is that fair enough? You decide to marry a white woman, carefully plotting your ascendance towards a higher form of human existence: with all the fears, irreversible ruptures, and mandatory exiles that such an alienated situation necessarily entails.

So much time and labor expended, so many trials and tests lived through, made it possible for you to open your body and heart to a Gaul woman, whose ancestors—not so very long ago– were Romans... And you who have turned yourself into a Roman by virtue of your ambition to become thoroughly modern, aren't you–along with your recently wedded wife–now involved in a drama that is not unlike the kidnapping of the Sabines: sanctioned by law and the "sacred" bonds of matrimony? ...

Ha! So you married a Jewish woman... You must therefore know, having read all about the Jewish Holocaust in history books, the cost of the prayers and blood of the wretched of the earth... You surely remember that, in time of war, those in the enemy's camp wore different uniforms with different colors... Soldiers do not kill their fellow Man; it's the color of the enemy's uniform that they kill. These are, of course, matters that are not thought through; they are simply lived...

And the color of the body of your union lingers in the eyes of every passerby like a banal and ridiculous folktale...

But you know all of this very well, you who took such a modest friend for your partner, a friend who is for your heart what the oasis is for the desert... The two of you together are no longer Negro or White. There you stand, you and your wife, amid the anonymous masses who live in the margins of society: you are exiled, far from your own people, living as an invited if not particularly celebrated guest in her home–and she is happy to belong to you, just as bread belongs to the poor. The romantic happiness of reflexive inspiration, a carefree bovarysm, where a fragile sexuality folds and unfolds...

You are a couple whose love for one another is sealed with a vow, fragile children who rely upon each other; but, consider for a moment the gathering storm clouds: a thousand and one calamities are on the horizon, a laughable battle between reason and sentiment...

You are the saviors of virgin hope, wounded little birds; you are the hopeless splendor of the moon that illuminates the world, jubilant with prejudice, the hot sun that ripens men, the troubled waters where life itself flows—at the juncture of two civilizations.

You are the echo in the void of despair, the seed of a difficult future triumph, a terrible and wretched grain of dust that irritates the eyes, the syllable of censure in the human heart, and the spark from the cinders. You are the very life of bad conscience, the place where two minorities collide; that's what you are—that, and nature's fervor, its seeds, the folly of the world's order. Beware! Because you are thirstier than everyone else, you drink more deeply from the well of reason. You are the splendor of the splendid and the misery of the unconscious. You also stand for love, crazy and troubling love, spectacular and desperately beautiful love; that of the soul and body which secretly brings joy to your heavily burdened heart.

No one may ever acknowledge it, my little ones, but you have already been recognized, you whose absurd greatness resides in your soft power of refusal. A happiness built from a castle of varied and fragile stones, where the secret of secrets resides—which you know. You who dream of being delivered from evil.

It is through your love which is said to be incongruous and naturally disturbing, filled with impractical hopes that cannot possibly hold out against the wind, nor tolerate the world's foul odors, it is through you that the gift of commiseration and sin become immorality itself! Once their hearts and prejudices are cleansed of their faults, men offer you sacrifices in erratic cult rituals... Their sacrifices set before you, their bodies and souls retreat into the pious silence of unknown gods.

But the supreme mystery pleads on your behalf, the mystery of the human being. Amid so many sovereign authorities, of such imperishable and marvelous grandeur, decked out in so many colors of varying hues and bound by a thousand and one obligations, both permanent and ephemeral, a decoration now appears on the stage of your living flesh, imperceptible to the human eye, but known to you alone, like the luminous glow that emanates from the magnanimous…

Romantic fools, you are the very time that wears down the world. You flex your muscles and the spirit soars, woven from awkward symbols and perfumes that reek of the furnaces. A sun unlike any other swells within you, with no beginning, middle, or end, with an impoverished beauty: splendid exaltations surge forth, thrilling your souls, like the steady flames of a fire…

You created this couple from your own place in the universe, and you now hold on for dear life–creating from your own destiny a pedestal to build a monument of sand.

But you are love's wretched! The day when you at last begin to travel, after remaining silent for so long, will be dreadful indeed! The wave-washed shore of your life may seem placid enough, but the constant ripples swelling to the surface reveal how your life is constantly in danger of dispersing in a thousand different directions…

Memories that are already dead to you, classified now as battles that are pointless to continue fighting, become entangled together, shriveling up, and then drifting away before they finally began to sink into the ebb and flow of your perpetual resentment.

Your vacuous gaze before the mirror reveals the future possibilities of your love… Every reflection, every passion, every joy and fear and act of defiance, everything that has ushered the shadow of death into your own private universe, is relived in the silent odor that fills your nostrils, that sickens you now and makes you feel lightheaded.

You will live through every single one of these desperate moments, standing completely and utterly alone. You will know the hour of indecision, which is nonetheless terribly real, the bleak hour when the public parks and gardens know only deathly silence and the darkness of night. You will feel what it means to live in a world that is eager to destroy you and all those who are like you–all those whom it quietly deposits on some forlorn park bench, their shoulders erect but their heads slumped down, as they ruminate over the wreckage of their lives...

Never will you know what it means to be hungry for love, but you will know sorrow. You will know a sadness that no one else may claim...

Passively imitating the lifeless gaze of the malicious people whom you encounter, you will suddenly be over-whelmed by the living silence of your memories, recalling all your misfortunes. They will steal back upon you so softly, so profoundly, leaving you powerless and broken–and you will long for these unsettling thoughts to drift off and leave you in peace...

If you are sufficiently mature, you may escape this fate, provided you never leave France; that is, that you remain an exceptional and highly privileged Negro, black-rabble in permanent exile. But if you are young and inexperienced, the sun will bear down upon you, its scintillating eye piercing your innermost being from its orbit in space, and you will know solitude and mourning... To find respite, you will do everything you can to see that your love survives–while fully aware of where all of this is headed...

You will capsize, no doubt, but ordinary heroism will also help you regain your equilibrium as a couple. The couple that you are. Its ebb and flow. Without end. The words that you speak. From time to time, you will be reduced to silence... But words will come back to you during these times of silence, brief utterances that you will address to one another, words of encouragement, indifference, and disagreement. These are matters of which the heart knows not how to speak. Here, the heart is reduced to silence, as if ashamed...

And so if you, as a mixed couple, can survive all of this, a new and somber standard, like the ashes that ascend from a concealed flame, may just yet...

LETTER TO ALL THOSE WHO DON'T KNOW WHAT A NEGRO IS, OR WHO HAVE FORGOTTEN WHAT IT MEANS TO BE WHITE

Dear All Those Unfamiliar With *The New Illustrated Larousse,*

"The French man is not a racist," it has often been remarked. But without his knowing it, certain ideologies have been drilled into him, from elementary school to the university, by way of education, and then by way of media outlets, or thanks to the findings of the "experts": ethnologists, sociologists, so-called philosophers, and politicians... Each has contributed to shaping his point-of-view, guiding his actions, and dictating his speech.

Attitudes about race are often shaped in elementary schools, in middle schools, and in high schools. They can be observed every day in the streets, in fact, almost everywhere. At any given time, one may collide with this inescapable reality: Black vs. White.

A fundamental "truth" is inculcated into Whites: Negroes are cannibals, savages, sometimes nice but always ill-smelling. And, as tribal rivals, they are ceaselessly engaged in violent conflicts with one another—it goes without saying, they also offer human sacrifices, along with other atrocities. Their civilization seems so ridiculous that, whenever Negroes are spotted wearing indigenous garb on the streets of France, they leave the impression of having erupted from prehistoric times. Why, a simple frockcoat would be their salvation! Yet, they walk around in preposterous straw hats, exposing their naked legs to the world at large... A civilization of pure folk-lore, whose impoverished nature could certainly profit if they would only import certain useful items...

This is why we must do whatever we can to civilize them, to save them from hunger... The man on the street, if you press him, will tell you that he doesn't know the difference between a Negro and an unleashed penis, or a half-civilized baboon...

By way of contrast, the word "white" is bound up with the most redeeming and seductive adjectives. White is the color of innocence, purity, virginity, truth, day, and light. In musical scores, a white note is equivalent to two black notes. The word white is synonymous with *cleanliness*. Similarly, the verb "to whiten" has several different meanings, for instance, when a cook "whitens" food by throwing it into the pot to boil. To "whiten" is clearly a civilizing act...

In medical science, *to whiten* means *to mask*; in a similar vein, one speaks of medical treatments that whiten the patient.

In the process, the verb *to whiten* takes on the meaning of *to be rehabilitated*. A lawyer, for instance, may *whiten* a criminal, or one may *whiten* oneself or be *whitened*, after performing a disreputable action.

In any case, it is obvious that to be white means to be clean, pure, innocent–and the word *blanditiae*, which is less common today, is synonymous with charm, seduction, etc.

As the old proverb has it, "Whitening a Negro's head is waste of good soap." This time honored saying is echoed in similar idioms like to give someone a "carte blanche" or "that's mighty white of you..."

✌✑

Thus it is that language makes of the White the prototype of the ideal man, whereas the Negro is the exact reverse.

And yet, paradoxically, the White is sometimes described as a ... Negro in that very same language! Here and there, it turns out, one comes across pejorative references with respect to our ancestors, the Gauls.

Thus, one speaks derisively of the "white space" that remains on the page; that is to say, the *empty* spaces between words; as the saying also goes, one sometimes writes a *blank check*, one acts *ex nihilo*; which is to say, like a Negro; in other words, without carefully considering one's actions... like a tin-horn [*blancbec*]!

Better yet, the White man — yes, it's true — may unexpectedly find himself referred to as someone who is "underdeveloped": for the word *Blanc* formerly designated the lowest form of currency, a coin with almost no value. As the old saying goes, "six *blancs* are equivalent to two *sous* and a half."

Certain philologists have argued that this curious adage may shed light upon the true origins of our ancestors, the Gauls, which have hitherto remained unconfirmed. But, it's probably safe to bet that even though "six *blancs* are equivalent to two sous and a half," none of this reveals much about the history of trade among the Gauls (even if the trafficking of white women among the Gauls is an established fact), at least in the days of Vercingétorix and Astérix...

᎒᠃᠃᠃

And here's another troubling and strange fact, one that may disrupt the serenity of many a pale face: white also happens to be the color of ghosts, of *revenants*. In other words, white is the color of those phantoms that no longer belong to the material realm...

Could this be the reason why so many of the French feel the need to pass for people of color (in other words, aristocrats) by taking a sunbath, so that they can turn their flesh bronze, especially in the Winter when it is so fashionable to sport a tan?

Troubling.... troubling... to encounter such a custom in a land where whites are so highly esteemed, and where these same people, once they lose their tans, hurry off to buy stockings to hide their purple-veined legs! And the illusion is perfect! All that remains now is for someone to market ultra-white socks for Negro women who want to reverse the process.

Do the French who came to Africa under the banner of "Cooperation" ever get asked if the word white (whose meaning we have just unpacked) implies, by extension, an archaic sociopolitical order bearing the adjective "white"? For instance, in the Franco era in Spain, one formerly spoke of "the Spanish White"; or, in the Soviet Union of Stalin or Khrushchev, one spoke of "White Russians." In both instances, white meant royalist. The question remains to be asked: if France is truly a Republican nation, does this mean that it is therefore a Negro nation (rather than a white one)?

Here's another problem: What was the cause for the revolution of May 68?

The bulbous and inflammatory portion of a zit is called a "whitey" or a "whitehead": like the white head of a State. But doesn't it make more sense to speak of a zit as an "old red"–or, even, as a "red-head"? For it is beyond dispute that a zit has more red in it than white!

Here then is the solution to the problem of May 68: there was, at least for a brief instant, the threat of a red peril on the streets of Paris, which was quickly repressed, for the white head rapidly rose to the surface and restored order, without which only that which is utterly vile, threatening, and appalling — in short, all that is black–would have prevailed. This then is probably why the black flag disappeared beneath the city streets...

⇗⇖

Thus, despite all the coalminers who live here, France couldn't quite transform itself into a land of Negroes.

For the word black, first and foremost, signifies all that is dirty or filthy. It also means everything that is sad, dismal, even when referring to "black humor," which evokes the "black tumor," and "the black death." A *black destiny* is one that is irremediably gloomy. Moreover, a *black soul* implies the utmost base form of degradation imaginable. In the French language, when someone's reputation is "blackened," it means that his name has been dragged through the mud. And of course, we all know what a "*bête noir*" means!

We commonly complain about those who see "the dark side" of everything, or those who "darken our prospects," and, in the French language, a coward is said to "avoir le noir," which literally means "to have the black."

It is worth noting also that the French refer to a person who is excluded or ostracized as "*blacqueboulé*," or "black-balled," which no doubt comes from the English word "*black*."

The word "black" inevitably brings us to notions of evil, sadness, and the demonic. As a case in point, one might cite the common French expression "he's more black than he is devilish," which may be translated as "he's not as wicked as he seems."

When it comes to France then, we must firmly reject the proposition that this land of liberty, fraternity, and equality despite its policy of "cooperation" with Negroes–is itself Negro. No, no, and no again! It just isn't so!

And if in popular usage *to be black* means *to be drunk*, it must also be remembered that, among Whites, all that is linked to death also comes to be associated with the Black. Hence, the white man decks himself out in black on his wedding day, for he is laying to rest his life of celibacy.

❧❧

Perhaps this is the reason why, in Africa, those in mourning deck themselves out … in white!

An African school kid, a black cockroach haunting the public schools, once asked his French classmate, a white idiot who was better educated than he was, if the reason that *priests wear black* is to symbolize their vows renouncing the pleasures of the flesh.

"Why, yes," replied the white idiot.

"But then does that mean that the school's blackboard represents the renunciation of everything that you learned before coming to school?"

"Yes, that's true too," replied the white idiot, who was slightly more lucid than those who hail from Nanterre.

"But don't you find it strange," the young cockroach wondered aloud, "that, in the world of fashion, black is also associated with all that is elegant and chic?"

"An exception," his friend replied, "but it confirms the rule."

తుల

The lesson to be drawn: France is not Negro, for God created White people and Black people in order to keep them apart.

Suffice it to say that the underdeveloped man is a human being only in a negative sense—as a Black: a monkey without a red butt. The monkey is what he is: you should never believe a word that comes from his mouth: first, because he can't speak and, second, because he's a terrible liar. He does, however, know how to scowl and wrinkle his brow: this is why he gets prematurely old in comparison with the human being.

తుల

The White alone has a name, the Black only has nicknames: Negro, Abibi, Bibine, Boudouboudou, Alibi, etc.

This is why the *tchadanthrope*, which was recently discovered in Chad, that is to say, in Africa, was given such a harmonious name, for when it was excavated, it loudly sneezed *a-tchadoum*! In doing so, it spat out the dark side of its soul, which led those at the digging to conclude that it could not be a white man, but only a crusty old Negro…

To put all this in mathematical terms:

First equation: one Black + one Black = How many?

Answer: one Black + one Black = still another Black: in any event, something that is totally worthless.

Second equation: one Black man + one White woman = How many?

Answer: one Black man + one White woman = ½ White, which should surprise no one…

Third equation: two half-Whites + one White woman = How many?

Answer: two half-Whites + one White woman = Goodbye, Black Africa! This is the ultimate outcome of Independence.

The lesson to be drawn: Is France Negro or is it not Negro?

Answer: you might simply flip through the pages of any local telephone directory, if you want to know whether or not African people have any real future living in the French suburbs…

LETTER TO NON-RACISTS

Dear Descendants of Our Ancestors, the Gauls,

Late at night, in order to better see one another, owls say, "I love you," from behind their glasses. But, in front of curious children, they put on the most severe expression, transforming themselves into dragons with glowing eyes... As recounted in tales of old, men learned from the owls, imitating their glowering stares in order to scare off possible enemies and thus profit from the mystery of the night: In short, they turned themselves into Blacks.

But Blacks didn't have any money in those days, so they had to migrate towards *l'Afric* [Africa / the cash]...

And what a continent it proved to be! One night, the moon drew the shape of a circle, carefully tracing out the design of underdevelopment. In humble gratitude for this divine blessing, and in accord with the dictates of nature, Blacks decided that they would henceforth remain men of the bush, careful to keep upwind from all other men. Does that surprise you? Don't you know that the less a Negro makes an effort to become civilized, the more his civilization is diminished in stature?

Hair plays an important role in this regard, for, as we all know, the Black is nappy-headed in more than mere outward appearance. Thus it happens, by virtue of a curious logic, that the Black always ends up getting entangled in everything that has to do with Negroes.

Their land has been baptized black Africa, as opposed to white Africa, which is nonetheless populated by Whites who came from out of the blue. The black-rabble refers to the herd of blacks that didn't simply appear from out of the blue.

Thus, as is also the case with microbes, Negroes swim in the troubled waters of civilization, where, like the dead, they lie in rest, but with one leg cocked up, while the other is always half a step behind.

But in the eyes of the civilized world, Africans are just like monkeys. The higher a monkey climbs, the more it exposes its hairy butt. The only cure is to give the monkey a good kick in the butt, in order to cure it once and for all of the desire for assistance, offered to the underdeveloped countries by those who make a living wringing their hands over the Third World.

It is true that Negroes are unfortunate. But if they work like black slaves, it is because they waste so much time butchering the French language that they end up getting worn out and have to stop to take a breather.

Thus it happens that people in Africa know nothing about the springtime of life, for, of course, Spring never comes to Africa.... Between the ages of ten and twenty, young people wonder what they are going to be when they grow up: black or white. Once they choose to be White, they take off for Europe.

Once there, the elite few weep over the vanquished gods from days past, which languish under the ashes of History. They place all their hopes in progress but end up getting blamed for being backwards...

Having lost his innocence from the Fall of Eve, the Black would love to find it again in the words and gestures of Charley DeGaulle, as if it were concealed somewhere in his long-winded speeches and modest offers of assistance. But his stirring appeals finally get jumbled up with all his strange mumblings, whenever the General, with his shoulders swaying to the music, ruminates upon his grandiose visions, like the Vercingetorix of Africa. "French men and women, I need your help! We must save black music..." he recently proclaimed, while speaking of the imperiled art-works of Biafra.

From that day forward, we have witnessed the rise of a new canon of black classics, one that would certainly please "our ancestors the Gauls," and one that has been fashioned in the friendly spirit of assimilation and "cooperation"–in other words, a canon of "black classics" that suits the tastes of the Occident, such as black music lamenting the Negro drama.

The music of the Negro drama, as the Sons of Empire of the Independent Night were informed, gave birth to Negro spirituals, jazz, the blues, the twist, the jerk, the Madison, the cha-chacha, and every other variety of contemporary music, the modern classics. Thus it happened that, in order to fulfill his destiny as a musical genius and to more expertly sing of the world's ills, Beethoven decided he'd best become a black man. The only white man who saw through Beethoven's forg-eries was apparently Adolph Hitler, who denounced him as a fraudulent white man, but no one took Hitler seriously, and so today Beethoven is still thought of as a White! Later, all of this was so upsetting to Beethoven that he composed the Pastoral Symphony just to prove to everyone that he was White–when, as we all know, only a Black man can be a true musical genius!

Lord, have mercy upon us! ...

Brother Gauls living among us, doesn't it seem to you that a Black man is actually a cow? For, no one can deny that his skin is black, and I don't mean black in the way that a poor White man can turn black, not even a coal-miner!

The White man is superior to a Black man because he doesn't allow anyone to give him any gifts, given the fact that he is already such a fully developed man. You can't give him dark skin, for instance, since he prefers to pay for it himself on his expensive vacations where he goes to get his tan. Hence, one of the great advantages of being White is that you get to be both White and Black at the same time...

"I understand you perfectly," the Great Man explained to all those clamoring to be paid the minimum wage [S.M.I.G.], while cackling at the same time that they had had enough of being treated like colonized Negroes by High Finance...

How is it then that a White Man can ever really know that he's not a Negro? First of all, he must not lose sight of how the black-rabble live.

Among the black-rabble, for instance, the African woman struggles to keep evil temptations at bay with a kind of sadistic desperation, each and every morning as she readies herself for a trip to the public marketplace–the doctor of the Third World's hunger–oblivious as she is to the grandiose schemes of her generous father, the General, with his heavy sacks of French francs. The men, who are more macho, prefer to bash their illiterate skulls against the walls. As for the children, they hug their bellies in their hands and wail in agony, until they at last fall into silence.

(If you've seen a sight like this in your own home, you'll know for certain whether you are a White or a Negro...)

❧❧

In truth, the Sons of the Independent Night do not commonly behave in this manner. They are Blacks, as we all know. A Black man is a man. He is not a woman. He is filthy and disgraceful. He is a masculine type; unlike all others in his social interactions.

From the earliest days of the world's creation, he has rarely taken a bath, which explains how he got so black in first place. He once laughed so loudly that he turned the world's flowers moist with his sweet saliva. For the Black man lives on honey. He is a bear that quickly grows angry and lives a lonely life among his fellows.

He is also simple-minded and highly ridiculous: in fact, the Black man has white hands, white teeth, white eyes, and white feet. Everything else is black, so black that you can't see anything except the whites of his eyes! For further proof of his underdevelopment, just take a look at his size, for the average height of a Black man is a meter and eighty-four.

When people speak of "the road to development," they are actually thinking of Pygmies, who are so-named because the pigment of their skin is uniquely deficient...

Yet, we must be careful not to rush to the hasty conclusion that the Black man is a zebra. The Black man is most certainly not a zebra. If he were, he would have stripes that would be visible to the naked eye. Not being a zebra, the Black is very intelligent. He is a being whom existence transformed into a terrible wretch, a village idiot from the primitive horde.

Do you come from the horde? Are you primitive? No? Then, you are not a Negro. If you have any lingering doubts, you may rest assured: You are merely a barbarian. You are no longer a beast.

Are you educated? I mean, is your culture really and truly your own? Yes? Once again, you may leave such worries to the naked monkeys, for you are assuredly not a Negro...

For a corroded and vacuous form of knowledge weighs down upon the brains of all those with somber skin tones, those who have made the brutal discovery of their own worthlessness, and who have abandoned themselves to the intoxicating futility of that insight. (Is every resident of Marseilles secretly a Negro but unaware of that fact? Whoever is next in line, step right up!) On the Champs Elysée, the black-rabble waxes lyrical on the Rights of Man, especially when it concerns money, as the African minister tries to take it all in, winding his way through the crowds like an errant ass. Lord Jesus, may the ass you rode on Palm Sunday not take offense! *Amen*!

But, the black-rabble was delivered from its primitive condition as soon as it, with an *unapologetic and resounding* "yes," transformed itself into the cash cow of the General, the liberating father.

Problem: If the Illustrious Head of the French state is the father of the Negroes, can we conclude that he too is a Negro? Nothing could be further from the truth: for how could the President of the French Republic possibly be a Negro?

❦

Now the Black man who has turned himself into an individual is a brilliant figure. The proof? He always shines his shoes before voting "yes" in public elections. He drinks, sleeps, travels to France, schleps off here and there, drags his black ass everywhere. He stretches out to take a nap wherever he pleases, plummets deep into every aspect of French culture by trumpeting its universality, for which the gods punish him by swooping down him to scrub his Negro head white — obviously a waste of good soap.

Don't scorn Negroes by tying knots in their nappy black heads, just to kill time...

For the underdeveloped no longer eats his neighbors and has even begun to exhibit civilized traits. He now knows how to speak and laugh in a civilized fashion. He has developed a taste for sausage with Verdun sauce, as well as fine salads with dressing.

He also haunts the tailor shops of Rue de la Paix, in order to forget the Congo, timidly drooling over the bright window displays in the evening.

But then, how can you really be certain that he's a Negro when it's dark outside, and you are inside, separated from your underdeveloped customer by an opaque glass window? Easy enough solved... Behind every Chinese curtain, a Negro most certainly crouches. But be careful, for he is not your run-of-themill sort of Negro: he is a refined Negro!

Thus it is that, each day in Africa, the Chinese say "thank you" on account of the Black cause: the Chinese need more living space, and it's up to Blacks to wolf down the European tourists, who have come to make their fortune. Since the flesh of a European tourist is so tender and refined, the Black man hardly need move his bowels after digesting one. For, not a bit of that good White meat is left to waste. It is all mysteriously transformed...

In spite of himself, the Black man transforms Nature into night's vast chamber pot. When it comes to producing human fertilizer, he is a truly gifted amateur, always ready to do his modest part in the fight against hunger and ever prepared to contribute to his country's agricultural stability.

Who else has hair like rotten cauliflower?
Who else has lips that sprawl like leaves fresh on the vine (and that no one wants to kiss)? Who else has an ass like a watermelon and nostrils as brown as day-old lettuce? No one, but the Black man!
Well, almost no one; for, we mustn't forget the chimpanzee!

అఆ

Oh, naked monkey of indisputable French origins and healthy hue, are you a Negro?
As a helpful guideline, here is a technique to help you distinguish Black monkeys from White monkeys (since it has elsewhere been established that both groups share a common ancestor, the Gauls.) Fix your eyes for a moment on the Negro: first, the common street sweeper, *cluck, cluck, cluck!* Then, the student, *cluck, cluck!* Or, the ambassador, *cluck!* Just stare at him for a while and watch him cluck like a wet chicken:

1) He will be disturbed by your gaze: Should this happen, if he says *leave me alone*, then all is clear. If he responds in this way, it means that he is merely putting up a professional front, but that he is a cannibal to the soles of his shoes. You may therefore safely conclude that you are dealing with one hungry street sweeper.

2) Take a good long look at the Son of Night, preferably during the winter when there's lots of snow. Fix your eyes upon him for a long moment, and then rub your hands together. Stop for a moment, and then repeat this gesture. He begins to imitate you. Do you see? Shh… Wait a minute. You will hear him say in a sneering voice, while stamping the ground, "Ugh! Me cold! Me clap hands!" Now, should this happen, you'll know you are in the presence of an ambassador. The proof? He has just discovered the benefits of in-door heating. In other words, he is a White-Negro, more Royalist

than the king himself and whiter than the most lily-white White man. (Be careful not to confuse the White-Negroes and the Negro-Whites, who are captives of hunger and money, unpaid debts, overtime, a dog's life.)

3) Finally, the last case. Towards midnight, on an obscure street that flits with comely silhouette shadows (indiscernible male and female shadows in the night), listen carefully, and you will hear a descendant of the black Gauls say: "This is really fantastic! I love night-time! No one can see me!" (And then, he'll burst into laughter.)

No doubt, he is a student of the Humanities: a slacker, a thief, a rogue, who leads a life with bizarre values… Which leads us to formulate the following theorem: *our ancestors are most certainly the Gauls because if they weren't, they wouldn't have black descendants in France…*

It is said that the Gauls were savages, but this can't possibly be true! For it was the Blacks who started this malicious rumor, when they wrongly assumed that the Gauls were what they weren't, and that they weren't what they actually were…

Thus we had to wait until the development of French colonialism in Africa to overturn the pernicious myth that France was one of Africa's colonizers.

So, if there is a black problem in France, it is only because once civilized people began sitting on implements called chairs, they began to feel themselves to be superior to the black-rabble, who actually fell out of trees and landed flat on the earth where they began moaning and groaning about their abominable skin color, ceaselessly pursued by the implacable blessings of the goddess of misery.

To escape the evils of the latter, and to avoid becoming turned into Negroes in the midst of their own civilization, the Whites decided to use their time to buy up all the money. But, seeing that they weren't completely white (does a White man even have hands, one wonders?), but also not completely Negro, they grew less enthusiastic about playing the lottery, as they were aware that the revenue that is generated by the lottery always ends up in the hands of the French lady who is embossed on the coin, as opposed to the winnings that wind up in the hands of the horse doctors–who know very well that the fastest horses tend to be afflicted with galloping phthisis.

Thus it is that the Mediterranean climate, which is so conducive to intellectual thought, secretly transforms the melodramas of the Negroes into the most ghastly sounding music imaginable–which is performed for the enjoyment of petty stockholders with the good fortune to be born white.

Alas, such is not the case for Africa, which is destined to remain the land of impoverished Negroes, for as long as it remains warm in these countries, there will never be enough doors to keep Africa's house well-ventilated; hence, its Negroes will have no choice but to climb through the cracked window of civilization.

≈≈≈

A Negro, it should be clear, is not simply a white man who has black skin. Even within his own civilization, his frizzy hair is an index of his stupidity.

You think that yourself in quiet moments, do you not? … But you fear that if you say so you will be labeled a racist! Well, consider the following: even though Blacks are able to think up all kinds of excuses for their failures, they justify their stupidity in their own eyes by maligning all those who don't themselves imitate the lifestyles of African peoples. Incapable of turning themselves white, and therefore going mad with despair, their jealousy has become so great that they really should dye their hair green. At least that way, they could give the rest of the world a good laugh…

Thus if you who are a White man are labeled a racist, treat your insolent Negro accuser as a man of profound insight; if he tells you that you yourself are a Negro like him, and therefore no better than him, tell him that it just isn't so. If he keeps arguing with you, just repeat back to him in his own words everything that he says to you. In no time at all, he will be begging you to stop.

Why is that so, you may ask? Because the poor little Negro, who doesn't have a penny to his name, knows very well that, by the time Christmas rolls around, he will be reduced to singing to himself in falsetto, just to keep himself amused...

It should be clear then that a measured form of cooperation is inevitable wherever the évoulés, who love to flirt, groom themselves and gaze in the mirror at their own reflection, primping themselves on behalf of France, which, for its part, doesn't hesitate to play along.

❦

To make the message of my letter even plainer, it may be wise to recall precisely how it was that Blacks first became the children of the General.

Before there were Whites, there were only Blacks... Africa was therefore rich but without being underdeveloped.

In general, as there was no de Gaulle or any of his like, there was also no such thing as a Civil Community; there were only empires and emperors, and there was no proletariat on the horizon. Here and there, it's true, you might come across a few individuals who were all decked out like human beings...

The rest was an empty jungle filled with nappy-headed anthropoids: a herd of morons.

Besides the morons, there were a few bright men who sold the morons—at a handsome price—along the coastal regions.

The bright ones would sneak down to the coastal regions to play hide and seek. They'd lie in wait and then... pop! The herd of morons would soon embark for the high seas.

The herd moaned, bleated, and bellyached: thus began the trade in ebony goods, which helped to stock up many a larder... Thus, having acquired a taste for it, the local slave chiefs took for themselves the same name: *Turlututu*, which means, "the eternally unsatisfied ones," or, alternately, *Tara-*

tata. Invariably, their first name was *Grè-grè-ti*, which means, "I regret," in the best Negro-Frenchdoggerel. Thus, the local trade flourished, albeit with some regrets. But, this didn't stop them for long. The slave would be turned over, and then he was sometimes sent back. This made them black with anger. They didn't turn red with anger, of course, but black. Sometimes they would welcome the returned slaves, especially when they were hungry. For, they made pretty good eating, or so it was said.

❧❧

"Onward! In God's Name!" cried the army of helmeted invaders: and, once the Blacks were pushed against the wall and then conquered, they were colonized in short order.

This is my bread, this is my blood, said the Whites, who then lived in glass houses and made mannequins of themselves for all civilized peoples to emulate. They were quite happy with themselves. In the nights, they were so immaculate that they glowed for hours on end. Their shibboleth was the phrase "Omo *makes you whiter than white.*"

❧❧

Civilization, politics, economics, mosquitoes, Europhoria, Negrology.... There were so many difficult conundrums for the priests and the educators—all of them whites, which is to say, men and women of good intent, whose souls were not black...

How are we to understand and love one another? The word "racist" had not yet come into being. On the other hand, the word "fascist" did exist, and each time you were attacked simply because of your black face, you did have the right to shout, "Fascist! Fascist!"

Which in the best French may be translated as, "'Der good banana 'der bouts. No need be angry, bossman!"

After which, you would grow calm and allow yourself to be carried home in a hammock, so long as you were White. In these days, all Whites were Negro kings.

Is that still the case today? Who are the true Negroes?

To answer this question, one must first hear the secret History of the Independence of the Empire of the Night.

❧

Once upon a time, in the faraway land of Negrobabes, there was a very hot young babe who attracted a lot of attention, for she had all the allure of nobility (Zapata was her family name). The passions of this gentle creature, whose family named her "Binta" for the sweet little child that she was, combined with the elucubrationary tendencies of the Whites, finally led to her downfall, for these foreign guests took to wandering into her bed late in the nights.

Each time that a White man climbed into her bed, Binta would say, "*Kiss-kiss, toupati tomati?*"

(By which she meant, "Who is it, please?")

"*Nay,*" replied the White man. (Walls having ears, the White man was careful not to speak French.)

"*Who?*" Binta replied, who was heating up.

"*Nay,*" said the White Man (by which he meant, "It's me.")

"*Who?*" Binta said again, who was by now so hot and bothered that she could hardly believe her senses.

"*Nay, nay,*" the quivering White man said in the voice of a goat.

Thus, Binta happily welcomed him into her bed, and the White man stumbled about in the darkness, braying "*Nay, nay…,*" as he fondled her.

This was how Binta came to be baptized as "Naynay." Thereafter, Binta–Naynay, for those closest to her–would blush (turning red on the inside too, of course) each time they compared her to a swallow, for certainly she enjoyed a good swallow. She wondered why her black body seemed so beautiful to the Whites, why her lovers often spoke to her of the virtues of this migratory bird…

Naynay, the little black bird, wore upon her head a fine duvet that grew frizzy whenever it rained. "It's not very pretty," the little bird said, meaning her coiffure.

So to give her hair the fine, satiny sheen of the beauties of the West, Naynay, the little black swallow, warmed up a pan of Astra margarine, which she then poured on her head, in the hopes that it would make her light up like a star: and the band played on, as she danced to the tune of self-determination...

Alas, Naynay turned bald. Her hopes of conking her hair, so that her flowing locks could be paraded in the carpeted lounges of the foreign embassies, were now completely dashed. The Blacks moaned and groaned, for their national superstar was no longer able to generate as much income, not to mention the fact that there was a great deal of speculation regarding the true color of the band members trumpeting self-determination: socialists, optimistic centrists, pessimistic centrists, engaged Whites, disengaged Whites, revolutionary Reds, perilous Yellows, shiftless Blacks, etc.

Local authorities, alerted by those with a vested interest, as well as those who trafficked in mirages, got wind of the matter: it made headlines and resulted in Cartiérism.

The hell with it! I'll make this easier: Since Naynay was still alive, and since she had lost the chance to gain the favors of a great many men, gulp, the whole sorry business was hardly ever discussed. In any event, she had fallen ill, it seemed. She was beset by diarrhea of the mouth, an incurable passion for squandering money, megalomania, abject poverty, and inescapable notoriety. (Who could have foreseen it? Naynay now began associating with an exclusive circle of Inscrutable-Asians, the Third World.) So, let's be frank, old friends: There's no denying that, every now and then, Naynay certainly showed us a good time. Sometimes, she got a little out of control, there's no denying that either, and so, morally, we have an obligation to help her break her bad habits.

This matter being both stirring and inspiring, it is incumbent upon each international partner to take responsibility for his own slice of the pie!

But by then... Binta had turned herself into a clown (as often remarked by You-Know-Who about the dirty Negro agitators of May 68, who stirred up the Katanga rebels). She was sick, anemic, undernourished, and underdeveloped.

Yikes! Her ability to purchase goods? Zippo! Her ability to be happy? Uncertain. The Whites would no longer climb into bed with her. She was now independent. Hee, hee!

⊰⊱

The Blacks feared that no one would "take them seriously." But they were taken seriously, all right, since, in those days, they were treated like big, dopey teenagers. So, in order to give them what they deserved, the Whites relied on diplomacy for purposes of negotiation: for all the rest, they paid in cash. Long live Switzerland!

But some of the less discrete neighbors got wind of what was happening (in Africa, there are many trade winds), and they began to speak of *la politique des blocs*, just to irritate an old friend by stirring up the pot. All of this was pretty sacred stuff, so, of course, there were a lot of irritated people. Folks began hurling phrases in one another's faces: "Join the French commonwealth or tell the French to buggar off?" *Eurafrique* or *Heure-Afrique* [Euro-Africa or the Hour of Africa]?"

The experts finally hammered out a solution:
"Look, guys," they said, "laugh or don't laugh, it's up to you. But, you have to laugh at least a little, just to keep them guessing. It's simply a P.R. strategy. You see what we're saying?
So, let's all laugh together. Long live liberty, commonweal, and independence! Hip hip hip! Now, give me your word!"
"Urr…urr.. [*Heure … heure..*]" laughed the Black man, "Long live French Africa!"
"Better yet," the White man offered, "Long live Negro France!"
"Hee haw! If that's what you prefer," replied the Son of Darkness.
It was pure Cooperation. The next morning, Assistance to Underdeveloped Countries was born. There were lots of photographers. On the television, you could see a lot of

250

people waving their hands. The Children of the Fatherland were on the march...

⋘⋙

And yet, a great number of Whites felt confused about their new relationship to Negroes. They did want to help Naynay, having occasionally run into her, and they felt they should make an effort to keep in touch with her. In any event, they felt that this was a minimal requirement if Whites and Blacks ever hoped to reconcile their differences....

These blackened Whites returned to France and discussed the matter with Charles, who grasped that it wasn't by interbreeding that the race was going to be strengthened.

From that day forward, an enormous question mark has haunted each and every imagination. For the White man, the main question is as follows: "To be or not to be ... Negro?"

But in order to not be divested of all his prejudices, most of them were buried away in his unconscious...

What are the Negroes doing in France? This question will someday have to be answered. But at least for now, we should have the courage to admit that, if it really is true that Africa itself doesn't exist, that Africa is merely an extension of Gaul civilization, then the plight of certain sick individuals, like our friend Naynay, is going to have a very different meaning for us.

For their part, the French, thanks to coffee that is imported from African countries, can now treat and even cure diabetes: by way of a coffee enema. This cure works best when sugar is mixed with the coffee.

LETTER TO NEGRO KINGS TEMPORARILY RESIDING IN FRANCE

Dear Whites,

Certainly, oh yes — material riches, in your eyes, you say, count for nothing...

But those who claim to despise money are no different from those who claim to execrate civilization, hard work, talent, virtue, and values. When imbecility of spirit, a primitive mentality, or crass egotism make it impossible to perform a good deed without perverting it, the good that might have been is dragged through the mud and then despised–though without awareness of the fact that, when we do so, we are actually blaming something that we ourselves have perverted.

Crapulent scoundrels despise hard work, the man who rationalizes his own laziness blames society for all his woes, and the sophist preaches against money and colonialism. Who, after all, hasn't been colonized?

And, no doubt, you, in the middle class — who may be astounded to learn that you too have been colonized–may nonetheless agree that the underdeveloped morons, who are enslaved by their passions, would probably become even more insufferable, should they ever strike it rich. There are some people, as a wise man once remarked, who even lose by winning. More wealth for them would only mean more worries, as is the case for those poor louts, the Negroes... To multiply your needs by the hundreds, to have to strut around like an ostentatious peacock, to be required to open a hundred embassies abroad because some other proud country has opened fifty of them—and then, God forbid, should they open sixty, you'd have to build two hundred—all of this would amount to burying yourself in difficulties far worse than those that result from your poverty.

But to govern yourself in a respectable manner, to know when to quit accepting help even though foreign "assistance" continues to rain down upon the Third World, to employ the resources already at hand to actually develop your own country, to put one's people to work, and not from the backseat of a Rolls Royce or Bentley, and to balance a deficient budget: all of this entails far more than hurling anti-colonialist insults to placate the black-rabble. Rule by begging or bragging is a form of false wisdom at best.

For if it's hardly desirable to be a common fool who is poor, you're probably even worse off being a common fool who is rich…

❦

Negro kings, due to your political mistakes of every stripe, you have placed Africa under a spotlight, a blinding light that shines upon us in our obscurity…

Certainly, you cry to the United Nations about your miseries, shedding tears, which are hot enough to cook the goose of your own civilization, which has become derailed, thanks to you!

And the shackles from your ambiguous marriage to the United States of Europe and to other places are so heavy that you now need to walk on all fours just to hold up under its weight. But your blunders have been so stupendous that the very fleas on your hide long to abandon you.

On the other hand, how clairvoyant Nature can be! She pushes all the Blacks into Africa, knowing very well that the locals, just like the French hired-guns who have become their Heads of State, can survive merely by eating the bugs that they pull from their ears, first so they can better hear, and, second, to satisfy their hungry bellies…

❧❧

You have many questions for France — although, strange to say, it has no questions for you! You're in a big hurry to get hold of those heavy French francs, in spite of the fact that you're forbidden to take dollars or rubles, which are irritating to the touch.

Dropped from out of the blue in order to take a stroll through the civilized world, you end up in the pocket of the socialists, riding the very ponies that only five minutes earlier...

A mediocre student with terrible grades, you ape the voice of the Republic by speaking to the clouds, in order to forget the horrors of your political prisons...

Next, you go out for a stroll, out again on one of your endless rounds of official visits to the portals of prosperity, where you recite a speech that was penned by an associate who has bought in to your ragged ideology

But here, two equally evil enemies square off. To better use and abuse the Francophones, you decide to get baptized in the Church of the Cooperation, and you take for yourself the name of Alfred, just so you can pass for one of the descendants of Alfred de Vigny, who all get good grades in French...

The stupidity of your massive capital transfers to Switzerland is so corrosive, and your dishonesty so fetid, that Africa now smells of shit because of you.

Oh, you dirty, second-rate school boys! You are all cheaters! You have set a generation back to prehistoric times, merely because you snuck a peak at the book of a civilization that was more than happy to oblige you.

You are building a civilization without being true builders yourself, and you are destroying another one, ever since you gained admittance to Parliament, where Human Rights and Citizenship are championed. Meanwhile, it is permitted for you to assert the will to build Africa in the streets of Europe, but on the condition that you piss off, as far as anything else is concerned....

Long live...! Long live...! Long live...! Negro France, it is high time for you to pick yourself up off the ground, like a woman without a suitor who is fully prepared to do her part to knead the dough. What do say you, my fine black sweetheart?

Instead, you are encouraged merely because there are a few less plagues raging in your own backyard, and that currently do damage on a hitherto unprecedented scale.

∝∾

Blindly guided in even the slightest steps you take, the least of your actions and gestures, all dictated to you by the Negrofied Whites whom you call "technical assistants" (the gorillas who haunt your spiritual life), you'll do anything that will increase your popularity and show that progress has been made on the road to development. In effect, you have transformed yourself into a militarized nymphomaniac...

But, beware! Beware of the hangover that will surely come after your weekend cultural festivities! Beware of the coming collision between the train that you've boarded and that of your people, which may result in the death of millions, an irreversible catastrophe of terrifying proportions.

In this case, we will not be talking about a mere putsch, but a revolution.

But, let's be clear about something: I do not stand in judgment against you: for, who among us has never indulged in the follies of youth?

As the snow now falls upon your French-speaking States, you skate upon the thin ice of the limitations that have been imposed from the outside, a crass adventurism that finds its origins in other climes. And so, I say to you "Best of luck!", but "Watch out for cracks in the ice!"

LETTER TO ALL THOSE WHO ENJOY THE COMPANY OF NEGROES

Dear Amateur Miscegenists,

First of all, a little astrology.

The Earth moves because she is like a small child searching for her mother in the infinite abyss of space.

The Earth has a father, which is the Sun, and a mother, which is the Moon, brothers and sisters, which are the stars, who wink at her and tease her because she is not the center of the universe; for, if this was the case, she would be perfect, rather than the badly made orange that she is, teeming with Negroes and Chinamen, money and hunger, not to mention all the miseries, savage beasts, and jungles.

When the Earth was the center of the universe, she was an utter paradise. But when she lost her center of gravity, she became ridiculous. Thus was born the Negro of our ancestors, the Gauls.

The sky, which hung too low, hindered the Negro women whenever they cried for assistance in their struggles to be liberated. One day, the cry for independence across the entire continent was so resounding that it frightened the sky, causing it to retreat to the very place that it occupies today. Hence, God was at last able to dissociate himself from the problems of the world's proletariats, starting with the Blacks.

... Everything went well enough, despite all the misery caused by God's abandonment of the world, until one day when a conflict broke out between the Sky and the Earth.

Singing Negro spirituals, the Earth ascended to the Sky to inform God of the urgency of the black problem.

The Sky, with the help of God, thundered. And the rain poured down upon the Earth's spine, which eased the Sky's conscience. From that day forward, the Black man dared to speak his mind, and the White man lent him his ears. It was a miracle! For the White man had been deaf for so long. Then God caught a bad cold because of the tears of the black-rabble. But he abstained from blowing his nose, so as not to throw the world's equilibrium out of balance. Moreover, he chose to make himself invisible.

❧❀

So it goes! Since it has now become fashionable, let's tell everyone that we are no longer cannibals: better yet, let's swear it! Now that this question is settled, we can say instead that we are countries with *emerging industries*, that we are now civilized people…

You! You, who enjoy the company of Negroes, know very well that they are not cannibals: otherwise, how could you possibly respond to me?!?…

❧❀

Another reflection: how do you account for hunger in African countries, since they are essentially agricultural? (The rules of hospitality loom so large in black societies that it can easily be shown that they are built upon an ethics of unlimited co-responsibility for the other.) With a population density of 0.94% per square kilometer, which is, more or less, constant across the continent, and with record numbers of exports to the Rue Mouffetard and the Rue Madeleine, including fruits, vegetables, rice, and diverse cereals, how can we possibly explain Africa's hunger?

Only as follows: *Negroes were so weakened by famine that they could no longer stand up to gather all the bananas, oranges, avocados, etc.*

Since they could only crawl about on their hands and knees, they begged the white man not to abandon them in their plight and to do them the favor of hauling away everything that was edible...

Hence, it only follows that a White man who cannot safely assert to his wife or mistress that he can do a far better job of making love than all the puny little Negroes in the world is no man at all: he's nothing more than a technocrat.

As a technician in the bedroom, he must be well past his first youth, for we all know that the best dishes are prepared from well-worn pots.

৵৶

But, happily for Negro France, the Whites who most enjoy spending time in the company of Blacks are not themselves obsessed with the desire for sex with exotic Negroes...

There are also those who enjoy being fleeced by advertisements, the validity of which it never occurs to them to question, imploring them to "save the children dying from hunger, *oye oye oye*, in the remote deserts of Africa"; and so they rush about gathering their pennies to help the poor little Negroes with swollen bellies.

And the money weeps as much as all the poor little Negroes, since it knows very well how much of it will not end up in the hands of those for whom it was intended...

For there are certainly a great number of Whites who live very comfortably on the Third World's hunger; and, because there are so many itches that are constantly in need of scratching, the Heads of black States, in their turn, have no qualms about the "small" but indispensable levies that end up in their own wallets...

All of this makes me wonder... How is it that, during the colonial era, it never occurred to anyone to make a fuss about Africa's hunger (even though all the conditions on the ground seemed to favor this fabulous French Union with its multiple colonies?)... It was no doubt necessary to wait till the era of "independence" in order to begin levying taxes from all the good souls back home, the blindly pious who are stirred by the crocodile tears of the professional weepers, and who are only too happy to disburse the funds that are necessary to support their country's overseas investments?...

Hmm... Perhaps it's wiser to protect my reputation for being underdeveloped rather than to ask so many troubling questions...

And, besides, maybe the problem of Africa's underdevelopment can be resolved by relying upon homegrown remedies... As a matter of fact, one advantage of being a cannibal is that, instead of dying a natural death, you may be eaten at a young age.

❦

But there are many women who associate with Blacks and yet don't end up marrying them. These women content themselves with merely sampling the goods.

Once safely married and leading a bourgeois existence, they profit from having learned how to turn a few African tricks, provided their husbands enjoy spending the night in a dancing hammock.

In fact, there are those who are quite happy to profit from the knowledge that has been acquired by their Venus de Milo—a goddess before whom they dream of becoming youthful initiates, as in antiquarian times—and also secretly dream of transforming themselves into a little mouse, so they might enjoy watching their goddess transformed into the concubine of a Negro sultan—the consummate Negro who knows how to give pleasure!

As for the White woman, she dreams *a priori* of the day when her incestuous desire for being sodomized by a black penis will finally be satisfied. Stirred by the power of her own libido, by her insatiable desire to transgress and enjoy the most sinful and forbidden pleasures, her little white buttocks—reem, reem, reem— clap with joy at the very thought...

Indeed, it is as if there is no creature who is better suited to bring out what is most perverse in the ebony lover: her pink skin and modest demeanor are well complemented by nature's shock absorbers: her fat white breasts, which assail you from the front, and her plump buttocks, which protect her from behind.

In order for her to hold fast to her Negro, and to populate France with more little Negroes (soon to be abandoned by Public Assistance), she needs to have a shapely ass and all the right curves. This will be more important for her than even the spices that she uses in cooking her husband's meals. For, when she lacks in these things, she tends to be as flat as a banana and far less slippery.

A White woman who keeps company with Negroes is therefore no ordinary woman.

The proof? Ever since France has begun to turn Negro, because of these enthusiasts of interracial sex, the production of toothpaste in France has dramatically increased: For the halitosis of the underdeveloped is so profound that it sometimes cools the ardor of the White woman's kisses.

The White woman who frequents Negroes is like the African peasant who tills the earth with a hoe, displaying his buttocks to the sky, which lacks in this accoutrement.

In dwelling upon these aspects of French society, allow me to make the following observation on behalf of those Whites who keep company with Negroes, whether they be male or female: let us never forget that we are engaged in a deadly battle against centuries of poor hygiene. So, to all you male and female Negroes out there, I can only implore you, for the benefit of your White lovers: For God's sake, it won't hurt you to take a bath every now and then!

As you are no doubt aware, it is due to the sweet law of Shaka-Shaka that the organs of female Negroes have two hot spots: an undisclosed centrifuge and somewhere along the elastic rim of the vulva.

All of this touches on obviously delicate matters, which you must do your best to penetrate. But, if you boldly press forward, you will certainly fathom these Negro mysteries!

As for you, the White woman who loves the Negro, beware that if the Negro's hair is particularly nappy in certain concealed places, he may be hiding some terrible secret from you. Should you happen to marry him, there may come a day when you ask him to roll over to display his naked flanks for you, just so you may know for certain that he has properly bathed: for, the stench that emanates from him may lead you to believe that he is harboring..... *Oh, the horror, the horror...!*

If you both found your way back to A'fric, you will need to get your ears pierced, so that you may know the caresses of his cousins, both male and female, their breasts, their desires, as well as your own, in fact, the desires of both of you. And, should you decide to live your entire life in such remote places, bear in mind that one of the great advantages of nose-piercing is that, after you're dead, it provides an excellent escape route for maggots and worms–preventing them from too rapidly feasting on your face...

✌ঔ৯

For, in the beginning, it was *Zamba* who created the sun in order to bring light to Africa. And, as we all know, among Blacks, the sun...

A cock crows, and so you lift yourself up on your elbows, opening your eyes just enough to see the light that streams into your room. At day's end, you behold the celestial heavens of God's creation, and you break into song at the sight of the stars above.

Throughout the day, while gazing into the water, you see only the sun's fire flitting across the surface.

In the afternoon, when you look down at your feet, you see only its shadow. There are twelve hours in each day. But, for you, there are twenty-four hours in each night, for you spend all of your days asleep. Thus passes the life of the White who has turned himself into a Negro, who has traveled to Africa under the banner of Cooperation.

You, who wish to follow his example, take note of the following:

You want to climb a palm tree, but you can't stop sweating.

You want to call out to your wife, but she can't stop sweating.

You lie down beneath her during a moment alone, but you both can't stop sweating.

Each night, the sun sets in the midst of a storm: sometimes, a real one, sometimes a political one... Every now and then, a billowy cloud, which floats high above you, is perforated by brilliant patches of light. You hear thunder in the distance. Another president has been deposed.

Soon enough, the rain begins to fall, a rain of promises, threats, or compromises. Thanks to the rain, you are constantly damp but never fully drenched

Under the sun and the rain, *Zamba* set her forest. The forest is immense and quite welcoming when intelligence agencies are in search of political agitators, who tend to disappear deep in the forest where they are difficult to find. Such is the underbelly of Independence.

I will not say anything further on this subject. There are some lessons that one can only learn by way of experience. However, allow me to remind you of a particularly edifying example, an incident that was witnessed by many.

However, I will refrain from revealing the name of the Association and country in question. It occurred in an African republic about a year ago.

A number of Americans arrived in a small city, one with about fifteen thousand residents. Upon arrival, they immediately visited the local dispensary, claiming that their private corporation wished to provide medical assistance to Africans. Hence, they announced that the dispensary would shortly be transformed into a full-fledged hospital.

With one condition: That forty children who were afflicted with river blindness be brought to the dispensary.

This caused considerable confusion among the locals. Where to find forty children with this disease? ...

But our Americans had cut an impressive figure in the nation's capital, and they had in their possession every official document imaginable in support of their mission. Numerous telegrams were dispatched at once. Ten days later, the forty children were there, exhausted from their journey, after having been packed onto two military trucks that kicked up enormous clouds of dust in their wake.

The children were unloaded from the trucks. Their fatigue, grime, and dirt from several days of hard travel delighted our American guests.

Immediately, the cameras began to roll. Nurses dressed in white, sporting a particular logo, which I will not name here, gently began to wash the dust from the children's eyes, before they had even had a chance to stretch their legs. Everything was captured on film.

Next, a long table was covered with an immaculate white sheet (casting a veil upon the primordial squalor)... And, in effect, this was the case, for the implements laid out on the white sheet formed a giant replica of the organization's logo... Bottles of medicine, vitamins, canned foods, cod liver oil, all of these items were carefully displayed on the white sheet, as devastated little Negroes, their lives one long and endless lament, gazed thankfully upon these various items.

The next few minutes were atrocious...

In effect, a nurse would station herself before a child and then hold out a spoonful of gruel. When the child opened his mouth, craning his frail and trembling neck, the nurse would slowly withdraw the spoon from the child's mouth. (For instance, as one might lure a fish with bait.) When the child began to cry, the camera would zoom in on his emaciated face. The nurse, with a look of infinite compassion, would then give a small morsel of food to the child.

It usually took about a quarter hour to film this scene.

The following day, there were no more Americans: they had taken off during the night... I learned later that the same scene had been performed in several neighboring African countries. Without variation.

... The dispensaries are all still there. They were never turned into hospitals. You can therefore imagine my surprise–mixed with a feeling of utter weariness and disgust–when I caught a glimpse on television of a couple of American movie stars, piously weeping about the misery of starving African pygmies, interspersed with images of these very same nurses who were fish-feeding the children with river blindness.

"Each year," groaned the movie star with a thick Anglo-Saxon accent, "each year, Organization X saves Y millions of children suffering from famine. But this is a drop in the bucket, for there are Z children who die of hunger every minute throughout the world. If Organization X is unable to remedy this tragedy, it is because its resources are too limited. That's why we have organized this telethon.... Please, open up your hearts and your checkbooks...."

Music. Laughter. Movie Stars. A fraud committed against human dignity, sold for a profit. And so I have a question for you.

How is it that France, which is renown for being a country of liberty, reason, and equilibrium, can be so blind? How can the French be stupid enough to believe that these Americans (who have not even begun to think about the *black problem* in their own country, where their President, his brother, and Martin Luther King were all recently assassinated) have now turned into tenderhearted angels who merely wish to help African children and want nothing in return!!!

If it is incumbent upon us to expose this colossal scam, this fraud that Africans are dying in droves of starvation, we should perhaps have no illusions about how many will be persuaded to our point of view: for, by now, the hunger racket has become a well-established institution.

I myself would prefer to go forever barefoot, like a "primitive," rather than walk a single step in the shoes of those who till the soil for the aforesaid institution, the scourge of Negro France.

None of this implies, however, that we, the other Negroes whom you associate with, some more remotely than others, are completely against working together in a spirit of cooperation. To do so is inevitable, since all of this has now become a part of History.

But nothing will come of any such efforts unless they are based upon objective information that may be verified by both sides, no matter how unsettling such information may initially seem. Barring this, the White man is destined to become the victim of a conformist anti-racism, and the Black man is destined to become an abrasive and alienated Jacobite–whether as an alibi or as a means of exonerating himself. This alibi will only serve to justify white colonialism, and to divert him from his funk, but nothing truly constructive can come of it.

After all, what African is ignorant of the fact that, long before the coming of the White Man, there was a colonialism of the black notables, as well as the Arab conquest? ...

In fact, the Black man only became a Negro on the day that the notable sold his domestic black servant to the slave traders. Then came the day that the Arab more fully developed this system by way of Muslim ideology (exporting a legal framework to accommodate slavery), in which the African most certainly remained a Negro. Even today, the Presidents of our Republics are considered by the Arabs to be little more than simple valets.

In our own days, if the truth be told, the intellectual black-rabble hurry off to Europe to acquire as much knowledge as possible, merely to gain an advantage over other Blacks (but also, no doubt, out of snobbery). The secret leprosy which gets them out of a fix at a cheap price, returns with a vengeance once they are back in their own countries, where they rail against the evils of white imperialism, all the while taking great pride in displaying to their fellow Blacks–often accompanied by a White woman, the true "Diploma of Civilization" — their multitude of honorary degrees, university certificates, acquired with some difficulty, thanks to the liberality of Grandfather Charley, the Gaul, whom he secretly idolizes.

❧❧

"All of this goes without saying," you may remark, but it is nonetheless better to say it, above all in Negro France, which is already a small embryo of what the United States will be in the year 2000.

Don't Negroes live well in France? Why would they want to return in droves to their homes, considering how easy it is to get French nationality, and considering they all came to France from historically French countries? And what remains of this mystery of the other Negro France, in the Antilles province... hmm... I mean in the French...

If you truly hope to live in France someday, here's a suggestion: learn to sing a few lyrics that are certain to win the acclaim of the entire French-speaking world. First, however, you must imagine that you are singing them to one of Béranger's inspiring melodics:

My breast,
Africa,
My breast is French,
But my milk belongs to me...

But then don't be too surprised when you find that France and Africa have–in the not too distant future — become entangled in the same racial dramas that the United States is living through today.

And, if we have not yet arrived at this point, it is only because there are so few highly educated Africans living in France. Up till now, Africa has turned France into its dumping ground, exporting only its unskilled laborers, the ragged street-sweepers who live in ghettos.

On the day when these same Negroes, who now seek to pass as Whites, and who harbor not so good intentions, who enjoy chasing after French women, and who are all in search of gainful employment, on the day when this teeming mass of French-speaking Negroes–a grab-bag of bastards and innocents alike, as true of all people everywhere–begins to pose a serious economic challenge to the status quo, then you can be certain that the French and Africans alike will regret that they have, on the one hand, sought to turn themselves into Negroes and, on the other hand, sought to turn themselves into Whites.

But there is no denying that the entire world seems to be going through a process of Negrofication. The time of coherent civilizations has come to an end. And if it has already come to pass that nations like Russia, Germany, Sweden, Norway, Italy, Switzerland, China, and so on, have, by virtue of the foreign assistance that they now export to Africa, begun the ill-advised process of transforming themselves into Negro-States, then one can only hope that at least France will be able to obviate the racial conflicts that are on the horizon, perhaps by sending its own surplus of Negroes to live on the moon.

Even there, living like morose cockroaches, these grave and dignified Negroes will no doubt still be able to wring out a luminous smile, as they strum upon their banjos and reflect upon the sad plight that brought them to their present conditions…

In order to whiten their black souls, if they don't first kill each other in inter-tribal warfare, they will seek more foreign assistance from other distant planets across the Milky Way. There, they will sing inspiring hymns, as sweet as Mama's milk, about how wonderful life on the moon is going to be someday, once it is finally developed. They'll patiently await the new era, just as one awaits the coming of the Messiah, with all the unctuous piety that one might expect of a senile old woman, whose mystical torpor is only matched by her cruelty.

They will jubilantly celebrate their new humanism, the birth of a new civilization in which they will imagine that they are citizens with full equal rights, merely because they have the right to vote, and then they will fall back into a life of utter misery, crrrraaaak!, fingers glued to the fly of their shorts.

Men who lack in sound judgment! Those of you who feel as harassed as the hare at a dog race! Who dread ending up on a cannibal's skewer! Who suffer from the indignities and miseries of life here on earth! Flee from Negro France at once! Flee the black-rabble—and try living on the moon!

❧❦

Should all these vermin go to the moon, Negroes with lighter skin tones, the Not-Quite White Negroes, who now earn little more than the minimum wage, would become the new top-dogs, the Negroes who give orders to the Negro Kings back home. And France, no longer threatened with the black peril, and having saved itself from the yellow peril at Diem Bien Phu, could enter the new millennium as if it was 1789 all over again!

It should therefore be clear why France today remains resolutely bourgeois, and why the revolution of May 68 was an exercise in sheer folly. As will soon enough be clear, the struggle between classes will be co-opted by consumer society...

When this happens, the traditional proletariat, which was the most revolutionary sector of the working class, will find itself displaced by Third World laborers, who will now be compelled to do France's "dirty work."

LETTER TO WOMEN WHO ARE LONELY AS NEGROES

Dear Gossips,

Unmarried women, you are very much like Negroes, for society has turned you into freaks and rejects, relegated to a life on the margins, not unlike the members of a minority group. The condescending and kindly anti-feminism of men—who are, in fact, obsequious and malicious wolves—is reminiscent of a colonialist attitude, one that sometimes flatters you but most often makes your heart grow heavy. It's a little like watching yourself die, but from a distance, is it not?
...

... For you too, when you give in to your anguish, cannot help but conclude that the problem is related to the very body you inhabit... We are talking about a feeling of frustration, one that you accept with a sad smile. Each day brings new and unforeseen difficulties... You open your door, walk down the street, in silence, smiling most when you are alone...

Your silence—which hides the secret of what remains of your elegance—speaks to your heart of all your miseries. You gaze into your own depths and are surprised at the indefinable feelings that well up. Sometimes, it even makes you blush, and you lower your beautiful eyes, which betray the calm fatigue that is born from a life without love.

You imagine that you have withheld nothing from life, and yet a strange surplus has begun to accumulate from somewhere inside you... Time rushes by, like at the wake of some undeclared armistice. Solitude, which is weirdly peaceful, where the melancholy of silence takes lonely walks in the night, at last brings you to the hollow understanding of what will become of the rest of your life, little by little, after you are completely resigned to your fate... And you can scarcely contemplate this interior horizon, the universe that marks the limits of who and what you are, without an exaggerated feeling of pain and horror...

"Come on," you tell yourself, as if a curtain just fell upon your lackluster performance. "Everything is going to be fine." It's just life. There's no joy in life without suffering too, and there's always hope... But you are a single woman, a sea creature born in the ocean's unfathomable depths: there is no ghost that haunts these waters that can save you from the destiny that belongs to you, and to you alone. You are wedded to the misery of your daily existence, ever driven by your child-like desire to be happy and free, like the birds that fly in the air. How you long to soar to far away lands and find a comfortable nest, where some mature man might possibly follow you! Once there, perhaps, you can start all over again...

But you have neither wings nor nest, and how is it that everything now aimlessly drifts, buzzes, and rattles about from deep inside of you? For the past is timidly measured by every breath that you take... It weighs your memories one after the other, as if fearful of what it may stumble upon... Behind the words that you utter in a low voice, it discerns the confessions that you wish to conceal, but that you repeat a thousand times over, no matter much you may try not to betray yourself — words that always lead you to the following conclusion: "I've wasted my entire life waiting for some weak force that I call 'love'... And, my God, I am so terribly afraid..."

Alas, the fish that dwells in your innermost depths has decomposed. You killed it when it swam in the exhalations of your bitterness, the essence of your dreams, the contradictory missives of your heart...

... It is only by chance that, somehow, the mysterious destiny that is your life will be revealed to you: men, your relationships with them, your dreams, the present, the past, its lessons, the future, the unknown, the unforeseen, your weariness—your days will finally blur together like a somber fog until you find that you have now grown old, too old to share your solitude with another. When that day comes, you will have nothing left but regrets and unfulfilled dreams. You will have become an ethereal and indifferent creature who haunts the world of those who no longer recognize you—incurably alone... And when, at last, your time is up, an entire universe will pass into non-being, for, after you, there is only death...

☙❧

You know very well that these fleeting visions reveal only partial truths, that they do not reveal the innermost essence of your being; and yet, they strengthen your resolve in unexpected ways, for they emanate with a peculiar odor that invades you, that frees you from the tyranny of a hateful contempt that had poisoned your powers of reasoning...

For you were certainly aware that no one is entirely unhappy who is still one hour from the morgue, who is able to keep at bay the ever-present spirit of contempt with an undying belief in oneself, however enfeebled.

In moments such as these, the gaze that one casts upon the world is not fully to be trusted, for it lacks in a certain tenderness. The world itself is transformed at such intervals into an exhausting abyss that leaves one skeptical of everything and completely disabled... And it was therefore not you, but an entirely different woman, who had crumpled under the weight of these anxieties...

Or, maybe it was you, but you cannot be faulted for doing everything in your power to redeem a failed life, after living so long in silence... You are so absentminded, so indifferent to those you meet, that it gives you pleasure to imagine that you have learned all these things from someone else, someone whom you address in lengthy and imaginary dialogues that are as long-winded as they are confused...

These dialogues flitted through your mind like so many buzzing insects. And the fluttering of their imaginary wings almost caused your throat to constrict in pain. Delusions of this nature at last became so ever-present, so fascinating, that you finally grew inattentive to those around you, even to your manner of dressing, and your professional life. But you were able, somehow, to take hold of the persistent problems in your daily interactions with others and lock them away in a neat little box, only to be re-opened at some future date–when you were better able to sort through them.

A life that was obscurely but indisputably Negro, which was born from confused feelings that overwhelmed you in moments of solitude, and that sprang from an indefinable experience of oppression, stealthily became at one with your own life– until, at last, you too found that you had become a ghost, yet another Negro to haunt the streets of Paris. Even in the workplace, your colleagues now seemed to have nothing to say to you. You could do little more than listen to the echo of your own wavering voice. The days followed, one after another, monotonously coming and going... And yet something was now different. You began to take notice of a rich symmetry beneath the dull regularity of your existence... And, suddenly, like an unexpected fissure in a crystal goblet, you felt that you had become the orphan of feminism...

∽ඐ∾

Clumsily pulling yourself to your feet, as if burdened by your own flesh, you seem not to expect anything further from life. It is only when you catch a glimpse of the grayness of your day-today existence, of your legs on the treadmill below you, which eternally slog onward, as if conscripted in the race to gain more time, more money, that your very body, the abysmal desert of your being, leads you to the inescapable conclusion that nothing is left for you now, nothing but a feeling of guilt... The lingering sensation of this internal collapse, of being hopelessly adrift, cannot save you from a feeling of anguish over your wasted youth...

You therefore have no choice but to gather up and assess the fragile traces of love that have deposited themselves in your body. You perform an inventory of your occasional liaisons, the affairs that never seemed to last. Did you expect too much? You remember how you whispered in his ear, the man you once loved, in the days before you began to drift apart. You spoke to him then, from this quiet place inside yourself... You cannot then deny that it doesn't matter so much whether you were married to him or not, for there is a certain concealed violence in all relationships, isn't there? Some unions may ravish the heart far more than those that are merely legal, leaving one utterly devastated and alone. Some may leave you adrift in the phosphorescence of an invisible peril, the terrible risk that is yourself. Morose. Anxious. Forever frozen in the present, which is something you don't really want to discuss...

It is because they so seldom speak that lovers separate... Or, maybe it is love that drives them apart, or the feeling of loss; but, in your case, you know very well that, during your lengthy monologues in silence, you really were only thinking of yourself, of the depths of your weariness. Black sand from unknown shores and seas–a feeling of dread so familiar that it was comforting... Sand, fragile, flecked with gray specks, caught in the undertow, where you were first cast ashore, but then at last arose, as if hoping to survive.

To live! Lord Almighty...

❧

... But you stare off at the sky, still dreaming... God? Man? ... Must you side with one or the other? Eyelids closed tightly, you take refuge in silence and in the very heaving of your lungs. You grow calm, but with your eyes shut to the rest of the world, you seem to have forgotten yourself, *to have become utterly resigned...*

Why do you put your hands to your face now in hopes of blocking a vision that you have already seen?...

So, it seems that all of this is not about your hidden fears: it is merely the lament of a haunted woman–a woman who cannot forget the trauma of discovering, quite by accident, an abomination that was committed by another woman, her own secret double. Consequently, you decide to wash your hands of the entire matter...

But in your dream, there was no end to this internal chatter. Aching to seize hold of this obscure power from within, this tension that came from long moments of solitude, you knew without admitting it that any spark of life that was still left in you came from your struggle to clasp hold of it, to make it concrete, to isolate and distill it: so that you could learn to summon it of your own volition. Even if this meant that your solitude would henceforth become unbearable for you... As your soul raged with thirst in silence. Plagued by mirages, the ugliness of your daily routines, rebellions, fleeting moments of happiness and laughter, followed by cold rage and the hope for something wholly unforeseen.

❧

For a long time, you thought about how you had once measured those moments when the floor suddenly dropped out from under your feet, leaving you suspended over a shadowy abyss: your own feeling of regret was what saved you–that, and the vague memory of happier days. You even thought of your childhood, the soft arms that had once rocked you to sleep. But, as you hung suspended over the abyss, you at last began to understand the terrible power that lies hidden in the shadows. You at last realized how useless it was to fight against it. For now you saw your struggle against the power of these ghosts as a battle that had taken place on a stage, a scene with props that had now been dismantled and locked away...

... You are no longer yourself but the very image of your despair. You have acquiesced to this specter that you now behold with a quiet joy. There is nothing left on the inside. Your thirst has been slaked. Now, you go for long walks, ambling here and there, idly chattering with some other embittered wretch. You go to great lengths to express your views, inane clichés that are on the lips of every other fool who crosses your path. And, as before, you silently take note of the filthy walls, the gray stones, tattered posters that speak to the world's hunger, but which, for you, now seem distasteful, hardly worth the effort that it takes to muster a yawn.

You have become a Negro who wants nothing to do with other Negroes, a Jew who has turned herself into an anti-Semite. Like so many other harassed members of the middle class, you simply close your eyes and do what you can to muddle your way through the days and nights. The agony of your life is by now painless, and you have made peace with it. There are even moments when you feel alive again, like a school kid during recess, times when life seems to smile at you. Once more, you open your eyes and reach out your hand...

And, it is with a feeling of serenity that you behold the specter of your own shadow that now wavers before you, an unexpected tremor of the heart...

And your life begins all over again. A procession of ambiguous images files past you, sights that you recall as in a forgotten dream, perplexing and unexpected visions, the daily suffering of those around you, the diverse colors of life—and money. Everywhere you look you see a world that has been transformed by the human thirst for consumption. You are dazzled by the blazing neon lights, which offer irrefutable evidence of a world of human activity and ceaseless labor...

And, in the midst of the monotonous and diffuse stream of questions that will henceforth frame your existence, you walk blindly towards your now spoiled place of refuge.

For you are a woman, and you are alone.

May Our Heavenly Father take you in His arms...

LETTER TO THE NEGRO PEARLS OF FRENCH EXPANSIONISM

Dear Romans,

You seem to have a taste for cultivating perfect specimens of black humanity, both in Africa and in Latin America, doing everything in your power to rekindle the greatness of Roman civilization. This is clearly a defining feature of French civilization. Yet, where will this taste for black pearls finally lead?

Is it a matter for rejoicing that, in the hearts and minds of great men, there is sufficient vanity and sufficient passion for conquest, to turn them into new Ceasar's, men who thirst for absolute power, and who, like Valéry's Monsieur Teste would be more than willing to trade academic immortality for the pleasures of solitude?

Beware liberal spirits here and elsewhere! You have never ceased to dream, and these dreams have inspired countless others, but deep inside you somehow feel that you have been thwarted…

But the exact opposite is true, as your very size should remind you. In fact, now is the time to demonstrate to the rest of the world that you have the right to exist, and that you are efficient on an international scale. You must show why your culture is relevant to the everyday lives of those peoples who bask in your bright light. And you must do so in a way that appeals to each and every constituency… But, do you really want to form an association of liberal spirits, as you claim? Is this really in your best interests?

For many of you, "advancing a noble cause" has become what is most important about your liberal ideology, its very reason for existing. Now you must do everything in your power to insure that your efforts, which were inspired by the tireless labor of many creative and diverse minds, are not squandered in vain, nor turned against you…

Who then will dare contest this divine right that is yours—which is lofty, useful, and noble, and which only serves to strengthen your resolve, as well as your political will? This is, of course, why you are always careful to exercise great prudence in granting pardon to those who challenge your authority…

It is, perhaps, the pride one feels in playing the role of master, a human being who enjoys boundless freedom, which now keeps you going. For, you are obviously incapable of renouncing the pretensions that sustain you. You fail to recognize yourself in the sweet old dotard that you have become. Is this a failure to see things as they are, or a matter of survival? What is unwholesome about all this is that your desire for eternal life seems to have become a professional necessity.

The most formidable risk, without a doubt, of la mission civilisatrice in the French-speaking world, also implicit in the politics of Coopération, is that the Negro, whose humiliated pride is the impetus behind his ideas, has begun to cultivate a liberty of spirit and action that borders on cynicism.

By necessity, of course, he is bound to France. But this bond will endure for the Negro only so long as it is expedient. This will also be true of the shape that his politics eventually take.

❧

The conservative political parties of every nation seek to swell their ranks with the guardians of culture, those who will unambiguously sing its praises.

And this is not by chance.

The Messianism that is implied by Coopération and the official policy in which the French language is promoted everywhere, naturally propel the ruling party towards adopting the easiest solutions, those that correspond to already preexisting structures: both psychological and collective ones. But, as we all know, perfect harmony is only achieved in the wake of conquest.

And the insufficiency of the political notions that now circulate throughout Negro France aptly demonstrates the lack of courage and the myopia of the French when it comes to the Third World's problems. For the average Frenchman, who likes to imagine that his hands are clean, tends to flee from all troubles of this nature, from worrying his head over difficult questions that do not concern him; as a matter of fact, he flees from anything that requires him to make a concerted effort. Thus, it is extremely difficult to make much progress in resolving these problems. It goes without saying that the Negro who casts his lot with this consumer civilization must not be faint of heart! ...

It must also be recognized that Negro France and French Africa will remain deadlocked, if neither the one nor the other ventures to articulate its fecund dissatisfaction at the current impasse. And, it is always possible to awaken one's faculty of adaptation.

A civilization that is based on the pursuit of material gain may find that it can thrive, even better than it did in previous days, by taking advantage of the irrationality and reflexive anti-racism of its populace, especially with the creative input of its brightest minds.

Negro France must do its part: It must immediately put its brains to work to help redress these urgent problems. On the other hand, French Africa should at last learn to feel some pride in itself, or it should simply hit the road.

But this particular France and this particular Africa cannot tolerate the thought of living together in harmony. Thus it was that they felt obliged to divest their unseemly coexistence of all ambiguity, through the internal coup d'état of racism.

And afterwards?

It may happen that the necessity of having to make a choice unleashes a newfound sense of what it means to be an individual– only to end by frustrating the individual and leading him to revolt. On the other hand, a new era of peace may be inaugurated, but one that is accompanied by a secret decadence... In both cases, there is regression, rather than progress.

And becoming what one is, according to a well-known formula, is a heroic task. De Gaulle himself, despite his strong and rich personality, or as a man who is faithful to the cultural values and ideology he espouses, can only be exonerated *after the fact*. For De Gaulle and his own Negro France, there is only the problem of *simplification*, but little thought is given to the question of method. He could at any time, if he so desired, interject the kind of sophisticated rigor that the Franco-Negro man inevitably experiences in his various interactions with others.

But, in De Gaulle's own case, there is no denying that everything seems to takes place as if the very formula of his soul was already predetermined by way of a series of complex and precise equations. And, like De Gaulle, each of us may also become a kind of algebraist of his own realities...

≪୨୭≫

To serve or not to serve. Everything takes place in Negro France as if the entire world consisted of nothing but the courageous little bourgeoisie who had, at some point in time, converted to Marxism.

But today, all those who reflexively cooperate situate themselves in the particular milieu where they happened to have been born. And the bourgeoisie, as much as the proletariat, do not question the inevitability of the separation of the classes.

All is reduced to categories that are as dreadful as they are comical, as if they somehow were especially invented for the technological era. In this uniformity, the Bolsheviks as well as the fascists are free to translate their preferences in terms of feeling…

But from whence comes the spleen that the average Frenchman feels for the grandeur that characterizes the politics of Negro France, and for the aid that is doled out to underdeveloped countries? From the impotence of this Frenchman when he realizes his inability to achieve such grandeur for himself, or even to conceive of it. It also comes from the remnants of the politically conquered power itself, the visible and irrefutable evidence of its former greatness, which tends to enervate the conquering power…

Here, despite all our efforts to keep them separate, serious-ness and lightness converge: and, when this happens, the colo-nial enterprise reveals itself as comical. And it is worth noting that the man who is purely French, as well as the man who is purely Negro, etc., are also figures of narrow-mindedness, however significant their cultural contributions. The point is not to cast blame upon Negro France or French Africa, but upon the gods of both—both of which are admirable but are finally dead-ends. By now, one no longer knows if these gods should be hated or loved, or if both should be worshiped at the same time—in order to minimize the risk. And there are plenty who mistake the desire to minimize risks for a gener-ous weakness, and, as a result, they will only share the wealth that they have accumulated with great reluctance. But it is, of course, good that a man should sometimes refrain from giving, so that he preserves the power to give in the future.

Ah! How fortunate we are to live through the good old days right now! How wonderful it is that we can, at least for the time being, make such a fuss over the black pearls of French culture! For now is the waning moment of cultural purities! Now is the time of the Negro! And, as we all know, the Negro is authorized to speak on matters of civilization, literature, Coopération, Negro-France, French Africa, racism, prejudice, the problems of underdevelopment! And, certainly, the Negro is quite articulate on such matters. His voice reverberates in the wilderness of abysmal ideologies, failed beginnings, dazzling illuminations, satirical jabs, and sword strokes in the water! ... No doubt, all of this must also be chalked up to the fact that we are living through the first moments of a fledgling hybrid civilization ... And yet, the time for making a decision is now. [...]

LETTER TO ALL RACISTS

Dear Intimate Enemies,

Although it is true that women are transformed into precious objects in the harems of our Negro Kings, the French woman–the type of woman whom you know very well–is a beautiful rose that lives in quick sand. You suck on her big toe as you watch her sinking into the sand, angling to get a better view of her shapely thighs. At last she disappears, fluttering like a stranded white pigeon. Death to the Negroes, and long live sodomy!

This French woman leaves nothing to chance: she plans her meals, the quarter-hour it takes for her to get her pedicure, the half-hour for her manicure, the time it takes to fix her hair, and every other waking moment of her day. She spends a good deal of her time making love with money and jewels–and sometimes, her husband. After her husband falls asleep, she stays by his side like a faithful watchdog, except for when she sneaks off to some hotel for momentary relief from guard duty...

Because he's never able to catch her at her game, her husband lives a melancholy life, for he knows very well what she's about. It is as if he dies a little bit every day, slowly, slowly, as if numbed by the repetitive stings of the lash... In short, he leads the life of a Negro, for in some hotel somewhere...

He thinks. He thinks. He thinks from inside his rib cage, suffocating for lack of air. With hardly a thought for the scandal he will create in the newspapers (which already know all about it), the husband reaches for his saber and revolver, which he conceals in his underwear, the true capital of France.

By now, hatred seeps from every pore of his body...

The husband goes out in search of his wife. His self-esteem and virility at stake, he pounces upon her. But the untamed shrew jumps up and escapes him, for she hasn't been waiting around, aimlessly fiddling with her brasserie. She takes a stab at him, swosh! She wounds him with her lying tongue! The husband bleeds.

The wife now bandages his wound, undressing him and helping him to once again stiffen his resolve. The woman who finds herself in this torturous situation fucks like a Negro: The very thought that she has turned her husband into her own little boy-toy makes her hot. For, while he is formally decked out in his struts and tails, she wears only her lace and garters.

Dear racists, it by your efforts that France will become great and will be saved from the Negro virus! You must keep up the good work! You must continue to refuse allowing your servants' quarters to be rented to Negroes—for, what would happen should too many of your wives learn to cry with pleasure? And, you know very well that most of the guests of Negroes can be there for only one reason...

Flee! Flee from the black plague! Never under any circumstances allow a black servant to work in your homes! For you would certainly come to regret his professional ethics... Do not allow any Negro whatsoever to enter into the sacred chambers of your beautiful apartment with, of course, one possible exception—and here, following the example of the *Négresco*, which was so named because it was the first palace to hire Negro servants — of the Negro woman, for, Lord knows, there are certainly times...

So, ladies, when you hear the stairs creaking outside your window, you may rest assured that it is only your Negro housekeeper who has been faithfully performing her duties...

In the streets, if you happen to come across a Negro, move quickly to the other side of the sidewalk, for there is no knowing what may happen to you. One evening, as you are strolling along the sidewalk, minding your own business, you might suddenly feel something poke you from behind–and you may be certain that it won't be a stray tree branch!

And let's be frank, dear ladies: your husbands do a lot of barking, but they do very little biting. So you might as well forget right now the silly notion that President of the French Republic would be willing to chase all the Negroes out of France, merely to please you! The fact is that nobody wants to hear your opinion about much of anything. In fact, it is a real pain in the ass for all concerned parties when you decide to give it.

But, don't take my word for it. Go ahead and speak your mind: We'll see how long it takes before you run out of breath...

Of course, I know that what I'm saying here is bound to disappoint you. You had naively imagined that the Negro was a simple and trustworthy man. You had even allowed him to become the Head of an African State; but, as it turns out, he seems to be little more than a mad man, a crude comedian who likes to tell bad jokes. You had all done him the service of declaring him to be a civilized man, and this is how he repays you! Why, in some places, he has even tried to turn himself into a kind of king among rats, the miserable communist rats! But it now seems quite clear that the Negro is a man who speaks out of both sides of his mouth.

You! You who are whiter than White: You are the color of natural champagne, white two times over because you are primordially white–the best of all whites! You are white as chicken meat– the most savory cut of meat for the most refined palates and the most delicate stomachs (whether it be White-on-Black, or Black-on-White), you are the purest sort of White, the White that becomes unconcealed in the midst of clear and empty fields of pure white, for, as you know, it is only in the open air of nature that one can breathe the purest and whitest oxygen, without which one will quickly turn green... Oh, you! You are a novice in the face of wholly new sensations! You seek to create an artificial paradise, simply by staying up late in the nights, by turning all your nights white, nights of riot and orgy, nights of sleeplessness, sleeping only when the evening is at its blackest, the hour when the Negroes secretly dance — Black-on-White: Oh, happy incest! –truths that are not roses! And, to accompany your aristocratic sexuality, your refined taste for glistening oysters, there is nothing better than a little dry white–the drier the better!–to clear your educated palate, as every part of your body is lovingly stroked, a succession of black delights.

Well, here it is then, a little something to go along with your morning breakfast of ripe black bananas, which you swallow with satisfaction, while spitting on Negroes' heads! I present to you a modest little dictionary of helpful terms, a kind of mibachibouzouk…

But, what is the meaning of this tirade, you ask? Who could be so niggardly, foul-mouthed, and unrefined as to call your gentle, elegant, and xenophobic sadism into question?

ॐॐॐ

Yep, it's me.

Rush hour: This is what has been going on non-stop since African nations declared their independence from you. The motorcades of Negro kings on their way to pay homage to De Gaulle have created a real traffic jam in Paris.

Jam jar: This is the portable refrigerator of the Blacks.

Indulgence: This word is uttered through France whenever, instead of punishing the black-rabble by refusing them financial assistance, the French write a check that saddles them with further debt.

Jesus: This word refers to the Son of the God of Coopération, the Father of Christian ideology, and the love for all mankind. His name is even more venerated than the blessed water of Lourdes, at the Élysée.

Light: the Whites have brought light to Blacks in the fullness of day, so that Blacks might better see how destitute and naked they truly are.

Honeymoon: This word is only to be found in White civilization. It refers to the period of time following the wedding of two white people who are in love; after these young folks have been married for awhile, instead of remaining like happy little children–in other words, instead of behaving like Negroes–they behave like ferocious bears and begin attacking one another.

Munch-munch: This expression refers to the savage habits of cannibalistic Negroes, for once tea biscuits were introduced among the more civilized whites, it was replaced by the expression *crunch-crunch.*

Pen-holder: a device that has, for some time now, served Negroes only too well, for they have not been slow in stealing it from Whites in order to put it to their own ends.

Ritornello: The stuttering sound that an African president makes when he comes to beg from the French, in terror of being left in total destitution. Generally, before making this abrasive sound, he falls upon his knees and then grovels before the General JesusDeGaulle.

Scruple: This is when the African is careful to show his report card to the civilized world, after having forged all his good grades.

Hubbub: A noise that may be heard across the African continent, whenever Third World people rant against colonialism.

Bragging: This is what the Black man does whenever he tries to pass himself off as a White.

Human: This refers to what we all truly are–Black as well as White–so long as we're not afraid to whip out our goods behind the men's room.

෴

Racists! My dear intimate enemies! You are truly foxes!

And the fox is a cunning animal. Like the fox, you have mastered the art of playing dead. Then you sneak back to the scene of the crime and cover up your dirty tracks, but not before leading the various dogs that run rampant in the underdeveloped world into the treacherous waters of nationalism.

Or, now playing the role of demagogue, you jump into these waters yourself, but not without a few tricks up your sleeve.

For, suddenly, you will swim off and leave the dogs floundering in the water, not sure which way to turn. Then you will peddle as far off as possible to keep them from imagining that they can live without you—in peace.

You especially enjoy making a grand entrance.

Although it's true that you're a human being, you are one of those formidable spirits with extremely sharp teeth. While no one can deny that you have a head, no one is quite sure about the existence of your tail, for you conceal it from us, like all the many creature comforts that your money buys for you.

Money is for you what water is for fish, and if you swim in aristocratic waters, it is because they are the reefs and shoals that are best suited for keeping you afloat. For if you ever tried to live in a world without your prejudices, you would no doubt sink like a rock!

But you swim—like the hippopotamus—in capitalism's oily waters. And all the little White children who revolt against you (for they have not yet accumulated much capital and so don't have much to lose) are Negroes of an altogether different species, totally oblivious to the ways of these black seahorses from warmer climes.

This is why anti-Negro and anti-Jewish sentiments ultimately serve your own interests, making you stronger than all those you seek to subjugate. Without them, you would be as flabby as a mollusk on a spoon. Racial prejudices are therefore extremely useful to you. They harden you by providing you with a rock-like protective shell.

This is also why those Whites who live in the U.S.A. very much need their "black problem," just as they need their Vietnam War.

For isn't it true that this device is ultimately far richer, and has more vitality (to the degree that it poses a greater threat) than the sexual revolution with its cult of eroticism? ...

The black problem therefore, in its most affective moments, swells like an enormous rugby ball, assuming a vaguely sexual form. Whenever this ball becomes slightly deflated, it's only because the viewing public can no longer afford to buy a ticket to enjoy the spectacle.

But the black problem itself awakens many fears. The Black man is constantly on the verge of a heart attack, terrified that he will be sent back to the morgue of an endless slavery. As a result, he is content to remain the archetype of the hard worker: a member of a cheap labor pool without any real voice at the heart of the enterprise.

Black problems can only be cleansed in blood baths. This is the only way that Blacks may at last come to grasp that they condemn themselves when they choose the path of the anemic– and then die of despair because they are no more than honey-tongued domestics

As for Negro France, it had best be on its guard against the fall-out from the black problem. Accidents can happen quite suddenly! A few million Negroes set up shop in your country, and there you have it…!

To avoid such contingencies, it suffices to interject a little bogus agony into the day-to-day lives of Negroes (blacks, or white trash): and, the easiest way to accomplish this goal is to nail them in the paternalistic coffin of high interest loans, credit debt, and lotteries.

In this way, you'll be certain to gain their votes during the next election, for you'll instill in them the hope of survival, merely because they imagine that they once came close to hitting the jackpot.

Thus, the advantage of a developed society is its ability to assign to specialists the task of creating–by way of a complex social ranking system that is reinforced through economic controls–Negroes, sub-Negroes, semi-Negroes, sub-Whites, near-Whites, and, finally, Whites…

Therein lies the miracle of specialization.

Moreover, this society of specialization knows very well how to turn the cult of human dignity into a routine game. For everything really turns on the axis of production. And production feeds capital because the latter serves the former. In this way, we are all condemned to toil for the richest of the rich. And this leaves us with two miserable choices: to be or not to be.

The only conclusion that can be drawn then is that you must be rich, if you don't want to be a Negro!

But then how can you ever become rich, if all the means, as well as the ends, are already taken? If you can never generate enough capital to be rich, unless you're already born with it? ... A tear for the black-rabble–Lord–for mercy's sake! ...

≪≫

Do I hear you begin to grumble, oh venerable *white man*? You must excuse me if I bring to your attention certain responsibilities that you prefer to ignore...

You are a racist! Well, stay that way, in the name of the Negro-Jew that you worship! For, isn't it true, *for both of us*, that– without our prejudices–we will become insufferably boring, like wavering ghosts?

[...]

LETTER TO THE GHOSTWRITERS OF FAMOUS WRITERS

Dear Black-rabble,

You are truly *nègre*, for you are blacks who are also ghostwriters! You guzzle beer like those who have spent many long winters in the dungeons of the King of Prussia, and then you harvest the fruits of your anonymity! Toss you a few coins, and you're content to sneak off and waste away in some other clime…

You are not even a manual laborer, for he at least earns a steady salary and may, without turning red, remain loyal to his profession. But you? You are an altogether different story! Where do you get the audacity to shamelessly confess that you have your very own pimp, who exploits your most crack-pot ideas, so that he may imbibe the opium of posthumous glory?

Should you reveal your true identity as an obscure drudge, you will not thereby gain in respect, for all are rightly cautious when it comes to the likes of you. The best that you can hope for is to be admired in retrospect.

In fact, it is always good for a writer who is destined to be famous to start with less than nothing, one sou and ten centimes, in the cause of a successful author fending off ogres, in the golden days of his glory… And it is often the case that the secret mouse of his glory days is a woman. You reverse this time-honored myth and thereby provoke the curiosity of the public, which does not hesitate to take you for a rat that nibbles upon library cheese, an intellectual who haunts the cellars and city streets—and a peddler of yellowed manuscripts, devoted to the thankless task of boiling pots for some incontinent, old geezer.

It is for all you poor birds of a feather that I, a Negro, decided to work like a White man: by thinking. Hee, hee!

I did this for you, for I did not want you to be turned into yet another Negro leper, which would then make things even more complicated for all the other Negroes out there, and all others who are blessed with miseries of this sort...

Here then, for your convenience, is a formula for denegrification, one that is, admittedly, crudely commercial. I am well aware that, as a rule, you prefer to pass yourself off as a respectable citizen, and so you gravitate towards detective stories or bodice rippers...

Would you like to discuss detective stories?

Then, when it's your turn, perhaps you can tell me a few things that you've learned about bodice rippers...

Ghostwriters [*Nègres*] of famous writers, you are terribly frustrated because your genius is castrated by the law of silence: I therefore propose to show you, in these pages, how you may become a ghostwriter and still remain white.

But you must follow my advice to the letter; for, otherwise, if it were proven that all Whites are as unfortunate as you, why would those who live in the Third World bother to lift themselves up and better their condition?

And so here it is.

I suggest that, henceforth, you make it a rule of thumb (in your work as a peddler of yellowed manuscripts) to do your utmost to craft the best possible detective story imaginable. You can do this by digging out the choicest literary pearls: its best descriptions, erotic details, suspense, and crime scenes, which may be found in formulaic anthologies, especially in the epilogues, containing the details leading up to the arrest of the guilty.

I am determined to bestow upon all you unhappy and cancer-infested writers of potboilers with a miraculous device, the likes of which you have never before seen. With this little gadget, you will be able to compose any number of literary works and thereby bring a smile to the lips of your employer. But you must rely exclusively (since we are on this subject) on the titles by famous detective writers: those masters of the *Série noire* [Black Series] (Carter Brown, James Hadley Chase, Peter Cheyney, John MacDonald, Robert Fish, Douglas Warner...), and those of the *Série blanche* [White Series], especially the authors of spy novels (*The Spy Who Came In From The Cold*), or those who write about "sensational" crime: Truman Capote, Hitchcock, Simenon, Agatha Christie, Jean Bruce, and so many others, published by Fayard and Masque, whether in "The Saint" Series (Leslie Charteris), or in the Mauve Series, or at Denoël (Sebastien Japrisot), or even Fleuve Noir or Presses Pockets.

This list, which is far from being exhaustive, has merit only to the extent that it may assist you upon the various paths that you will find it necessary to travel in order to write your own books...

Therefore, black-rabble, an enormous task awaits you. You must spend a great deal of time reading the many books compiled on this gigantic list. But the effort that you expend will not be in vain.

Here then is the magical recipe for your success. Your hard work as a ghostwriter [*pisse-copie*], or the Ghostwriter [*Nègre*] of a famous writer, should, here, permit you—much like the Surrealists—to concoct a Dadaist "exquisite corpse." I am, of course, speaking allegorically, for to become mired in intellectualism of any sort is ill advised for the likes of you...

For your books (if written according to this formula) should enable you to invent, according to the colors of your own imagination, ONE BILLION NOVELS, NO SWEAT!...

With this type of mechanism, you will have at your disposal all the ready-made dishes you could ever desire to serve up to your reading public: all you need do is find the right sauce to accompany the dish.

For, in the novel, in all novels, even the most descriptive ones, the décor is significant only when it sheds light on the inner world of the characters... When these descriptions are included in a documentary sense, they are mere filler, adding nothing to the story: description for its own sake is like a placebo, a fake drug that almost never does the trick... In other words, dear black-rabble, we observe what takes place on the outside, but it is not really the outside that we are observing. The art of the novel serves to remind us that there is a story to each one of our lives. Our own personal stories are often interrupted, but the novel represents the main events in a condensed or "thickened" form. It is precisely this "thickness" that inspires us to re-read our own lives in light of the novel. The entire art of the novelist consists in knowing how to underscore this thickness. In this way, one may finally come to grasp the meaning of the adage that 'beautiful books seem to be written in a language of their own'…

But, let's not get off track: after all, you are only a black ghostwriter, and so you should not aim too high. You are widely viewed as a kind of a worker on the chain gang: so avoid things that might distract you. And, don't torment yourself over literary themes that you hope to communicate. Just focus on your main task as a black ghostwriter who manufactures literature for consumption…

Here then is what I propose to you, in hopes that you may be able to come up with a consumable detective story.

It remains up to you to give it the largest possible framework so that your novel will be able to accommodate new and interesting material–which can compete with the best novels in today's marketplace and offer your readers a good story that is truly worthy of success. "Would you like to read one of the most fabulous detective stories ever written? Would you like to cook up, for your own pleasure, a really good detective story? Would you truly like that? Well, then you need only choose your sauce. Go ahead. It's great fun! It's as exciting, amusing, and quite simple!"

So, take a look at this: Here is a small sample of a book that you might write, but, of course, the possibilities are endless.…

Letter to the Ghostwriters of Famous Writers

Alphabetic Index of Themes (A to Z)	Table of Emotional Qualities	Text
	-1!•	He heard: If I put a bullet to my head, will you buy me some cognac first? Don't be stupid. You're not going to kill anyone tonight.
(example) SUSPENSE	1□	The spy stepped into the light and gazed at the other with a quizzical smile. He was tall for a Spaniard and wore loose trousers and a small farmer's vest. Around his neck, there was a coarse and uneven bit of lace, and his boots shone like silver. His eyes, which were buried deep in a face full of wrinkles, shone brightly from under the rim of his sombrero.
	2x	Why not? The stranger advanced slowly towards the door.
	3■	"You can kill anyone for me," shouted the other, desperately mad and searching for his own revolver. "Anyone! No matter how powerful! If I give you the word, you shoot him!" "One of us has to die," he said, taking out his revolver. "Whether I kill you, or you kill me doesn't make all that much difference. We'll just be letting the best booze in the world spill onto the open market." "Yes," said the other. "That's what I intend to do."
	4○	Someone laughed from the door. A brunette stood there, quite happy with herself. She laughed again, and her white teeth sparkled in the light of the setting sun. Then she came closer to the spy. She lowered her gun, slipped her fingers beneath his shirt, and began clawing at his chest with her nails. "I love you, honey," she said.

Authors	Genre	Titles	Legend
William P. McGivern	suspense	A Choice of Killers	-1!=humor
J.H. Chase	action	No Orchids for Miss Blandish	1"description
Ian Fleming		James Bond	2x suspense 3n
Ian Fleming	espionage	From Russia With Love	violence
Carter Brown	police comedy	The Crownof Diamonds	4¡ eroticism

This is how it works. Consider:

1) You read the text as you would any other book, from beginning to end, that is

   a   b   c   d   e

   -1!•   1□   2x   3■   4○

   and then you reassemble the text from the preceding page (humor–description–suspense–violence–eroticism), and consider:

2) You reconstruct the text by combining it as follows: *c, b, a, d, e*; or even *e, a, c, b, d*; or *d, c, e, b, a*.

3) Or, consider this: if *a* =1; *b* = 2: *c* = 3; *d* = 4; *e* = 5; the possible combinations, each of which can bring a new meaning to the text, may be as follows (to mention only a few!):

1,2,3,4,5	1,2,4,3,5	1,4,3,5,2
5,1,3,2,4	1,2,4,5,3	1,4,2,5,3
2,5,3,1,4	2,1,4,3,5	1,4,2,3,5
4,5,3,1,2	2,1,4,5,3	1,5,3,2,4
4,5,2,1,3	2,1,5,3,4	1,5,3,4,2
4,5,1,3,2	2,1,3,4,5	1,5,4,3,2
4,1,5,3,2	3,1,2,4,5	1,5,2,3,4
4,1,3,2,5	3,2,1,4,5	1,5,4,2,3
4,1,3,5,5	3,2,4,1,5	1,3,4,5,2
4,2,5,3,1	3,2,5,4,1	1,3,4,2,5

4,2,5,1,3	3,2,5,1,4	1,3,2,5,4
4,3,5,1,2	3,2,1,5,4	1,3,5,2,4
4,3,5,2,1	5,4,1,3,2	5,4,2,1,3
5,4,1,2,3	5,1,4,3,2	5,1,2,3,4
5,1,4,2,3	5,3,4,2,1	5,3,1,4,2
5,3,4,1,2	1,4,3,2,5	
etc.,etc.!...		

4) By selecting any one of the references that are listed in the "table of emotional qualities," and by connecting it with the pages that follow, you may reconstitute yet another text, one that suits your own tastes.

Do you prefer to create only police humor in order to keep your reading public entertained? Then you need do no more than endlessly combine those items that are listed in the corresponding column.

Moreover, my dear black-rabble, you will also satisfy the public's demand for EROTICISM, SUSPENSE, and VIOLENCE, by following these same methods. You simply read through the selections of eroticism, suspense, or violence that are listed in the indicated columns, and when you would like to add a bit of wickedness or blood to your tale, you stir in the appropriate coloring, one that suits your own tastes...

If you want to toss in a bit of Simeon, his descriptive portraits, for instance, or the long sections where he sets the stage for his dramas, then refer to the "DESCRIPTION" section, as it suits your tastes, or the "SUSPENSE" section, and then the "VIOLENCE" section, or the action of his choice, or your choice, as it seems fitting to you.

Just apply black to white... and the job will be done in no time!

To give you a better idea of this method, find below a few pages that may be "progressively" read:

N.B.: You can read in any possible and imaginable direction. In each instance, the story will never be the same, and the combinations are infinite.

THE GUINEA PIGS FOR EXPERIMENTATION

Alphabetic Index of Themes (A to Z)	Table of Emotional Qualities	Text
	-1!●	He heard: If I put a bullet to my head, will you buy me some cognac first? Don't be stupid. You're not going to kill anyone tonight.
(example) SUSPENSE	1□	The spy stepped into the light and gazed at the other with a quizzical smile. He was tall for a Spaniard and wore loose trousers and a small farmer's vest. Around his neck, there was a coarse and uneven bit of lace, and his boots shone like silver. His eyes, which were buried deep in a face full of wrinkles, shone brightly from under the rim of his sombrero.
	2x	Why not? The stranger advanced slowly towards the door. "One of us has to die," he said, taking out his revolver. "Whether I kill you, or you kill me doesn't make all that much difference. We'll just be letting the best booze in the world spill onto the open market."
	3■	"You can kill anyone for me," shouted the other, desperately mad and searching for his own revolver. "Anyone! No matter how powerful! If I give you the word, you shoot him!" "Yes," said the other. "That's what I intend to do."
	4○	Someone laughed from the door. A brunette stood there, quite happy with herself. She laughed again, and her white teeth sparkled in the light of the setting sun. Then she came closer to the spy. She lowered her gun, slipped her fingers beneath his shirt, and began clawing at his chest with her nails. "I love you, honey," she said.

Alphabetic Index of Themes (A to Z)	Table of Emotional Qualities	Text
(example) SUSPENSE	-1!●	The woman shook her head. Just once. "Oh my!" she cried. "That's not cheap wine. They'll lock you away for pulling a stunt like that. And if the Boss found out what we were up to, he'd make us dig all the way to China. What's the matter with you, Angie? You'd do just as well to buy a razor and cut your own throat, but not here! You'll bleed all over the rug."
	1□	Crack! Kaboom! "Christ almighty!" the spy exclaimed. He carefully put his fingers to the part of his forehead where he was wounded, and then felt his stomach. When you weigh a hundred and ten kilos, and you get whacked by a club that size, you are quite likely to be ruined forever. "You will pay for this!" he shouted in a panicked voice.
	2x	The woman's voice was hardened, harsh: "Angie! Angie, listen to me." "You thought you could control me, one way or another, isn't that so? Both of you?" "All right, Angie. All right. And you're some choirboy. A worthless piece of shit, but a choirboy all the same. So why don't you just take it to the cops? Without responding, he reached for his gun and pointed it at both of them.
	4○	But the woman walked toward his enemy. And he sensed at once that, behind her mask lurked a deeply evil nature, a hideous beast. It was enough to look at her to give you an electric jolt. Her eyes were nothing but blue porcelain. But the flames danced within them. Her legs were firm and smooth like ivory, and so were her shoulders.

Alphabetic Index of Themes (A to Z)	Table of Emotional Qualities	Text
	-1! •	"Is that enough for you? Is that all?"
	• 1 □ ? ○	"Listen to me, Angie. If this stuff's no good, I know where to find you. If there's someone who should be worried, it's you. So far, the kid's doing okay. But he better keep it up. The Boss doesn't want you hanging around here, so you better find yourself some new playmates, at least for the next two months. Everybody's got what was coming to them, and so now we can go our separate ways, right?" But to kill her? His mouth grew dry at the very idea that he might have actually gone through with it. He now had only one desire: to take her in his arms and let her feel his tenderness. He loved her small, heart-shaped face, her little chin, and the two tiny wrinkles between her eyebrows. "I didn't mean to scare you, Eva," he said. "I'm sorry. I..." "You idiot! You coward!" she shouted in a furious voice. "Get out of my sight right now, you son of a bitch." "Whore! I'll teach you how to talk to me!"
(example) SUSPENSE	3 ■	When he was about to fire, the stranger raised his arm; he held a riding crop in his hand, which he brought down upon his face, trying to force the gun from his hand. Twice, and then a third time, Angie sought to avoid the lash, but unsuccessfully. Step by step, lashing him from the left and then the right, he forced him into the hallway; a blow on his face sent him to his knees, groaning in pain, where he was beaten mercilessly. He seemed to hear a knocking at the door...
	4 ○	"Hi, honey," she said to in a happy voice. "Where are you off to? Unless it makes no difference to you. We're just alike, you and I. Take me anywhere you want, so long as it's far from here. And to think that I came here for the surfing! I might as well have gone to the North Pole! That's how it is, Daddy dearest... Do you like it with whips? I have a whole harem of treats in store for you. If you've got the money, the choice is yours. So how do you like it? With the knife or whip?"

LEGEND

-1!• Humor   3n Violence
1□ Description   4○ Eroticism
2x Suspense   •1□ Dingotism
                            ?○

Authors	Titles	Genre
William P. McGivern	*A Choice of Killers*	Suspense
J.H. Chase	*No Orchids for Miss Blandish*	Suspense
Ian Fleming	*James Bond*	Espionage
Ian Fleming	*From Russia With Love*	Espionage
Carter Brown	*The Crown of Diamonds*	Espionage
Agatha Christie	*Hercule Poirot's Christmas*	Psychology
J.H. Chase	*Eva*	Psychology
Simeon	*Maigret's First Case*	Drama
Stephen Marlowe	*On The Red Track*	Suspense
John Starr	*The Gold Jar*	Crime Annals
Joyce Porter	*Dover and the Unkindest Cut of All*	Police Comedy

And so, you see, the text could be read or combined in a million different ways, with an infinite number of possible meanings. You will have written, *en nègre* [as a ghostwriter], as many books as you could ever hope for: novels of mystery, intrigue, suspense, those that build up to a dramatic climax, as well as those that exploit the "flashback method," thousands of works, whereas, by reversing the process, you will end up with a new kind of mystery novel–one in which the plot's harrowing twists and turns are repackaged as historical narrative: in this case, you simply combine numbers 50, 30, 100, etc. to form an entirely new combination, one that can be reshuffled any number of times, in any number of directions.

This particular sample merely hints at the enormous quantity of books might be composed from the various titles and authors whom I have made here into my "guinea pigs," being the hungry little savage that I am.

Let me remind you again that this is only a modest example, one that reveals only a brief glimpse of all that is involved. For writing a novel in this way is not unlike performing exploratory surgery: Monotony and boredom are absolutely forbidden.

By adhering to this formula, dear black-rabble, by composing a new work with an eye towards the demands of the marketplace, *to become* the nègre [*ghostwriter*] *of a famous writer*, is to liberate yourself: it is a key to unlocking the boldest and most powerful combinations inherent in a language–which may thereafter be placed at your customers' disposal. It's a little like algebra, but algebra for small children.

This algebra does not involve the analysis of objects, but rather the analysis of actions. These actions are not themselves objects in their own right, but they are bound up with the basic structures of our existence–and reveal the innermost spiritual laws of suspense and blood, now made available for consideration.

And so, should you take this method to heart, assiduous in your application of its compositional techniques, the work that you perform as a ghostwriter will enable you, on your own merits, to write *The Thousand and One Nights* of the detective novel– the entire *Série Noir* [Black Series] in a single volume. But a volume that is born from a billion possible combinations, extracted from a billion preexisting titles.

Allow me, nonetheless, to alert you to a number of practical problems that may arise.

These will prove insurmountable if you fall into the trap of what I do not hesitate to call *cryptogrammamania*: the joyless game of chasing after petty trifles. In terms of the greater composition, these elements tend to recede like indistinct colors into the background, or they are like vague lines that fail to connect with the greater thematic elements of the fresco...

Be that as it may, to be the ghostwriter of a famous writer can be rewarding — and quite easy–if you can cash in on the public's affection: this is done through carefully selecting those texts containing attitudes and formulas that they themselves will find the most suitable to adopt. You will therefore perform double duty, as both a teacher and a researcher, flattering your readers' structures of expectation, while maintaining a perfectly clear conscience, for you, after all, are no more than a ghostwriter. Hence, you are free to laugh up your sleeve.

As a writer of detective stories, glossarist, and critic, you should be able to draft a recipe for all the meals you cook, but you should also be able to test their actual flavor. These are, of course, separate talents, but they are not entirely unrelated.

Your task is neither to interpret ambiguities, nor to justify what is finally incoherent, nor to analyze detective novels by means of compression, expansion, paraphrase, or close scrutiny with X-rays and seismographs, like some passive and naive reporter.

But, from under this gigantic heap of masterpieces of thought, whose material has been extracted from the archives of your blood, you must enter into the game of language and thereby create works of indisputable worth, works whose incomparable quality (and thus your motivations for composing them) cannot be denied.

It is therefore truly in your grasp to create a billion titles, the Bible for all literary fanatics: a genre that will rise up like a veritable fairy palace, an architectural wonder, speckled with descriptions, psychology, action, and blood, accompanied by fascinating tales of crime and punishment. A book that offers interminable insight upon the various references that you employ, as well as infinite possibilities for its future interpretation: You will set your own *Thousand and One Nights* upon a pedestal that will bring torturous agony to many of your readers, the height of despair for the literary bastards.

The reading public has sharp teeth and is ravenous to the point of delirium. It will remain so for you as long as you are careful to maintain in each of your combinations an apocalyptic dimension; that is, the total ensemble of diverse combinations which you draw together must foster in your readers the vertiginous terror that comes from standing too close to the abyss.

And so, there it is, my dear black-rabble, in a nutshell. For now, your genius is held hostage by your anonymity. It's up to you to show us what you've got!

Your fellow black ghostwriter

LETTER TO ASTÉRIX'S FATHERS

Dear Blissfully Ignorant Rogues,

Everyone lies to the average Frenchman.

And so we find ourselves the recipients of important missives that seem to come from another world.

In your farcical delirium, which is emphatically not innocent, you slyly wink at the public to measure the extent of its simplemindedness.

The preponderance of a certain nationalism, the theories of Tintin on the subject of Antiquity, the taste that you reveal for current events in your themes, combined with a daring but finally satiric pot-pourri of similar themes, show that you are complicit in the secret decline that is underway, and that makes the road to progress ever more difficult...

There was once a time when the vainglorious desire for cultural achievement, in all senses of the word, made of the French a being whom all efforts to oppose chaotically floundered... The sad impotence of those who resisted is competently illustrated in the literature of the past.

Why is that you have now decided to efface all hope from the spirit of those who still strive to achieve? It seems nearly miraculous! From this seemingly insignificant change comes an entirely new metamorphosis, a fertile new order, an impressive power that challenges and recreates a whole new species of la gauloiserie; that is, the art of telling vulgar jokes, lampooning and insulting everything in sight, all of which is packaged and sold at a profit by activist shopkeepers, who chuckle with black humor...

Ah, yes! Our ancestors the Gauls! Never will the French comprehend that it is precisely here, in this *gauloiserie* that they imagine they have renounced, that they have found an unexpected remedy for all their ills—one that is even more perfect and more pure.

And the mistake they make, in this instance, lies in their pretending to raise (whether in ethical or religious terms, or even in some moralistic sense) a serious problem, which is, at heart, little more than a matter of hygiene...

Once it is acknowledged that Astérix is little more than a technique to encourage good hygiene, it should be obvious that the mere existence of such a widely celebrated tool may circumvent the future explosion of the black problem in France. Could this be due to the fact that the author (although not the animator) is ... a Negro?! Admittedly, he is of mixed origins, but he is a Negro all the same—one with a handsome head of frizzy hair! ...

As for Astérix, in order to defeat the black problem in France—the problem of the Gauls and Romans, or, the problem of the Negroes and the Whites, to put it simply — it suffices to rely upon funny gadgets, channeling this difficult social problem in a positive way and, at the same time, appearing to overcome it.

This pretentious feat is pulled off in a manner that is both funny and wisely naïve.

In doing so, the adventures of Astérix deftly serve as a comic outlet for the pent up frustrations of Negro France, frustrations that are mitigated when one accepts the premise that they refer to ancient times.

It is not difficult to perceive in all this a familiar psychological dynamic at work, the necessity of the scapegoat—and, in this case, a ridiculous one, to boot. And, as we all know, the scapegoat played an important role in nearly all the religions of antiquity, most obviously in the case of the Christian religion (Is not Jesus, 'the Lamb of God,' who is crucified for the sins of the world?). In our own days, this dynamic is alive and well, although it manifests itself in insidiously refined and often imperceptible forms. Moral of the story: Black Africa was fucked from the start. So, we'd best pull the plug on the billions that are being thrown away on assistance to under-developed countries. Long live France, the great hexagon!

The hidden lesson behind Astérix's many farces may be summed up as follows: Because individualism has destroyed nearly all forms of traditional authority, it has become a matter of vital necessity in our days to recreate new forms of authority to prevent the outbreak of chaos.

LETTER TO PHILISTINE *NEGROPHILES*

Dear Jesuits,

With the raging hunger of energetic monks, the concierges of Négritude (as they loudly proclaimed that Africa was one of the most culturally sophisticated of all the marginal civilizations, its jerry-rigged folklore a dazzling wonder from the world's underbelly–with the help of the professional hucksters who make a living by shedding tears while living like fat cats on Africa's dramas and most idiotic myths–even as it rots with the mildew of forgotten treasures), were able to fool the entire world into believing that this venerable old continent has absolutely no body, no heart, nor (metaphysical) life, outside of the way it is described by the philistines: I mean the shameless and irresponsible negrophiles who act with total impunity...

Of course, these scoundrels have by now become quite dexterous in their pharisaism, and so they do not dare to deny what the rest of us have, little by little, gradually come to realize– and not only us, but many others across the world–which is the obvious fact that there is no such thing as a "black problem" in and of itself. For there is only the problem of the economic–and the violent conflicts that accompany this problem–(and such conflicts do not, in other places throughout the world, differ all that much, whether they emanate from the left or the right): the role of the Man who is black is certainly spectacular in such conflicts, but only because he brings a certain color to them.

And thus, restored to the true color of his skin, but now shorn of its inconvenient human dignity, which is so often strutted out in times of war and conflict, he can be reduced to a cardboard figure of the underdeveloped wretch. In fact, his skin becomes the very emblem of the economic curse that nature has bestowed upon him.

This is why, today, second only to the Congo, it is Biafra that speaks to us the most. For in this case, we can no longer pretend that it is merely a question of cultivating the happy and abundant farmlands of a depopulated Africa, whose happiness was merely baptized by the arrival of the White Man: here, the false glitter of White colonialism collides with the actual dramas of the black world; here, at last, it is impossible to close our eyes to an Africa whose image has been grotesquely distorted by the blind ideologues and travel writers....

For the traditions of the legends from this continent, baptized in torture, reveal certain truths that are not reducible to the sleepy-eyed views of those who assign to Negroes the miserable vocation of somber beggars, worthy of no more than a leprous glory and a crown of slobber. The timeless drama—often laughable—of the Sons of the Night.

No one can deny the reality of the misery, the disorder that comes with underdevelopment, the oppression that indeed exists, the fact of slavery, the fruits of prayer, blood, and violence, and all the other problems that are intrinsic to our diverse cultures.

This is why one must denounce in a deceptively bombastic voice the snobbism of all those who, even now, wear themselves out singing hymns about Africa's undiscovered museums and the delights of its tropical gardens. The convulsive infantilism of these snobs, whose insipid vitality plays directly into the hands of the Negrophiles, not to mention the most reactionary sections of the black population, reinforces the worst sort of slave mentality— which consists in defining oneself, not in relation to oneself and to authentically African realities, but exclusively in relation to the concerns of the White man and to the canons of White civilization.

Letter to Philistine Negrophiles

If *négritude* is in any way still relevant, it is only relevant insofar as it may serve as a kind of stage upon which new dramas may be played out. The goal of these new dramas, however, would not be to erect yet more altars and idols to a hundred myths, none of which address or correspond to authentic Africa realities; at present, however, *négritude* is little more than a barnyard riot of chimeras in which the imaginations of the merchants of ideology may run amok, a hastily cobbled scaffolding upon which a thousand lies have been erected—lies that are, most likely, intended to reassure the stock market that Africa's unruly primitives harbor some redeeming value, despite the anxieties of the petty investors.

The truth is that the various journalists, sociologists, ethnologists, Africanists, literary types, Negrophile "specialists," and so on, who write about Africa, are seeking to invent an Africa that can serve as a backdrop for them to reveal to the entire world their own genius. Under the pretext of serving Africa, they do everything in their power to imprison it within the *magic lamp of literature.*

What else may we call this strange situation, in which a White man who has never set foot in Africa, outside of a few pseudo-cultural incursions, nonetheless imagines that he is authorized to write about it? Or, in what effectively amounts to the same thing, a Black man, who is acculturated to White society at too early an age, and who lives in African society, but without comprehending it, becomes an "expert" writer? ...A literary cult with a fixed *code* and a stale, Negro-African stench, one that is exclusively comprised of elements intended to "reassure" the status quo: a sloppy chef's stew that is one-part bananas, one-part Negro folklore, one-part philosophy.

৵৽

It is, of course, true that the black problem in France is not as urgent as the black problem in the U.S.A., and that there is no legalized form of racial segregation in France, a nation where, not so very long ago, the second most powerful elected official was Gaston Monnerville, the senator from Lot.

It is also true that, in addition to black laborers and students, there are some 15,000 Senegalese residents in France. In fact, there are more Dahomean physicians in Paris than there are in Dahomey itself. It is also estimated that 75,000 blacks from Guadeloupe live in France, and every year there are about 10,000 more new arrivals...

And for most inhabitants of the West Indies, Madagascar, or the African continent, Paris remains an intellectual Mecca.

But it is crucial to not shut one's eyes to the facts in the name of a so-called anti-racism, which is actually a paternalism authorizing Whites to assume responsibility for the destiny of Blacks, and which encourages the Negro—at the first sight of trouble—to flee into the warm embrace of the French Republic...

It is not, however, the right to be a foreigner that I am calling into question. After all, there are plenty of French people living in African countries today, who live much better in Africa than they could ever dream of living in their own native land.

My modest hope is merely that French and African peoples do not, under the influence of sibylline ideologies, chart an irreversible course into dangerous waters, while remaining oblivious to the actual challenges that now confront both.

Translated by Christopher Wise & Michel Tinguiri.

Notes

1. [*Translator's note*]: Ouologuem alternately uses the terms *Nègre*, translated here as "Negro," and *Noir*, translated here as "Black." Although the English language term Negro is now archaic, it was in usage at the date that this book first appeared. The French term *nègre* alternately means "negro" and "ghostwriter." As will be clear, the term *nègre* (or "negro") tends to be a pejorative term for Ouologuem whereas the term *noir* (or "black") tends to be merely descriptive. We have refrained from employing the English word "nigger," which is used in Ralph Manheim's earlier translation of *Le devoir de violence* (for instance, we translate Ouologuem's term *négraille* as "black-rabble" rather than "niggertrash"). This editorial choice is not motivated out of fear of offending the reader (it is doubtful that the reader who is easily offended will bother to read Ouologuem in the first place), but rather because the term "nigger" does not accurately convey what is most commonly intended by the French word *negre*, which is far closer to either "negro" or "black" than the stridently offensive term "nigger."

2. [*Translator's note*]: The minimum wage in France.

3. The French words *Afric* and *Afrique* are phonologically equivalent. The French word *fric* is slang for cash. With this play on words, Ouologuem emphasizes the problem of cash flow (or financial capital) in Africa along with more general social problems of Africa.

The Thousand and One Bibles of Sex

by Otto Rudolph

Note to the Reader

This book will no doubt astonish the reader; but as I have gone to the trouble of offering it to him, he must show enough indulgence not to complain about its scandalous nature.

May the reader come to see instead that the man who makes love, if he is lucky, finally reaches a point where he no longer ponders the ethical meaning of the act. In fact, he does not think at all. He lives. He longs only to be true to himself, and he learns what it means to be alive.

Whether we may like this fact or not, all healthy couples are erotic, each according to its own fashion. And this book is a document. It is a veil that is lifted upon the private lives of diverse couples. You might even know such people. The hidden life of a couple is, of course, an intensely private matter, but it is not therefore unworthy of consideration.

I nonetheless make no pretensions of teaching my readers anything: I merely ask them not to censor me, nor to be shocked, but to instead join with me in seeking to understand.

In the end, our judgment about such matters is superfluous. For we are dealing with human beings, and we would not ourselves be fully human if we did not seek to understand the world as it is. [...]

NOTICE

It is the destiny of sex to seem less romantic than desire. This is no doubt the practical lesson we learn from classicism, which places love and perversion upon an equal footing. The romantic cult of guilt, by way of contrast, is the gospel proclaiming that the sexual act is the secret reason for all human tragedies.

And the diverse worlds of the orgasm and of sexual pleasure are thereby reduced to spite and malice. The genius of eroticism is that it guards its own secrets.

And so, we should hardly be surprised that, after searching for so long, and then finding (or missing) the cult of Eros, our sexuality may lull us into the dream of a thousand and one utopias. Here, the body learns what it may, and pleasure awakens in us our true genius, somewhere between the claims of hearth and pulpit.

But, the commonality of the acts that we perform, as well as similarities in our reactions, motivations, tender feelings, and sexual pleasures—be they serious, meditative, oppressive, or unrestrained—do not, however, authorize us to conclude that there is a single norm in matters of human sexuality. A single truth. For sex constantly takes us by surprise. The body, for its part, interrogates. And the mind learns to see. In the meantime, the sentinel of desire trembles when caught off guard. This is how it is for those who are new to eroticism…

As for the simplest form of love, the natural coupling or twosome, it is the flowering of "unique friendships" and is inextricable from the diverse circumstances of the lives of those involved. But it nonetheless entails a sensual encounter with an other who is irreducibly different from us. This is why the discoveries that follow sometimes give rise—in imitation of rites that are born in shadowy regions that never deceive us—to religions in which pleasure itself assumes a prophetic role. Such is the case of the fabulous voyage disclosing the "poker-confessions" of Utto Rudolph, confessions that I have entitled here, "The Thousand and One Bibles of Sex."

Here is how this book came to be published: last November, a well-known Parisian aristocrat telelphoned me at Éditions du Seuil. After a long and feverish preamble in which he introduced

318

himself, he asked if we could meet to discuss an important matter. True sincerity being such a rare thing, I had my doubts about the motives behind his warm aristocratic rhetoric. What did he really want from me?

In any event, I agreed to meet him, and he gave me a manuscript—a heavy tôme of 2,400 pages. None of this seemed out of the ordinary. But, I noticed at once the idiomatic nature of the prose: it seemed to be a book of erotic adventures in which the concrete details themselves, randomly dispersed amid the multifarious and intense passions recounted, brought to light the hidden essence of sexuality.

It was a manuscript of concealed Bibles, a codex of sexual religion born from long and delirious walks in the night, a revelation attuned to the pleasures of the flesh, the sound of an ancient blood that throbs in the temples…

I decided, with the consent of the manuscript's owner, to entitle these "poker-confessions": The Thousand and One Bibles of Sex. For Utto Rudolph (a well-known personality) had selected (after trial and error) which entries from these diverse notebooks to include amid thousands of possibilities. In total, three hundred couples had agreed to recall and record their memoirs: people from the liberal professions, the world of spectacles, and commerce… Despite their extremely intense erotic life, the 600 respondents left much to be desired in their approach to matters of pornographic style. Besides a lack of eloquence and a certain redundancy, their prose was stereotypical in diction and littered with commonplace slang expressions. The collection was certainly an unkempt, teeming, living, and authentic document, but it eschewed all aesthetic considerations and was reminiscent of countless other indigestible publications in which eroticism and its faults are confounded. I mean, for instance, the sex manuals that can serve just as well in an anatomy course, but, when it comes to questions of psychology, offer us nothing whatsoever—or, at least, nothing worth talking about.

By disguising his identity with a pseudonym, Utto Rodolf (a well-known aristocrat) assures the anonymity of all those who participated in contributing to this unusual document. Thus, Utto Rudolph authorized me to further question some of the partici-

pants over the telephone. In other words, he sought an editorial guide and advisor.

As certain erotic passages of my novel The Duty of Violence *seemed to him more than plausible, Utto Rudolph believed that he could rely on me to perform the role of literary executor. I agreed to accept this responsibility, after first consulting with the diverse members of the jury of the Prix Renaudot, who had bestowed this award upon my first novel. They did not look unfavorably upon my initiative; hence, I became the manuscript's craftsman, correcting its many faults and abridging it to a manageable size. Once confronted with the task of excising certain details of the participants' erotic lives, it became no longer—with perhaps one or two rare exceptions—a book about eroticism, at least not strictly speaking: for there are finally no tastes that are foreign to our nature, above all tastes for the unspeakable[...]*

...Eroticism is certainly the concern of us all. But it should be clear that I myself have no interest in specializing in this domain. This book therefore represents my first—and last—foray into this genre. And, if I took it upon myself to present The Thousand and One Bibles of Sex, *it is in part because a number of African nations decided to ban my first novel* The Duty of Violence, *due to its unapologetic eroticism. In the eyes of some Heads of State, I was irresponsible or uncultured, since I had dared to say that Black people actually make love. Others said that I was pandering to racist French people, who took great delight in seeing a Black denigrate the morals of fellow Blacks. Fine. It's good to be primitive—of that, there can be no doubt—but, it is unforgivable to be childish and narrow-minded. Too bad for the childish and narrow-minded censors among us.*

YAMBO OUOLOGUEM

Poker Confession X

Prehistory! They wore blue-jeans, and prehistory was all around them! Here, they discovered the exoticism of an entire universe in Turkish slippers, in worn-out sandals, naked feet, naked arms, naked legs: over there, traders of small goods squatted near merchandise, polishing their precious trinkets: tailors of fine embroidery, jewelers, saddle-makers, ragged beggars, merchants haggling with wives in imperial purple: and, all of this the result of a strange coincidence, a forced landing at Robertsfield! Their voyage was a throwback to days before the modern era!

Dropping from the coppery storm clouds, their airplane had reeled off course and fallen out of the blue, blown to earth on the last winds of Sirocco... But this was nothing new to them.

They lived a carefree existence, undaunted by the shocks of the road. Tourism meant perpetual and boundless freedom for them. Leaving the warmth and humidity of the Ivory Coast, and then Sierra Leone, they arrived on the Guinea Coast, at Liberia... They heard the terrible roar of the Ocean, they survived Africa's tornadoes, the violent winds that blew down the coconut trees and buffeted the children on the road to Sinkor, in the residential district of Monrovia... The dry season, burning and dusty, had lasted for months. Now, it was the time of the monsoon, which brought fertile rains and apocalyptic nights... The storms had strewn the coconut palms to infinity, along the shores of the Atlantic with its marauding sharks that swim in the surf. The frothy waves pounded the shore in the nights, sweeping away all those who were careless enough to walk along its edges.

The countryside was luxuriously baroque, with its folklore overflowing with carmine, bougainvillea, hibiscus, amaryllis, vermilion, weirdly shaped orchards, and diabolical colors...

Pineapples, oranges, grapefruits, lemons, coconuts, fresh or treated in copra, sugary mangos, luscious papayas, khaki, gourd-shaped jackfruit—they tasted it all, reveling in the discovery of the magnificent trees, the ebony trees, the raffia trees, the giant bamboo trees, and, most of all, the baobab trees and their fruits– monkey-bread with a bitter taste.

John imported cocoa and coffee in the Vait Country, which was located north of Monrovia. Willy, his cousin, was a member of the government of President Tubman, loved by some, hated by others.

But Samuel, his friend, was said to be mixed up in the diamond trade. Rumor had it that he played an important role in running the country's mines for diamonds, pyrite, copper, iron, and gold, but his involvement was shrouded in secrecy. To even mention the semi-precious gems of quartz, tourmaline, and rubies, was a taboo subject for the Whites. Those who spoke of it found themselves carted off to Headquarters, where they were interrogated with harsh and violent measures.

None of this detoured Emmanuelle, Regis, Harry, and Vive, including the presence of Nazis, the most prominent of whom were a local doctor and the owner of an airplane taxi-service. It was well known, in any event, that the doctor operated on his patients while inebriated, and that he was not officially licensed. The Nazi, apoplectic and besodden with whiskey, spent his nights listening to the songs of his younger colleague, a Hitler devotee. Stripped of his profession in France, this other physician was said to be responsible for the onset of paralysis in the legs of several children, following the careless administration of Tetracoque vaccinations. Such was the atmosphere of the country at large, where Whites married Blacks to profit from the legal system of this territory that was offered by the American government to freed black slaves, who could, in the names of their children, enjoy the dual benefits of being both Black and White. And, it never failed that, once their fortune was made, they left for vacation in Europe and never returned, abandoning their African wives and children. Above all, they profited from the overwhelming racism of the Blacks among them.

Thus it was that, one day, Regis and Vive decided to tour Monrovia, guided by their boy. During their walk, their boy was approached by another boy. A few harsh words were exchanged between them, before they went their separate ways. Curious, Vive asked their boy, who was of the Bassa race, why they were so hostile to one another.

"Oh! It is nothing. Missy," he said in response. "I only wanted to know if he was Bassa, like me. Since he wasn't, I had nothing further to say to him. He is a stupid." This is how the various races of this country–the Bassa, Kru, Mandigo, Bulom, and Gora– treat one another.

... Besides the members of these races, one also finds in the American colony clock-makers, hotel-owners, travel agents, pharmacists, agents of foreign corporations–Nestlé and Coca-Cola–a large number of displaced Americans and others who have no history, miscellaneous specialists, but also Lebanese businessmen.

Hence, after their weeklong stay, Regis, Vive, Emmanuelle and Harry were more than ready to depart. At the President's zoo at Totota, an Irishman welcomed them, a caretaker of twenty-seven species of serpents, including cobras, grass-snakes, and poisonous mambas. The Irishman was very proud to have on display the largest scorpion in the world, which was about twelve thumbs in length. The scorpion was dried out and set under glass, next to other enormous dried-out insects, including wasps and praying mantises.

The guests were light-hearted and flirtatious, but nothing happened between them.

After the Molossol caviar, the Slivovitz (a type of vodka) was offered by the German and the Yugoslav who were also at the party. There were also in attendance two captains of Peruvian fishing boats, a Greek architect, and an agent of the Swiss-Air Company. The gathering was cordial, nothing more. Those in attendance informed the Parisians that, earlier that day, the young girls from the Vai country—their thighs gooey with blood—had undergone the ritual of having their clitorises amputated, in the name of ancestral custom.

Two black Americans, who wore their colonial helmets even during their meal, said that they must turn in early, for the next morning was the Sabbath. There were a great number of religious groups for a country that was so small, including congregations of Catholics, Protestants, Lutherans, Baptists, and Anabaptists. Many Blacks also frequented the homes of the sorcerers. After the departure of the pious and helmeted Black Americans, who had left a bad taste in the mouths of the other guests, they all went their separate ways that evening.

✥

Artists of eroticism, Regis, Harry, Vive, and Emmanuelle agreed among themselves to go on safari–to Chad and Kenya. Those who hunted in these places included stockbrokers, filmmakers, painters, politicians, businessmen, liberals, photographers, and architects.

For Regis and his companions, Africa dazzled them: its Black women with their insolent breasts, pretty girls in spangled boubous wearing no undergarments, their slatternly and nonchalant manner of walking, their pleasant figures, firm buttocks and thighs, nappy cunts—electrifying when rubbed against the male pubis—their exposed flesh under the hot sun, the robust nature of their open sensuality, born from the climate, bodies overflowing and voluptuous under African skies. Thanks to the safari, and the intoxication to which it gave birth, they came into contact with an uncanny and aggressive style of sexuality, a sensation that evoked for them the violent eroticism of the bullfight.

When the matador artfully kills the bull before thousands of spectators, the art of putting the bull to death awakens the most basic instincts of those gathered, taxing the last resources of both man and beast.

Nothing in their adventure caused any profound upheavals in the conditions of their existence, but it awakened in them a feeling of delirium, the desire for adventure and domination. What they encountered was pure bullfighting, the estrangement from their ordinary lives, the civilization of exoticism, and the corporeal fact of blood...

But the safari was blissfully restful and pleasurable as well. There was something both stirring and urbane about the love of the hunt, especially the crude brutality that it unleashed in the women among them.

After the shocks of the journey, they spent the evening at Fort-Lamy in Chad, on the banks of the Chari, delighting in the opulent breasts of the women, the small, tight asses of the men, the air-conditioned rooms, showers, toilets, wet-bars, and restaurants; then they journeyed to N'Gaoundéré, the ranch of N'Gaoundaba, the falls of Tello, the nature reserve of Benoué, with its lions, giraffes, elephants, buffalo, and hippopatmuses. Later, in Kenya, Regis and his friends stayed for the longest period of time at a comfortable four-star hotel, only a few kilometers from the domestic barbarism that surrounded them. Why not indulge in the myth of the fantastic, of unknown horizons and faraway skies? ...

... One lovely Kenyan afternoon, after much drinking, they stayed awake all night with a group of Belgians, Germans, Danes, Swedes, Americans, and Italians. They removed all their clothes, the women as well as the men.

When dawn came, rosy and warlike in its amber, it was Vive who, frolicking along the ocean shore, proposed that the four of them visit a nature reserve. With the guide, it would make five in total. Now, of course, there were certain limits that they did not allow themselves to transgress...

But, one of the greatest pleasures of the amateur traveler is to pay little heed to such prohibitions.

Harry, Vive, Regis, and Emmanuelle therefore decided to look for a guide.

They found him the next afternoon. They also rented a Land Rover, a 4x4 jeep-truck. The voyage was set for the next morning, at dawn.

Not traveling with any other group, the four French tourists met up with their guide at N..., where they stayed in African-style huts, which were equipped with ultra-modern comforts. They took a long detour, touring the savannah that basked under the blue sky. That afternoon, after their meal, it was time for a quiet siesta.

Then, around four o'clock, when the sun was not so hot, they continued their journey...

After thirty kilometers, there was a fork in the road.

They had a great appetite for the countryside, its vegetation, the diverse species of birds flying within their view: they approached the border of the reserve and were thinking about taking a shortcut towards the sea, so they might return to their original point of departure, the hotel.

To live in this way, free of all constraints, greatly amused them. The black guide understood a little French, but his knowledge was so rudimentary that the four others were able to arrange the most daring indiscretions without the knowledge of their guide, a Black who had been civilized by a refined English gentleman.

An hour or so later, finding an inviting spot, they decided it was time to stop. The guide raised the hood of the jeep-truck, letting the engine cool down, and filling the radiator with a tin of water.

The women began to undress before disappearing behind a thicket. There was not much to shelter them from Ali's line of vision—but what did it matter? Regis pushed Vive onto the ivy, and Harry, finding a more remote spot under the shadow of a tree, occupied himself with Emmanuelle. The couples could not see one another, but they could certainly hear one another in the pure air of the afternoon…

… Somewhere, to the left, there was a noise.

It was a lion—but Regis and Vive, who were entranced, could not yet believe what they were seeing. The lion watched them with slit yellow eyes from behind a thicket of gorse, bramble, and wild henna.

Raising themselves up on their elbows, the couple saw its red tongue and the sharp fangs of its black mouth. Either the wind—or the beast's anger—caused the mane around its neck to tremble.

Why not say it outright? They were terrified. Vive tried to hide herself by laying flat on the grass. Regis slowly lifted himself up, noticing that Harry was nowhere to be seen. Ali was also far away. The lovers slowly stood up. That was when the lion leaped…

They had no time to flee. They stood at thirty meters' distance, frozen in place. Their distress was obvious. They had not brought any guns with them—it was the one condition that the guide had imposed upon them before agreeing to become their guide. Not a single gun! And if the lion…

But Regis seems to understand. He has not yet dared to look the lion straight in the eyes. No. Not yet.

… Regis stands motionless… He looks over at Harry. His face is as stolid as a mask. The others have now seen the lion and begin to creep closer, perhaps expecting to find their mangled bodies.

Regis softly sits down. He instructs Vive to sit as well. The others hesitate. They hold sharp sticks in their hands. How can they help their friends, who are in so much danger?

Regis puts one arm on a tall shrub nearby. Then another. He slowly approaches the lion, fixing his eyes upon it. He stares right into its slit pupils. He whispers for Vive to imitate him. And this whisper of Regis echoes yet another whisper that comes from the mouth of their black guide…

The guide slowly undresses. He approaches the lion from the left, downwind. He whispers. He tells the others to stay calm. Above all, they must stay very calm… The black guide is now nude. He wears only a cotton loincloth that is tied by a rope. He looks for something in the shrubs. There… not far from the moss and a cluster of mushrooms.

Why does the black guide make such a grumbling noise? The lion turns its head towards this grumbling and sees the Black, who holds a stick in his hand. His hand makes a sweeping motion across the space before his eyes, before dropping to his side. His hand sweeps the space again. It is a sign to the couples to get up and move.

The black guide whispers, and the two couples at last understand. They change places, following the eyes and movements of the Black.

They stop once they are downwind from the lion.

The lion can still see them, but he growls less now, for the smell of the couple is not as strong, neither the odor of sperm on Vive's thighs, or the sticky fluids that drip from Regis's member.

Why doesn't the guide, who stands behind the lion, take flight?

When Vive makes the slightest effort to lift herself from the ground, the lion growls again, swatting insects with its tail, and clawing at the air with his left paw.

All of a sudden, Regis understands: the lion is in heat and knows that they are nude and making love.

Regis tells Vive, who is twenty meters from the lion, to sit down and turn her head towards the face of the beast. A single bounce, and the lion will crush them with all its weight...

Regis, his eyes riveted upon the eyes of the lion, bites himself on the lower lip, hard. It is as if, by feeling this sharp pain, he seeks to become more aware of his own presence, and to avoid doing something stupid. Under the gaze of Regis, the lion docilely crouches down. It shakes its mane, its body trembling.

Regis lifts one of Vive's legs. He softly orders her to wrap her other leg around his back. Now, he mounts her, penetrating her soft flesh, all the while watching the lion. The beast begins to drool, as the fleece of its tail coils around its lumbering paws, rubbing the bushy end of its tail against its penis, humping its back in a measured rhythm.

Its penis emerges from its furry sheath, and the beast rubs it like a cat. The beast comes nearer to the couple, gently repeating these rubbing motions. But Regis now lowers Vive's soft round ass, and the lion stops in surprise.

The man now whispers.

It is Harry who starts things up again. Harry makes an effort to look at the lion, straight in the eyes, for a long time, without blinking. In the end, it is the lion that blinks and recoils a little. It raises itself up and then rolls around on its back. The beast seems to have misplaced its member, its testicles that are as stolid as the calf of a man's legs. Now it again flogs its penis with the end of its tail and then stops. The animal is furious. It roars. Will it pounce, the criminal beast?

Bewildered, the beast watches the man and woman. It does not know where to go. Vive and Regis, Emmanuelle and Harry— still copulating—form two distinct groups. Eight eyes are riveted upon the eyes of the lion. The eyes of the couples get bigger: they slowly look over at the black guide, who is nude. He carries in one hand a gourd that is filled with honey; in the other, he carries the long branch of a tree, which is forked at the end. There are sheaves of grass tied to the branches. There are also various flowers with stalks that trickle with sap.

The Black approaches the lion. The Black raises his arm. And the forked branch with the sheaves of grass is gently rubbed against the flanks of the lion. The lion turns. The Black nimbly bounces back and turns his body in unison with the lion. The branch now strokes the anus of the beast, making soft circular motions. The man now sets the gourd upon the ground. He tips it over on the grass, and the honey flows... With his free hand, the guide clutches at the branch. He pushes it, ever so softly, now timidly masturbating the lion's member. With the other fork of the branch, he inserts the soft tip into the lion's anus, which contracts in pleasure. He steps closer, as the lion pants unevenly.

He takes yet another step, pouring more honey from the gourd. The Black makes mimicking gestures for them, and the two couples now understand that the branch is medicinal with soporific effects. The two couples exchange partners under the eyes of the lion, which makes a grousing sound.

The Black comes closer, taking small steps. He continues his soft motions with the branch. With each step, he comes a little closer, his hands clutching the branch. There... Closer... Closer still...

The Black effortlessly substitutes the branch with its grassy tips with the warmth of his hand, which he moistens with saliva. He clutches the lion's organ in his hand. The forked branch props up the back paws of the lion, and so the Black is now able to come closer. He puts his other hand on the beast's testicles and begins to masturbate it. Slowly at first, and then with a more lively cadence.

The end of the forked branch is planted in the soft earth, near the hind paws. The man becomes exasperated, masturbating the lion with increasingly rigorous strokes.

The lion roared so ferociously that all jumped up. His lava was yellow like an egg-yolk, thick and abundant like the contents of an ostrich egg, spewing in every direction. The lion struck at the air with its claws, his penis trembling as he kicked away the forked branch.

The medicinal herbs were dispersed in Harry's direction, beside him and behind him. That was when Ali understood the danger.

For a while now, the honey had been attracting wasps, bees, and butterflies. They could be seen hovering over the drippings of the honey. Butterflies fluttered at the opening of the gourd. Buzzing around its base was an enormous swarm of bees: but, there were also dozens of wasps that flew about.

Ali put his hands on his head. He unraveled his meager turban, bottling the opening of the gourd with the cloth.

The glassy-eyed lion roared, its flanks palpitating in agitation. It was a moment of passing weakness—they had to take advantage of it. The beast could suddenly turn into a raging assassin.

Because the lion had shown his displeasure when he kicked over the herbs, because for nearly an hour they had been compelled to dupe the obstinate beast, the lion's ejaculation had merely unleashed his desire to tyrannize, to threaten, and to paralyze the men and women who had brought him so much pleasure. Ali lowered his right hand to the earth. He quickly made a ball of clay, which he rapidly separated in two parts. Standing against the wind, he moistened the balls of clay with his saliva and made a prodigious leap at the beast...

In an act of incredible bravery, he stuffed the two clay balls into the nostrils of the startled beast. The lion thundered, lifting its claws. That was when Ali hurled the gourd into the roaring mouth of the lion.

The paw of the beast came down, but Ali lurched to avoid the blow, falling flat under the beast's neck, which he strangled with two hands.

The lion choked, panting for air. It shook its mane, doing everything it could—unsuccessfully—to spit out the gourd.

"Run for it!" shouted the guide.

From a squatting position, his face trembling with terror, the guide bolted forward, as fast as his two legs would carry him.

When he felt the breath of the lion at his heels, he hurled himself into the beast in a frenzy of anger and despair, tumbling upon his back, his elbows against the earth. After his act of reflexive bravery, he now let himself fall backwards in a burst of savage joy—for he had heard the clear crack of the gourd against the palate of the beast.

Ali came back to where the others lay. He courteously gathered up Emmanuelle's peigne, which was strewn on the ground, ten meters way. He picked up Vive's purse, in which he found a cigarette. He lit a cigarette, while stroking his erect member.

The man watched the lion with a non-chalant air. He was more interested in stroking himself now. Meanwhile, the lion howled and writhed about, furious, slobbering, jumping in the air with pitiful leaps, falling backwards, bewildered. Its tongue was full of blood and mucous, as the lion clawed in vain at the wasps and bees that flew in every direction, stinging its raspy tongue and enflaming its throat. Filled with insane fury, the lion clawed at its own swollen tongue and disheveled mane. Howling in agony, its mouth gaped open revealing its naked, pink tonsils. From the abyss of the lion's mouth, blood and scum flowed onto the earth...

Translated by Christopher Wise

Suggestions for Further Reading

There are by now a great many critical essays that have been written on *Le devoir de violence*, less so with respect to Yambo Ouologuem's other writings. Some of the most important essays have been assembled in my book *Yambo Ouologuem: Postcolonial Writer, Islamic Militant* (Boulder, Colorado: Lynne Rienner Publishers, 1999). This book includes essays by Thomas Hale, Wole Soyinka, Kwame Anthony Appiah, Tunde Fatunde, Chris Dunton, and Eric Sellin among others. It also includes accounts of interviews conducted with Yambo Ouologuem in 1997, "In Search of Yambo Ouologuem" and "Yambo Ouologuem Among the Tidjaniya." A longer version of "In Search of Yambo Ouologuem" was originally published in *Research in African Literatures*, Vol. 29, No. 2 (Summer 1998): 159-182. The standard for criticism in Ouologuem remains Thomas Hale's *Scribe, Griot, Novelist* (Gainesville: the University of Florida Press, 1992). Regrettably, a great deal of criticism of Ouologuem remains uninformed by West African history and cultural realities. This can be remedied through study of related texts such as Thomas Hale's and Nouhou Malio's *The Epic of Askia Muhammad* (Bloomington & Indianapolis, Indiana: the University of Indiana Press, 1996); John Hunwick's *Timbuktu & the Songhay Empire* (Leiden: Brill, 1999); Marcel Griaule's *Conversations with Ogotemmeli* (London: Oxford University Press, 1970); as well as my book *The Desert Shore: Literatures of the Sahel* (Boulder, Colorado: Lynne Rienner Publishers), and my forthcoming translation of al Hajj Mahmud Kati's

The Tarikh al fettâch. Readers might also see David Robinson's *The Holy War of Umar Tal* (Oxford: Clarendon Press, 1985). Also, see my forthcoming book of edited translations *The Chronicles of al Hajj Umar Tall, a Fulani Jihadist*. A film documentary on Ouologuem is also currently in the works, produced and directed by Jean Frédéric de Hasque, entitled *Un homme en colère qui se tait* (Michigan Films).

Appendix:
"In Defense of Yambo Ouologuem"

by Kaye Whiteman

Early in May the *Times Literary Supplement* published a remarkable piece of character assassination. The victim was the Malian novelist Yambo Ouologuem, whose first novel, *Le devoir de violence* (*Bound to Violence* in English translation) won the Prix Renaudot in Paris in 1968. The method was to take up almost a full page of the TLS with reproductions of pages from two novels: *Le devoir de violence* and Graham Greene's *It's a Battlefield*. The aim was to show that over three pages Ouologuem had plagiarized Graham Greene, with various slight alterations and insertions. Any reader could conclude, says the TLS, that the one text is a "loose but stylish version" of the other. The paper then refers to an article by Eric Sellin, in a journal[1] published by the African and Afro Research Institute at the University of Texas, which makes a similar point about *Le devoir de vio-lence* and an earlier winner of the Prix Goncourt André Schwartz-Bart's *Le dernier de justes*. Sellin points out strik-ing similarities in the opening and closing paragraphs of the book, insinuating strong derivation.

All this leads TLS to conclude: "On its appearance in the United States *Bound to Violence* was trumpeted as 'the first truly African novel' a claim which now looks more than a little sick." Then, heavily ironic: "Or is M. Ouologuem on to something: a style of literary imperialism intended as revenge for the much chronicled sins of territorial imperialists?" This was considered sufficiently important by *The Times* to run the story of the exposé by its sister paper on its front page, with the follow-up about how Graham Greene had drawn the attention of the publishers to the similarity of the two passages and the book had subsequently been withdrawn from publication. Similar action had been taken by publishers in France and the USA.

What did Ouologuem have to say? *The Times* said they were unable to contact him. His only published reply has been an oracular piece in *Le Figaro littéraire* early in June in which he says that the relevant passages, referring to both Schwartz-Bart and Graham Greene had been in quotation marks in his original manuscript, and that he had several times referred to "borrowings" that he had made for *Le devoir*, in a number of different interviews and talks. But his defense, above all rationale behind the "borrowings" seemed confused.

There is, in fact, a very good case in his defense, that deserves to be heard. First of all, *Le devoir de violence* is full of literary allusions and quotations, some long, some short, some attributed, others not. Yambo has never made any secret of this, as he says, and from the moment the book appeared, this aspect of it has been discussed. There was a minor fuss in France, for instance, when *Le Canard Enchaîné* spotted a few lines from de Maupassant back in 1969 (*The Times* never unearthed this one). When I saw Yambo in his Paris flat recently he was much preoccupied by the new attacks, and was talking somberly in terms of conspiracy. He was in particular very caustic about the whole relationship of white literary circles, especially publishers, with black writers.

To demonstrate the injustice of the charges against him, he spent some time taking me through his original hand-written manuscript (in an old exercise book) of *Le devoir de violence* showing me all the places where there had been quotation marks, if not actual mentions of his literary allusions and quotations. He gave me a fairly comprehensive run-down on all the other authors he might be accused of plagiarizing, including the 16th century Portuguese explorer Lope di Pigafeta, and a modern detective story by John Mac-donald (the basis of the sequence containing the asp killing), as well as traditional epic sources in Arabic, Bambara and Amharic, and even French colonial documents that he says are still in secret archives. I saw, for instance, where he had written "here ends *The Last of the Just*,"[2] a reference omitted like so many others, for whatever reason, from the published version. But it is, in truth, a fairly chaotic script, much erased and amended, with a multitude of little pieces of paper inserted and clipped into pages, some of which have been lost. And it only demonstrates what is completely apparent anyway, that the so-called plagiarism is a stylistic technique to further the purposes of the novel.

Yambo compares it to the techniques of what is called the new novel, or even the work of some modern film-makers in which clips from the films of others are inserted. In a collage it is the arrangement and the juxtaposition which are impor-tant. If he quoted Greene, he says, it was a kind of homage, and that particular passage was intended as a dramatic coun-terpoint to the bestial passage which follows — a piece about a normal relationship as a prelude to a sequence of abnormal degradation. The same reasoning applies to the Maupassant "borrowing," and to the quote from Emily Dickinson which A. N. Mensah of the University of Ghana, Legon, writing in a university quarterly,[3] attacking Ouologuem for literary excess, finds so incomprehensible. "The little echo of Emily Dickinson introduces feelings into that episode in the novel which are entirely out of place. The poem which is echoed is a calm reflective poem—and that is exactly what Ouologuem's novel is not." This, unbeknown to A. N. Mensah, is exactly the point.

Taking the work as a whole, no charge could possibly be made that the "borrowings" were in any way to supple-ment any literary inadequacy on Yambo's part. You may like or dislike the way he writes, but there is no denying his talent for words. I see no reason for those who praised the book to now feel embarrassed, just as those who attacked it should now feel they have gained new ammunition, although those who saw it as brilliant pastiche can perhaps feel reinforced in their view.

What is needed, however, is a full list of acknowledgments (Green, Maupassant, Pigafeta *et al*): even better would be a full-scale annotated *Le devoir de violence*, enough to provide satisfying fodder for university seminars for decades. If anything the fascination of the book has been enhanced by the controversy. And to those who say it is less of an "African novel," one should note that the style of allusion and quotation is *par excellence*, as Yambo says, that of the griots.

West Africa, July 21, 1972.

NOTES

1. *Research in African Literatures* (Vol. 2. No. 2).
2. In a letter to the Times Literary Supplement, the French publisher of *Bound to Violence* quotes a letter from Schwartz-Bart in 1968, prior to publication saying, "I am in no way worried by the use that has been made of *Dernier des Justes*...I have always looked on my books as apple trees, happy that my apples be eaten and happy if now and again one is taken and planted in different soil."
3. *Universitas, An Inter-Faculty Quarterly*, Vol. 1, No. 3, published by the University of Ghana, Legon.